Fire Prevention Applications

by Brett Lacey & Paul Valentine

Published by
Fire Protection Publications • Oklahoma State University
Stillwater, Oklahoma

RECYCLABLE

Project Manager: Rachel Hutchinson
Developing Editor: John Joerschke
Design: Ann Moffat
Layout: Missy Reese
Indexer: Nancy Kopper

ISBN 0-87939-257-6

Library of Congress Number: 2005920656

First Edition

First Printing, April 2005

10   9   8   7   6   5   4   3   2   *Printed in the United States of America*

"Listen to me: I've seen the ashes of past fires, fires of thousands of years old. I know what's going to happen. The Flames will come. I have no doubt about that whatsoever."

Isaac Asimov and
Robert Silverberg,
Nightfall

Contents

About the Authors x

Acknowledgements xi

Chapter 1: Introduction 1

Chapter 2: History and Development of Fire Prevention 7

   FESHE Objectives 8

   Why Study Fire Prevention History? 9

   Early Fire Prevention Laws 10

   American Fire Tragedies 10

      Iroquois Theater (1903), Chicago, Illinois 11

      Triangle Shirtwaist (1911), New York, New York 11

      Coconut Grove (1942), Boston, Massachusetts 13

      Our Lady of Angels School (1958), Chicago, Illinois 13

      Beverly Hills Supper Club (1977), Southgate, Kentucky 14

      MGM Grand Hotel (1980), Las Vegas, Nevada 15

      Happy Land Social Club (1990), Bronx, New York 15

      Food Processing Plant (1991), Hamlet, North Carolina 16

   Where Do We Go From Here? 17

      "America Burning" 19

      Greater Emphasis on Fire Prevention 20

      Better Training and Education 20

      Public Fire Safety Education 21

      Neglected Areas of Research 23

   Research Organizations 24

      Private Organizations 24

      Federal Fire Protection Organizations 25

      State and Local Organizations 26

   Summary 27

Chapter 3: Codes and Standards 33

   FESHE Objectives 34

   What Are Codes? 35

   Insurance Services Office 36

   What Are Standards? 37

   Appendices 38

   Federal Laws and Properties 39

   State Laws and Statutes 40

   Local Laws and Ordinances 41

   General Principles of Fire Codes and Standards 41

      Appeals Procedures 42

   Building Codes 44

   Building Departments 44

   Model Code Organizations 45

   How NFPA Codes Are Developed 46

   Model Codes and NFPA Codes 46

The Reality of Fire Codes 47

Performance-Based Codes 47

Summary 50

Chapter 4: Development and Implementation of Fire Prevention Bureaus 55

FESHE Objectives 56

Fire Prevention as a Public Business 57

Ensure the Organization's Mission Statement Includes the Fire Prevention Bureau's Primary Function 60

Ensure the Fire Prevention Bureau Is Part of the Fire Department's Strategic Planning Process 63

Determine the Level of Fire Prevention Services 66

Retain and Motivate Staff 67

Adjust the Organization as Needed While Monitoring the Environment for Internal and External Changes and Opportunities 71

Summary 73

Chapter 5: Fire Prevention Bureau Organizational Structure and Function 79

FESHE Objectives 80

Administration 81

    Explanation and Scope 81

    Identify the Staffing Levels to Provide the Desired Level of Services 83

    Determine the Optimum Organizational Framework for the Staffing Levels to Provide the Desired Level of Services 85

    Staffing Options for a Bureau 87

    Staffing with Sworn Personnel 90

    Staffing with Civilian Personnel 90

    Outsourcing Fire Prevention Services 92

    Staffing a Fire Prevention Bureau in Volunteer Departments ... 95

Tasks Within the Bureau 95

    Fire Protection Engineering or Plans Examination Section 95

    Fire and Life Safety Education 99

    Fire Inspection and Code Enforcement 100

    Public Information 103

    Preincident Planning 104

    Fire Investigations 106

    Occupant Service Section 108

    Wildland Risk Management 109

    Training 110

Summary 111

Chapter 6: Risk Assessment 117

FESHE Objectives 118

Defining Risk 119

What is a Risk Assessment? 121

    Risk Impact 121

    Risk Perception 121

Why Do a Risk Assessment? 122

Issues to Address in the Risk Assessment 123

What Does Your Public View as Their Level of Acceptable Risk?............123

Paradigm Shifts...125

The Truth Hurts...127

How to Engage the Public On Risk 127

The Nuts and Bolts..129

Summary **131**

Chapter 7: Fire and Life Safety Education............................. 135

FESHE Objectives **136**

What Is Fire and Life Safety Education? **137**

Why is Fire Safety Education Important? **138**

History of Fire and Life Safety Education **139**

Does Fire and Life Safety Education Really Work? **144**

What Do the National Statistics Show? 146

Planning a Fire and Life Safety Education Program..........................**147**

Designing Presentations **149**

Targeting Your Audience..150

Fire and Life Safety Education Topics...152

Fire and Life Safety Education Programs..152

What Makes a Great Presentation?..154

Getting Your Message Out...**155**

Summary **156**

Chapter 8: Public Information Officer: A How-To 163

FESHE Objectives **164**

The Importance of Public Information **165**

PIO Skills **167**

Community Relations...168

Media Relations 168

Written Communication...177

Public Speaking...179

Audio / Visual Presentations 180

Fire Department Operations and Functions 181

Legal Issues and Responsibilities **181**

Summary of Strategy and Tactics for the PIO **181**

Summary **182**

Chapter 9: Fire Investigations 187

FESHE Objectives **188**

Why Investigate Fires? **189**

Significance 189

Fire Investigation as Fire Prevention 189

Benefits of Fire Investigation 190

Identifying Trends 192

Responsibility..**196**

Basic Investigation Training, Equipment, and Procedures **197**

Training...198

Equipment...199

Determining Origin and Cause 200

Arson Investigation **201**

Training and Equipment..202

Procedures...203

Toward a Long-Term Solution 209

Summary **210**

Chapter 10: Construction Document Review **215**

FESHE Objectives **216**

Introduction **217**

The Construction Document Review Team **219**

Building Officials 219

Insurance Rating Bureau 220

State Fire Marshals...220

Fire Department 220

The Construction Document Review and Permit Coordination Process ...**222**

Step 1: Determine Need 222

Step 2: Contact Design Professional..................................222

Step 3: Preparation of Conceptual Design 224

Step 4: Construction Document Submittal for Review 224

Step 5: Construction Document Review.............................234

Step 6: Generating Construction Document Review Comments.........234

Step 7: Construction Document Revision Submittal.................235

Step 8: Construction Document Revision Approval or Denial.............235

Step 9: Permit Application and Issuance 235

Step 10: Construction Begins..236

Step 11: Construction Inspection 238

Step 12: Construction Complete 238

Step 13: Certificate of Occupancy Issued 238

Step 14: Occupant Moves In 239

Step 15: Business License Approval....................................239

Step 16: Periodic Fire Inspections......................................239

Significance of a Good Construction Document Review Process..........239

Summary **240**

Chapter 11: Fire Inspection Procedures................................**243**

FESHE Objectives **244**

Why Conduct Fire Inspections?..**245**

Implementing Inspections **246**

Step 1: Analyze 246

Step 2: Determine the Enforceable Regulations............247

Step 3: Determine Inspector's Level of Training 247

Step 4: Establish Organizational Fire Inspection Policies and
Procedures..249

Fire Inspection Priorities **250**

Preparing for Fire Inspections **251**

Occupancy Hazards 252

Fire Inspection Public Relations...254

Conducting the Inspection..**256**

Interior Inspections 258

Exterior Inspections 259

Fire Inspection Evaluation 259

Fire Inspection Steps 259

Record Keeping 261

Summary 262

Chapter 12: Identification and Protection of Hazards 269

FESHE Objectives 270

Types of Hazards 271

Identify the Target 272

Think Strategically in the Target Identification Process 273

Develop a Target Protection Plan 274

Identify Your Resources 275

Involve Your Team 275

Reevaluate the Plan 276

Solutions for Control 276

Suppression and Control 277

Detection and Alarm 279

Fire Department Operations 280

Product Manufacture and Performance Control 282

Compartmentation 283

Occupant Safety 284

Performance-Based Design 289

Summary 290

Chapter 13: Wildland Fire Mitigation 297

FESHE Objectives 298

Wildfire and the Environment 299

What Is Wildfire? 301

Historical Forest Service Issues 302

Current Threats and Risks 303

Causes of Wildfire 305

Factors Determining Risk 306

Wildfire Management 306

Interagency Cooperation 306

Fire and Life Safety Education 307

Prevention Tools 308

Prevention and Mitigation 312

Suppression 314

Paradigm Shifts in Wildfire Management 315

Summary 315

Chapter 14: Using Technology to Improve Fire Prevention

Efforts 321

FESHE Objectives 322

Technology and Change 323

Global Information Systems 329

Are We There Yet . . . Is Technological Advancement Over? 329

Summary 331

Chapter Review Exercise Answers 335

Bibliography 367

Glossary 373

Index 377

About the Authors

Brett is currently the Fire Marshal for the Colorado Springs, Colorado fire department. He has served on various technical committees including NFPA 1031, IFSTA committee for Inspection Practices, and the Colorado Fire Marshal's Association Code Committee. Brett has completed various classes at the Center for Creative Leadership in Colorado Springs, CO and has served on various State committees.

He holds an Associate's degree in Fire Protection Technology as well as a Bachelor's degree in Fire Protection and Safety Engineering Technology from Oklahoma State University. He is a Professional Engineer and Certified Safety Professional. He has attended numerous classes at the National Fire Academy and has been a speaker/lecturer at various national conferences including NFPA, IAFC, Colorado Mitigation and Wildfire Conference, and Colorado Safety Educators Conference.

He has been an instructor for two community colleges and has been employed in the private sector as an HPR Loss Control Representative and Safety Engineer. He has over 24 years experience in the fire service in both a professional and volunteer capacity, as a nationally registered paramedic, firefighter, and fire protection engineer.

You can contact the author at:
Colorado Springs Fire Department
Office of the Fire Marshal
375 Printers Parkway
Colorado Springs, Colorado 80910
(719) 385-7355
blacey@springsgov.com

Paul Valentine's fire service career began as a volunteer firefighter with the Stillwater, Oklahoma fire department. Paul presently serves as Fire Marshal for the Mount Prospect Fire Department in Mount Prospect, Illinois. Prior to the position of Fire Marshal, he was the fire protection engineer for the Mount Prospect Fire Department. He has worked for the Mount Prospect Fire Department for 13 years and has five years of fire protection engineering experience at a Department of Energy research laboratory and as a Loss Control Consultant in the insurance industry. He has a Bachelor of Science Degree in Fire Protection and Safety Engineering Technology from Oklahoma State University and a Master of Science Degree in Management and Organizational Behavior from Benedictine University. He is a graduate from the National Fire Academy's Executive Fire Officer Program. Paul has been an instructor at a local community college and for various fire service certification courses. He has served on many International Fire Service Training Association (IFSTA) committees and as a member of the IFSTA Executive Board. He is also a principal committee member of the NFPA Fire Marshal Professional Qualification Standard.

You can contact the author at:
R. Paul Valentine
1515 Fender Road
Naperville, Illinois 60565
paulvalentine@wowway.com

Acknowledgements

I would like to thank foremost my wife, Marie, for her patience and support in allowing me the space, time, and periodic frustration in writing this book. Thank you to Michael and especially Logan and Keagan for your patience and understanding while I locked myself up for days at a time. I am indebted to so many other people who, throughout my career, provided me with so much information, mentoring, opportunities, and ideas: to my parents, Milt and Marlene, and to Owen Berg, Jim Gleason, Rich Strassia, Mike Jambrosic, Bob Barton, Larry Borgelt, Pat Brock, Jim Hansen, J.J. Adame, Jesse Guzman, Vicki Doner, Michael Borden, Frannie Brester, Frank Carter, Bill Mills, Manuel Navarro, Michael Gower, John Gibbons, Bob Weller, Ed Kirtley, Brenda Quinones, all of my staff, and many others whom I don't mean to leave out, but there are too many to list.

All of these people have argued with me, struggled with me, put up with me, but in the end helped me learn and work through so many things. I am especially grateful to Paul Valentine who allowed me the opportunity to work with him on this book. Without his patience and ability to cover my back, I couldn't have got my parts done. Thanks, too, again to Frannie, who did her best to make us look like we have done this before.

Brett

I would like to thank my wife, Kellie, for her encouragement, patience, continued support, and willingness to put up with my bits of frustration while writing this book. I could not have done it without her! A warm-hearted thanks to my kids, Lucas, Rachel, and Sarah, who graciously allowed me to take time away from them while I worked on this project. Thank you to my parents, Richard and Peggy; without them I would not have been provided with so many opportunities. I feel fortunate to have had my father's example of hard work and dedication to the fire service to be the greatest influence on my career.

I am grateful for those people who throughout my career have continued to take the time to share their ideas with me and help me through many challenges. These individuals unconditionally help me whenever I ask them. (Trust me, I ask them often!) Although too many to list, these people include Doug Forsman, Bob Barr, Dr. Jim Straseske, Gary Jensen, Larry Borgelt, Pat Brock, Jim Schifiliti, Jim Hansen, Ed Cavello, Mike Figolah, Tony Huemann, Buz Livingston, Henry Dawson, John Malcolm, Denny Thill, and the entire Mount Prospect Fire Department.

Lastly, I owe a great deal of gratitude and acknowledgement to my good friend and partner in this project, Brett Lacey. His insight and dedication to fire prevention is commendable. I am fortunate to have had the opportunity to work with him.

Paul

Chapter 1
Introduction

The United States faces many challenges in the 21st century. The threat of terrorism on our soil is more prevalent than ever. We now have government officials at the federal, state, and local levels responsible for Homeland Security. Amid, all of this, the fire department remains one of the most critical players, if not the most critical player, in protecting our citizens. Although fire departments are forced to do more with less, the types of services they are called upon to handle are escalating. The changing roles of the fire service necessitate an ever-increasing demand for fire prevention efforts. The reality is the fire service will not be able to continue increasing and maintaining human resources for emergency response the way we traditionally have in the past.

> The fire department is among the most critical players in protecting American citizens.

According to the National Fire Protection Association's (NFPA) fire analysis and research division, public fire departments in 2001 responded to 1,734,500 fires in the United States. This equates to a fire department responding to a fire somewhere in the United States every 18 seconds. Every 34 minutes one of those fires was in a home. Every 170 minutes a fire death occurred in a home. In fact, fire deaths in the home account for over 80 percent of civilian fire deaths.

As a country, we appear to be on the cutting edge of technology, but we still suffer multiple life loss from fires (**Figure 1.1**). During the writing of this book, Rhode Island suffered one of the most tragic loss-of-life fires this country has seen, a nightclub fire very similar to several others in years past in other parts of our country. Most, if not all, of these incidents could either be prevented or mitigated through fire prevention and mitigation programs developed to meet the needs of the community. Each community must establish a level of fire prevention effort that meets its needs. The fire prevention efforts needed in one community may differ from those needed in another. Does that make one community better than the other? Not necessarily; it all boils down to determining the level of service and protection that citizens expect and then developing a program

Figure 1.1 One of the main reasons we work so hard to prevent fires is to protect our brothers and sisters who serve in this fine service. The Professional Fallen Firefighters Memorial serves as a reminder that nearly every day, a firefighter in this country dies in the line of duty. Preventing these deaths saves our public and our family.

that meets or exceeds those expectations. The costs and available funding in conjunction with the perceived benefits of the service will determine the level of service to be provided. Determining the necessary level of protection and then selling the need for that protection is the fire protection professional's greatest challenge.

As the cost of fire suppression escalates along with the costs that result from the devastation of fire, the demand will increase for preventing fires from occurring or, at the very least, mitigating their effects (**Figure 1.2**). There will be a greater focus on built-in fire protection systems to control the fire

Figure 1.2 Most people associate fire departments with suppression activities, which are a reactive function. Damage has already occurred.

until fire department personnel arrive. As a disproportionate number of fire deaths continue to occur in our country's homes, suppression systems, such as sprinklers, in residences will become more prevalent. Residential sprinklers will be the next generation of home fire protection. There is no dispute that prevention is and will continue to be less costly by far than responding to a fire incident after it has occurred.

Our continuing great need to prevent fires and overall community injuries and deaths from occurring is obvious. However, fire departments cannot do this alone. They need to look for opportunities to build coalitions and make the prevention of fires and injuries a combined effort. The following chapters examine some methods to build those coalitions and ways to prevent or mitigate fires. Unfortunately in this country, obtaining staffing for fire prevention efforts is more difficult than obtaining firefighters or paramedics. The public is enamored with firefighters as heroes, perceiving our response capabilities as our most important job (**Figure 1.3**). Unfortunately, we continue to emphasize tragic events and the heroic efforts and resources expended in fire fighting rather than the benefits of good prevention or mitigation practices. Why?

Because keeping an incident from becoming serious or preventing it from occurring at all is not dramatic, it is not newsworthy, and if nothing terrible happens, nobody notices. Our firefighters' visibility sends a clear message that they will be there to "save the day," which they certainly will do whenever they can. However, as a profession we need to work smarter and better at keeping the day from getting so bad that it needs to be saved.

Figure 1.3 Fire department personnel are responsible for inspections and other fire prevention functions, which include activities such as operational support at large fire incidents.

The grass-roots level of our fire service needs a paradigm shift in which we become as proud of prevention and mitigation as we are of emergency response. This is not intended to take anything away from our response capabilities, for human activities will lead inevitably to accidents, failures, and breakdowns. However, we must elevate our efforts to the next level and give much greater emphasis to prevention and mitigation than we do currently.

In this book we decided to take a different approach toward fire prevention activities. We emphasize a holistic approach to fire protection that encompasses not only fire suppression but community involvement in fire prevention efforts. Many other texts provide tremendous detailed explanations and descriptions of dealing with specific hazards such as not storing gasoline next to water heaters. We wanted to address a more global philosophy, if you will, of community based fire prevention and how it can be designed and developed to work specifically within any community.

> The grass-roots level of our fire service needs to become as proud of prevention and mitigation as we are of emergency response.

In the chapters that follow we will start by examining the history of fire prevention efforts and end with the methods and opportunities available using the latest technology to help prevent fires and injuries. We also will discuss at length the roles of prevention versus mitigation and the utilization of risk management techniques to focus our fire prevention efforts in the right direction. Fire prevention efforts involve engineering appropriate solutions to eliminate or reduce fire hazards, educating the public on the appropriate behaviors to prevent and mitigate their risk, and enforcing the appropriate fire safety codes and standards. This text will explore methods to apply each of these principles to produce the community's desired level of fire prevention services. Not only must we deliver the expected level of service for our community, but we must also have a means of prioritizing what gets done first.

> The "Three *Es*" of fire prevention are engineering, education, and enforcement.

We hope this text is informative, but more than that we hope it challenges you to think "outside of the box." We do not pretend to know everything about fire prevention. What we do propose, however, is the notion that if we all work together and make more people aware of the issues, firefighter safety will be enhanced, community safety will be enhanced, and our vocation will rise to a much higher professional level than ever before.

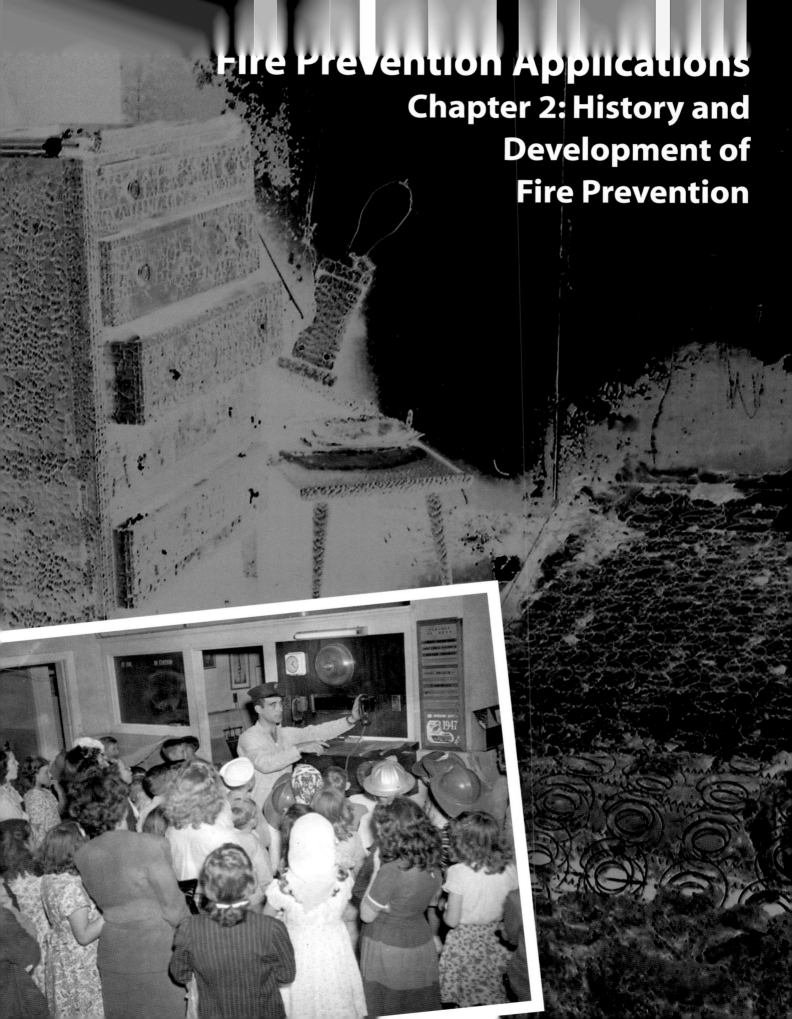

Fire Prevention Applications
Chapter 2: History and Development of Fire Prevention

FESHE COURSE OBJECTIVES

1. Define the national fire problem and the main issues relating thereto.*

2. Understand the fundamentals of the history of fire prevention.

3. Explain the importance of learning the history of fire prevention.

4. Recognize significant fires that have occurred in the United States and identify similar lessons learned from each fire.

U.S. Fire Administration Objective

Chapter 2

History and Development of Fire Prevention

Why Study Fire Prevention History?

You may wonder, "What is the point of learning what has happened in the past?" Is it really important for fire prevention professionals to know about fires that occurred before they even began their careers? When will fire prevention professionals ever use historical information? How are historical fire case studies relevant to the daily tasks they perform?

A knowledge of the relevance of historical fire events lays the groundwork for understanding how we got where we are today in the field of fire prevention (**Figure 2.1**). Most all of the national codes adopted by municipalities were created or modified as the result of tragic incidents. As a society, we tend to react to devastating situations by trying to prevent them from recurring. The public outcry to these types of events can be found in the form of stricter or modified laws, as was the case in many of the devastating fires that have occurred in the United States.

Studying historical fires lays the groundwork for understanding today's field of fire prevention.

Figure 2.1 Fully understanding twenty-first century fire prevention methods requires a fundamental knowledge of the profession's history.

There are many situations in fire prevention professionals' careers when they will be asked to explain "Why do we need to do that?" or "What is the purpose or intent of this code requirement?" If they understand what led to the development of fundamental requirements found in most of the model codes, they will be capable of explaining the purpose of or reasoning for code requirements. Case studies of historical fires give fire protection professionals the ability to recognize existing building hazards that are similar to conditions that contributed to historical fires. This in itself can help fire protection professionals prevent or mitigate similar events.

The concept of fire prevention is not new to the 21st century. As early as 24 B.C., large portions of Rome were destroyed by fire. Caesar Augustus stationed an estimated 600 servants at the city gates to fight the fires. After another disastrous fire in 6 A.D., Augustus instituted a Corps of Vigils. The corps was composed of slaves who patrolled the city for fires and alerted the citizens when a fire occurred. Over the next 500 years, this led to dividing the city into districts and developing ranking officers for each district. This is very similar to how fire departments are organized today in many of the larger cities across the United States. The districts in Rome had an estimated 7,000 vigils who were dressed and equipped with buckets and axes. They also took on the duty of fire prevention by enforcing fire prevention laws and punishing offenders.

Early Fire Prevention Laws

Laws to prevent fires were issued as early as 1189 when the first lord mayor of London mandated that houses were to be built of stone with slate or burnt tile. These laws also banned thatch roofs to prevent fires from spreading from one building to another. They required a 16-foot by 3-foot party wall to separate buildings from each other. A party wall is a noncombustible wall constructed to prevent the spread of fire from one building to the next. Buildings had to have rings so firefighters could pull them down with fire hooks during a fire to create a firebreak. Early fire apparatus carried these hooks along with ladders and were commonly referred to as hook and ladder companies.

Fire prevention laws reached the New World soon after the arrival of Europeans. In 1608, Jamestown was destroyed by fire.

American Fire Tragedies

As the United States evolved into the prosperous country of today, many fires resulted in large life loss. Some of the most notable fires that directly influenced many of the codes enforced today throughout the country include:

- Iroquois Theater, 1903
- Triangle Shirtwaist, 1911
- Coconut Grove, 1942
- Our Lady of Angels School, 1958
- Beverly Hills Supper Club, 1977
- MGM Grand Hotel, 1980
- Happy Land Social Club, 1990
- Food Processing Plant, 1991

Iroquois Theater (1903), Chicago, Illinois

The Iroquois Theater fire in Chicago, Illinois, resulted in 602 deaths. It was one of the worst theater disasters in American history. According to reports, the building was said to be fireproof. At the time of the fire, the permissible occupant load of the building was 1,602, but an estimated 1,774 persons were in the building.[1] Few of the exits were marked and some were covered with draperies. Some of the doors were locked with levers that the occupants did not know how to operate.

The fire is believed to have started when one of the spotlights ignited the draperies.[2] After the fire broke out, one of the stagehands tried to extinguish it, and only a few of the occupants started to evacuate. In fact, witnesses stated that the orchestra continued to play in an attempt to avert panic and to calm patrons.

As the fire from the draperies spread to the drop scenery, those wishing to evacuate had difficulty because of the large number of occupants blocking travel paths, acrid smoke that obscured visibility, and poorly identified and locked or blocked exit doors. The fire grew so rapidly that many of those who perished were in or near their seats. Officials found bodies stacked as many as four high near many of the exits.

The fire provided a number of lessons:

- Stages need to be protected by automatic sprinklers. At the time of the fire, the building had none.

- Draperies, such as the stage curtain, need to be fire resistive.

- Permitted occupant load limits must be obeyed.

- Finally, employees need to be trained in evacuation procedures.

Triangle Shirtwaist (1911), New York, New York

The industrial fire at the Triangle Shirtwaist factory in New York City resulted in 145 deaths. This is still the largest life-loss industrial fire in American history. It is also significant because of the codes that were developed in its aftermath.

The building where the fire occurred was a ten-story loft building occupied by approximately 500 employees. Each floor was approximately 10,000 square feet. The building had wood floors and wood trim. Two exit stairs were available for the occupants. The building had no automatic fire sprinklers installed at the time of the fire.

The fire started near quitting time on the eighth floor of the factory. It is believed to have begun in a rag bin.[3] When the fire started, workers tried to extinguish it. The smoke from the fire traveled rapidly to the other floors through the stairwells. The doors apparently were at least partly open, contributing greatly to the spread of fire and smoke. In a very short time, the fire had spread over the entire fire floor and began moving out of the windows to the other floors. Many workers on the ninth floor became aware of the fire when the flames pierced through the exterior windows.

Workers on the eighth floor tried to exit one of the stairwells and found the door locked. After a time, they managed to open the door, although their difficulty was increased because the door opened inward. Once the door finally was opened, people evidently rushed into the stairway. Some of occupants evacuating in the stairwell fell down to the seventh floor landing, where evacuees began to pile up on the stairs. According to reports, a police officer ran up the stairs to help and assisted in untangling the pile-up. An estimated 125 workers escaped down the stairwell. Other workers on the eighth floor climbed out of the windows onto a narrow fire escape. Some fell from the fire escape, and others were able to reenter the building at the sixth-floor and exit the facility.

The workers on the ninth floor tried to escape down a stair but that door was also locked. Some workers perished trying to escape down the elevator shafts; others tried to escape the flames by going to the window ledges and jumping to their deaths. The fire department tried to extinguish the fire from the outside with large streams of water, but the floors were too high for the water to penetrate. By the time firefighters extinguished the fire using hose lines supplied from hose outlets in stairwells, the upper three floors were burned, with all of their wood trim and finish consumed by the flames. Many lessons were learned from this incident:

- One of the most significant findings was that a building's means of egress must include a sufficient number of stairs in fire resistant shafts with rated fire doors at each opening. Even today, the model building codes as well as the Life Safety Code use this fundamental principle to provide occupants of a building a means of safe escape in an emergency. The concept of providing a protected means of escape through rated exit enclosures is still one of the basic code principles taught to architects and engineers.

- As with the other tragic fires with large loss of life, the need to install automatic sprinklers was also underscored. This is especially true in industrial occupancies with many combustibles.

- The need to conduct evacuation drills in industrial occupancies was also identified. At the National Fire Protection Association's annual meeting in May 1911, R. H. Newborn presented a paper on exit drills and educating factory workers.[4] A year later Mr. Newborn's paper became the NFPA's first safety-to-life publication under the title "Exit Drills in Factories, Schools, Department Stores, and Theaters."

Some good did evolve out of one of America's worst industrial fire tragedies. The National Fire Protection Association code requirements for the workplace, particularly exiting provisions, changed substantially as a result of this fire. After a number of meetings and discussions regarding topics such as fire escapes, evacuation, and sprinklers, the NFPA Committee on Safety to Life was formed in 1921. The committee's work began by expanding previous committees' publications regarding exits and related features for all occupancies and then evolved into the first publication of NFPA's Building Exits Code in 1927.[5] This later became what is known today as the Life Safety Code.

Coconut Grove (1942), Boston, Massachusetts

In 1942, another fire occurred that would also help to foster future building codes and later editions of the Life Safety Code. In one of Boston's most popular nightclubs, a fire claimed the lives of 491 patrons and injured another 200. The original reinforced-concrete building had undergone several additions over the years. There were no automatic sprinklers. The dance floor on the main floor could accommodate about 500 persons. Adjacent to the large dance floor was a room decorated with paper palm trees and a mix of other combustible decorations including cloth coverings on the walls and ceilings. A number of tables and chairs scattered throughout the space blocked or obstructed the building's six exits. Some of the exit doors were covered with drapes or even locked to control access. The primary means of egress into the club was a single revolving door. An estimated 1,000 patrons were inside at the time of the fire.[6]

According to reports, investigators believed the fire started in the basement lounge area. It spread rapidly because of the large amount of combustible decorations on the ceilings and walls. The rapidly traveling flames led the occupants to panic. The main entrance revolving door became jammed with people trying to escape. The flames and toxic gases produced during the fire killed many of those inside. Firefighters had difficulty entering the building because of the number of bodies stacked at the doors. The fire reportedly lasted only 12 minutes before it claimed the patrons' lives.

Several important findings came from this fire:

- The most notable lesson of the Coconut Grove fire was the significant role that combustible coverings and decorations can play in a fire situation. The combustible decorations, combined with both the lack of available exits and the absence of sprinkler protection, contributed substantially to the large loss of life.

- Like previous large loss-of-life fires, overcrowding and blocked or obstructed exits severely limited the occupants' ability to evacuate safely.

- Adequate enforcement of building codes and employee evacuation training also would have helped save lives.

Our Lady of Angels School (1958), Chicago, Illinois

A fire in a Chicago parochial school in 1958 took the lives of 90 students and 3 nuns. The fire originated in a pile of combustibles stored at the base of one of the stairways.[7] All but two of the building's stairways were open to the rest of the building. Many additions to the original building had been made without fire separations that would have limited the fire area. The building contained combustible interior finishes and combustible ceiling tile. It had no automatic fire sprinklers.

Students who indicated they smelled smoke were the first to notice the fire. Alerted teachers then went to find the principal, who was filling in for an ill teacher in another classroom and was not readily available. A significant delay followed before someone outside the school noticed the fire and found a phone to summon help. The students on the first floor began to evacuate.

Smoke and hot gases traveled rapidly up the open stairs. Smoke began to fill the halls and enter the classrooms through the transoms above the doors. Soon the fire had spread to a concealed space above the stairs. Shortly thereafter, the roof over the stairs collapsed. In an effort to escape the smoke and flames, some students jumped from the windows. Fire department ground ladders saved many students. Doing as they were instructed, other students perished while sitting at their desks. The lessons learned from this incident included:

- Automatic sprinklers with water flow alarms would have reduced or eliminated the loss of life at this incident.

- The open stairways created vertical passageways for the smoke to travel. Like the other fires, this event again demonstrated the need for enclosed stairs.

- The dangers of transoms over doors and combustible finishes were also identified.

Beverly Hills Supper Club (1977), Southgate, Kentucky

Thirty-five years after the Coconut Grove fire, another fire in a place of assembly took the lives of 162 people, injured 100 patrons, and caused injuries to firefighters. Factors contributing to the loss of life in this event were very similar to those in the Coconut Grove fire. Sadly, lessons learned several times over had yet to be heeded.

The Beverly Hills Supper Club was an irregular-shaped building approximately 240 feet by 260 feet. It had doubled in size after a fire destroyed the original building in 1970. The split-level building was divided into 18 large rooms with interconnecting corridors. It had no automatic sprinklers. The interior finishes along the walls and ceiling in many areas of the building were combustible.

According to reports, at the time of the fire an estimated 2,800 persons were present. Approximately 1,200 to 1,300 patrons were in the large Cabaret Room—three times the safe occupant load.[8] An insufficient number of exits were available in some areas of the building, and evidence indicated that some of the available exits were obstructed or locked. Moreover, some of the available exits were not clearly identified.

The fire possibly started from an electrical short in a plastered wall. Investigators believed it burned for some time before an employee discovered it, and an attempt to extinguish the fire delayed alerting the other occupants. When firefighters arrived, they found light smoke showing. They had difficulty entering portions of the building to conduct suppression and rescue operations because bodies near the exits blocked the doors. Many of the victims perished from smoke inhalation because they could not evacuate the building. During the incident the walls eventually collapsed.

The lessons learned from this fire are very similar to the others we have discussed:

- Automatic sprinklers would have reduced or eliminated the loss of life from fire.

- Exits need to be clearly marked and readily accessible to patrons.

- Exits must be free from obstruction or special locking arrangements.

- Combustible interior finishes again contributed to fire spread and the rapid development of smoke.

MGM Grand Hotel (1980), Las Vegas, Nevada

In 1980, a fire took place in Las Vegas, Nevada, at the MGM Grand, a 21-story high-rise hotel occupancy that also contained a large casino and convention facility. The building was only partially protected by sprinklers. The fire claimed 58 lives and caused 600 injuries to patrons and 35 injuries to fire fighters.

The fire is believed to have originated in the hotel's deli area.[9] The flames rolled out of the deli and continued inside a dropped ceiling into the casino area. The smoke rapidly spread to the high-rise portion of the complex traveling through stairways, seismic joints, elevator shafts, and the building's air handling system. Heavy smoke obscured the exits. During the event the high-rise evacuation signals did not sound. Victims were found trapped in stairwells, corridors, and even in their guest rooms.

The lessons learned included:

- A need for complete automatic sprinkler protection throughout and adequate fire separation construction in vertical openings, especially stairwells.

- The occupants' need for a means to leave the stairwell once they entered the stair enclosure. This was a significant finding at this event, and today the model building codes as well as the life safety code address requirements for re-entry from stairwells.

Happy Land Social Club (1990), Bronx, New York

A decade after the fire at the MGM Grand, a 1990 fire at a popular nightclub in the Bronx claimed the lives of 87 people. The building measured only 24-feet by 60-feet, typical of row-type occupancies found in the Bronx. A second-floor addition had been built on the original structure. When the addition took place, sprinkler protection was not extended to all areas. The building had two unenclosed stairways and combustible paneling along the interior walls.

The exit door contained a rolling security door. At the time of the fire, the rolling door was down and the exit was not readily apparent to the occupants. Other egress doors were locked and all of the exit doors had deadbolts.

Unlike the other case-study fires, this one was set intentionally. It originated in the main entrance area to the facility. An accelerant was poured and ignited. Upon the fire department's arrival, the flames were venting out the front doors. Although fire damage was limited to an area near the front door, the occupants could not escape because their only means of egress, the main entrance, was blocked by fire. Bodies were found near the entrance and on the second floor, where the smoke had traveled through the open stair to the second floor. The lessons learned from this fire were:

- A renewed emphasis on the need for complete automatic sprinklers.

- The critical importance of having at least two available exits.

Food Processing Plant (1991), Hamlet, North Carolina

Even though similar factors had contributed to previous large life-loss fires in the United States, the lessons learned did not prevent another industrial fire. Unlike the Triangle Shirtwaist Fire in 1911, the Hamlet, North Carolina food processing plant fire in 1991 occurred when technology was on the rise and many years after the establishment of fire codes. The fire spread rapidly and killed 25 people. Although the number of deaths is not as staggering as in the previous case studies, the event is relevant nonetheless because the factors contributing to the large loss of life were so similar to those in earlier years.

The food processing plant was a one-story, 33,000-square-foot building without automatic fire suppression. There had been several additions to the building. According to reports, when the fire started at 8:15 A.M., 90 employees were present.

The fire started when a hydraulic line ruptured and was ignited by a cooker. The burning hydraulic fluid sent dense smoke throughout the building obscuring visibility within minutes of the fire. The occupants tried to evacuate but encountered difficulty.

The fire investigation revealed that exterior exit doors were inoperable. Some were bolted on the outside, which prevented the occupants' escape. One of the primary means of escape was through a loading dock, but it was blocked by a semi-tractor trailer. Some employees were forced to take refuge in large coolers.

This event was significant not only to fire officials but also gained the attention of the United States Department of Labor. Shortly after the incident, the Department of Labor's Occupational Health and Safety Administration (OSHA) issued statements regarding the need to maintain a work environment safe from fire. The director of OSHA urged all employers to survey their workplace to ensure the availability of adequate exits as well as extinguishers and an evacuation plan.

The contributing factors in the food processing plant fire deaths were identical to those in the industrial fire that led to the development of the Life Safety Code. The lack of sufficient available exits combined with the absence of automatic sprinklers and an evacuation plan led to the deaths.

How can we prevent future tragedies? The answer is complex but achievable. Is there a problem with how we administer fire prevention programs? Yes; however, we have made more progress in the last 10 years than in the 50 before that. The rest of this chapter explores what has been discussed and proposed to address our future needs.

Where Do We Go From Here?

Where we go from here is a big question—a question that needs to be explored further by looking at the Wingspread Conference Reports on fire in America. The initial Wingspread Conference convened in 1966 in the Johnson, or Wingspread, House in Racine, Wisconsin. Three other conferences have followed, each 10 years apart, with the most recent in 1996. A virtual "Who's Who in the American Fire Service" has attended all of these conferences.[10] The purpose of the Wingspread conferences is to discuss issues of emerging interest and importance as well as to reevaluate our current roles and responsibilities as a fire service. These discussions have continued to advance an awareness of the diverse interests of fire departments, both volunteer or paid. The number and types of services being provided by various departments throughout the country are broad and numerous. The conferences have further determined that "each fire department must define its capabilities and educate its customers of reasonable expectations. The highest levels of service should be the challenge of every fire service organization."[11]

Six basic issues of national importance have emerged:

- *Customer Care.* The emergency services have an opportunity to increase their value at little cost by preparing the community to deal with natural disasters, fires, medical emergencies, and other incidents. These programs are not directly connected with emergency response or operations but in fact are more in line with prevention and mitigation functions such as public information and education.

- *Managed Care.* Escalating health care costs and insurance costs are driving more people than ever before to use 911 as their source of medical care. This discussion spawned ideas to radically change the delivery of emergency medical services. Again, this attempt at managed care is an opportunity for fire prevention bureaus or divisions to explore their potential in public education, wellness awareness education and information, and making the right decision.

- *Competition and Marketing.* Wingspread's intent was to recognize that if the fire service is to survive, it must market its services and demonstrate their value. We cover this in detail in our Public Information Officer chapter.

- *Service Delivery.* This topic speaks to deployment, response times, and service level objectives of the overall system. This book details risk management and planning, which is crucial in order to keep costs down and provide sufficient public protection. Increased prevention and planning functions can significantly lower the overhead costs of emergency response. This must be aggressively tackled if departments are going to survive in the future.

- *Wellness.* This issue addresses the need for fire service employees to make sure they are physically fit, mentally prepared, and emotionally healthy. In order to provide proper support and service, we must be at our best.

> The emergency services can increase their value at little cost by preparing the community to deal with emergencies.

> If the fire service is to survive, it must market its services and demonstrate their value.

✔ **service delivery**
deployment, response times, and service level objectives of the overall fire service system

✔ **wellness**
being physically fit, mentally prepared, and emotionally healthy

- **Political Realities.** This topic stresses the overall importance of good labor/management and customer relations to maximize our overall impact on our communities. Politics is a reality and the fire service must be better prepared to deal with it.

The conference also discussed seven "Ongoing Issues of National Importance." These included:

- **Leadership.** This discussion expressed a critical need for leadership development to move the fire service into the future, particularly with our dynamic environments and evolving political and fiscal challenges. Again, strong fire prevention and mitigation offers a good venue for strong leaders to emerge by providing high-level protection and service at minimal cost.

- **Prevention and Public Education.** This discussion again emphasized the need to expand this resource.

- **Training and Education.** This topic addresses managers' increasing their professional and leadership roles in order to remain credible to policy makers, administration, staff, and the public. The participants expressed the need to accomplish this through nationally recognized standards and certifications.

- **Fire and Life Safety Systems.** This issue concerns the need for adopting and supporting more codes and standards that mandate these protective systems' use. Again, this emphasizes the important need for fire prevention and mitigation program support.

- **Strategic Partnerships.** Participants explored the need for the fire service to reach out and enlist the support of other individuals and groups in accomplishing the overall mission of fire protection and emergency service response. Fire prevention bureaus are a good connection point because of the need to involve so many different organizations. We discuss this in several chapters in this book and cannot overemphasize its importance.

- **Data.** As discussed in this chapter, measurable data are crucial to understanding where we have been and where we are going. Fire prevention bureaus and divisions are major players in this role. Quality data and improved analysis are a must.

- **Environmental Issues.** These issues concern the need for the fire service to comply with local and federal laws in both mitigating incidents and providing for the safety and welfare of our employees and partners.

The Wingspread Conference reports provide insight on pressing issues. They are certainly not an exclusive list but a good foundation for future thinking. Ironically, where we are is largely where we have already been. The most important lesson from these conferences is our need to become familiar with the past to improve the future. Discussion and debate on these and other issues are vital to the success of our overall mission. Future Wingspread conferences will report our national progress and coming needs. Hopefully, the overall progressive thinking and strategic planning in prevention and mitigation that we propose in this text will help us to move in the appropriate direction.

"America Burning"

Ever since the destruction of Jamestown by fire in 1608, Americans continually have developed tougher codes to prevent such tragedies; however, as the case studies illustrate, devastating fires continue to occur. A big part of the reason for this is our failure to enact codes and legislation until after incidents occur. This keeps our fire prevention and mitigation efforts always at least one step behind the available technology. Not until the mid-1970s did the United States finally begin to take a proactive scientific approach to our fire problem. This research continues to improve year-by-year as technological advances enable us to better study fire behavior and its effects on design applications.

> Failure to enact codes and legislation until after incidents occur keeps fire prevention and mitigation efforts always at least one step behind the available technology.

For the serious fire protection professional, the detailed report *America Burning* is essential reading (copies of this report can be obtained from the U.S. Fire Administration in Emmitsburg, Maryland). Although a long document, it explains America's overall fire problem going into the 1970s and the issues that needed to be addressed. Many of the issues identified then still play a significant role in fire prevention in the 21st century. The report provides a detailed summary of findings and trends, which it then categorizes, with recommendations for mitigating the hazards we had already created and, unfortunately, continue to create.

Most destructive fires are caused by the careless actions of people, largely through apathy or ignorance.[12] When we speak of fire injury, we mean property damage, personal injury, fiscal impact, and the like. As a result of fire, in the early 1970s thousands of people were being killed or seriously injured. Many factors played a part in creating the fire environment that caused these injuries. *America Burning* identified a number of issues, some of which remain crucial to implementing successful fire prevention efforts[13]:

> Most destructive fires are caused by the careless actions of people, largely through apathy or ignorance.

- The nation needs to place more emphasis on fire prevention.
- The fire services need better training and education.
- Americans must be educated about fire safety.
- In both design and materials, the environment in which Americans live and work presents unnecessary hazards.
- The fire protection features of buildings need to be improved.
- Important areas of research are being neglected.

The needs identified almost 30 years ago are still the key elements for furthering our fire prevention efforts today. Although we are making great strides in most of these areas, a lot still must be done to achieve the goals and objectives outlined in this report.

Greater Emphasis on Fire Prevention

Fire service professionals must shift from overwhelmingly emphasizing response functions to stressing prevention functions.

America Burning identified several causes of our ongoing fire problem, but indifference is the biggest. People who have experienced a hostile fire firsthand will never forget it; however, most Americans think the dangers of fire's destructive powers are at worst very remote. The apathetic norm believes "It could never happen to me!" Indifference is prevalent even today, when it would seem most inexcusable. For example, there are those even in the fire service who are unaware of their field's state-of-the-art technology.[7] Many fire chiefs and their administrators alike talk about fire prevention but do little to promote or support it. Drawing attention to emergency operations and response programs is much easier because the BRT (Big Red Truck) is far more visible and evident, suggesting that equipment and method of fire protection is the way and the light. This rings true more than ever, particularly as a result of September 11, 2001. A great deal of attention is centered on the fire service response but little to fire prevention.

The public feeds this attitude. People are enthralled with "Big Red" as it comes screaming and honking down the street, while they think of the fire inspector visiting a business merely as a thorn in someone's side, interrupting their busy day. Is it not ironic that one can become a hero responding to a tragedy as it is unfolding, but an inspector who visits a business to prevent or greatly mitigate those tragedies is frequently viewed as a "badge heavy thug"? Fire service professionals must do more to shift the paradigm from overwhelmingly emphasizing response functions to stressing more proactive and efficient prevention functions.

Better Training and Education

Shortly after *America Burning*'s publication, the fire service was examined in detail. Considerable new research asked questions like "What other ways can we do things?" These studies identified planning as a major element of fire service organizational management. Attempts to finally identify and attack the "real" target became a focus for the fire service. Drawing much attention was the need for a National Fire Academy, not only to teach fire suppression and mitigation techniques but also to increase administrators' competencies in management and planning. The subsequent creation of this academy has fostered great effort to address the educational issues.

While the National Fire Academy's existence has helped fire prevention efforts tremendously, ironically it has at the same time compounded our problem. By its very nature, the mission of the fire service is extremely broad. Although it will vary from municipality to municipality or county to county, it typically involves a plethora of tasks. These can include EMS, fire fighting, USAR (urban search and rescue), emergency management, wildland fire fighting, hazardous materials response, and various recovery tasks, to name just a few. With these responsibilities comes the need to train firefighters to perform all of the tasks involved. Many departments have mandatory training requirements, allotting time for each shift. These requirements must be met between running calls, which is the principle reason for their existence, and performing numerous other duties.

If fire prevention work is as important as we believe, then departments must also factor in technical training on those functions. In reality, it becomes very difficult for a fire protection professional to be really good at so many different things. Fire prevention is our most important responsibility and must be a significant consideration in the fire service's overall mission; however, the methods of addressing this are complex.

If fire prevention work is as important as we believe, then departments must also factor in technical training on those functions.

Smaller departments can benefit significantly from the use of line personnel in performing inspection activities, but a large municipal department's much more extensive staff allows it to have more technically experienced personnel do proactive and aggressive fire prevention work. This is no different than relying on a technically trained USAR team to deal with a significant collapse rather than depending on one or two engine companies who may have never been involved in this type of incident, let alone received the specific training necessary. Chapter 5 further examines staffing and structuring of fire prevention bureaus to accomplish these complicated tasks.

These comments are not to criticize those departments, companies, or individuals who have had to perform tasks without adequate training. If you have been in fire prevention long enough, you are bound to have faced this situation. However, while training is critical both for operations and prevention, the time has come to carefully analyze how to conduct training in order to achieve the best results for the mission at hand. Maybe training engine companies on a little bit of everything is satisfactory. But maybe a very specific and dedicated training program for each group based on their responsibilities would better suit the local jurisdiction's needs and public demands.

Public Fire Safety Education

The need for public fire safety education comes back to the issue of apathy. The current news media are unlike anything we have ever seen. From the comfort of your living room or office you can watch tragic events unfold in real time halfway across the globe. This information transfer is marvelous in one respect; however, some suggest that it has numbed people to reality. Many people remember watching television, seeing the California Highway Patrol and Los Angeles Police Department chase O. J. Simpson down various freeways, joking about whether it was a movie or the real thing. So, while we can transmit photos, stories, interviews, and sometimes very graphic photos of tragic fire events, many people see them no differently than the made-for-television movie they watched the night before. They understand it happened and can recite many details, but the "realness," the significance of the event to their life, seems too removed to be credible.

So then, education must be interactive and animated. It must be timed appropriately, and it must match the immediate needs and values of the individuals we are trying to reach. If we are presenting an aggressive fire prevention program to a group of parents who are late picking up their kids from afternoon soccer or baseball, they are not likely to have a very committed interest. The presentation given to them where they currently are does not appear to relate to them at their present point in life and, therefore, does not demand their attention. They are distracted by more immediate events such as picking up their kids before they are left alone in a big park after dark. Our education efforts must better match the mainstream of communication, as it exists today. This may include e-mail, television spots, highway traffic message signs, as well as other means (**Figure 2.2**).

Figure 2.2 Our education efforts must better match the mainstream of communication as it exists today. This may include everything from e-mail and television spots to old-fashioned signboards.

In both design and materials, Americans' living and working environments present unnecessary hazards. Building designers pay minimal attention to fire safety in the buildings they design. These individuals and the owners who hire them unknowingly treat the model fire and life safety codes as "maximum" requirements, which all too often are watered down through the design and development process. Fire protection professionals are trained that fire codes are minimum requirements; however, these same people are frequently frustrated by the design community's misconception that fire code requirements are exaggerated and unnecessary maximum requirements.

Additionally, the types of materials we use in construction today typify the hazards of our living and working environment. In the early 1900s various fire research was done to determine time/temperature measurements of a typical large fire. The results were published and are still used today as the **Standard Fire Test**. The materials burned were wood, natural linens, and other ordinary combustible materials, generally considered class A materials.

Today, however, we have plastics, phenolics, glues, and other chemical compounds that have greatly changed the types of fires we face. While the Standard Test Fire had a fairly predictable and consistent curve, fires today are anything but standard. Many current code applications and designs still reference the Standard Test Fire. This is not a problem as long as designers and inspectors consider what has taken place since the Standard Test Fire was established and how it relates to the proposed construction. The Standard Test Fire gives fire protection professionals a good idea of a given design's or structure's relative performance. However, to make across-the-board comparisons of the Standard Test Fire performance to fire performance with today's materials is inappropriate. In these instances the fire protection professional may make determinations that necessitate applying the code more restrictively in order to provide more protection. The designer(s) may object, thinking the code official is being over-restrictive. For these reasons, the fire service must do a better job of educating designers in the potential outcomes of their proposals and in how their decisions affect designs based on the code requirements in effect. This does not mean that designs or decisions are bad; it just means that designers and officials have to be on the same page and better understand the overall impact of proposed designs and environments.

Neglected Areas of Research

Fire service research has actually been improving at an astonishing rate. For many years, the fire service did not do much research. Among the various reasons for this were the lack of funding as well as a lack of an academic focus. Technological limitations also played an important role as laborious and detailed computations could not be performed timely enough to be effective. With the advent of the personal computer and the improvement of minicomputers and high-end computers such as the Cray Supercomputer, our ability to perform research has increased exponentially, particularly over the last ten years. Many of us can remember running hydraulic programs to calculate sprinkler designs on small PCs that had to run all night; then, right when they were about to finish the iterations, they would crash due to insufficient memory. We have come a long way, in part thanks to the Internet, which has enabled us to share more information faster and obtain state-of-the-art research tools directly. Research needs to continue, but the fire service has made great strides and will only continue to improve.

✔ **Standard Fire Test**
published results of research that determined time/temperature measurements of a typical large fire in the early twentieth century

An additional finding in the commission's report was the fire service's inability to gather information and correlate nationwide trends or results. As late as the 1970s the fire service was ill equipped to handle this problem. "Time and time again—in listening to testimony, in studying the fire problem, in searching for solutions—this Commission found an appalling gap in data and information that effectively separated us from sure knowledge of various aspects of the fire problem."[14] Fire departments in large municipalities were addressing their local fire problems well; however, many were blind to trends prevalent in adjoining communities or nationwide because there was no good clearinghouse for sharing and comparing information. This was a significant and tragic lack of communication that, in effect, prevented any holistic fire prevention efforts for a number of years.

Research Organizations

Today a number of organizations at the local, state, and federal levels can assist fire prevention bureaus. The number of organizations is too many to discuss each in great detail, so we can note only a few here. The *Fire Protection Handbook*, nineteenth edition, published by the National Fire Protection Association, provides a detailed listing of organizations with fire protection interests.

Private Organizations

National Fire Protection Association The National Fire Protection Association (NFPA) based in Quincy, Massachusetts, promulgates fire codes and standards. Currently the NFPA publishes more than 210 codes and standards. These documents make a significant impact on all aspects of fire protection because they are considered the "standard of good practice" that forms a basis for legislation at all levels of the government from the local to the federal.

NFPA is an independent voluntary nonprofit organization that has over 60,000 members from industry, fire departments, architecture and engineering firms, and others. The revenues generated by their publications, membership dues, and seminars support the organization. The activities of NFPA are either technical or educational. An excellent resource for fire protection professionals is NFPA's one-stop data shop. They can provide summaries of incidents relating to a specific occupancy or type of fire.

Insurance Organizations The Factory Mutual System based in Norwood, Massachusetts, is well known for its loss prevention engineering, research, and training expertise. It can provide information on property loss prevention worldwide. It also provides technical reference manuals or *Factory Mutual Global Loss Prevention Data Books* that fire departments can obtain as a useful resource. These books not only provide Factory Mutual's recommended fire safety practices but also provide information on loss history that can be invaluable in making various risk management decisions.

Insurance Services Office, Inc. (ISO), provides a municipal grading service. Based on their ability to perform, fire departments are assigned a numerical grade of 1 to 10, with 10 as the lowest. The municipality's insurance premiums are then based on the fire department's grade.

Fire Testing Laboratories Underwriters Laboratories, Inc. (UL), is a not-for-profit organization whose purpose is to promote safety through scientific investigation, testing, and study of various materials and products. Fire protection professionals rely on UL and similar organizations to test fire protection equipment, such as fire extinguishers, sprinklers, and fire alarm components. Once equipment has been tested according to UL, it will bear the UL label. Many times fire protection professionals will verify through UL that a product is being installed or used in accordance with its UL listing.

Southwest Research Institute (SwRI) is another nonprofit organization devoted to government and industry. SwRI is divided into four sections focusing on different aspects of fire technology: Standard Testing Services, Fire Performance, Fire Chemistry, and the Applied Environmental Toxicology sections.

Another entity that performs testing and research is the Factory Mutual Research Corporation. This organization conducts research and development for property loss control and operates a third-party certification program commonly known as approvals. Similar to UL, Factory Mutual approves products and materials beneficial to loss prevention for their insured clients.

Professional Organizations A number of professional organizations have an interest in fire protection including the International Association of Fire Chiefs (IAFC), the International Association of Arson Investigators (IAAI), the International Association of Black Professional Fire Fighters (IABPFF), the International Association of Fire Fighters (IAFF), the Fire Marshals Association of North America (FMNA), Women in the Fire Service (WFS), and the Society of Fire Protection Engineers (SFPE). The many similar state or local organizations can be located by contacting your state fire marshal's office or other appropriate state agencies.

Many other professional organizations have a more specific mission within the overall interest of fire protection. An excellent resource for all fire protection professionals is the International Fire Service Training Association (IFSTA). The purpose of IFSTA is to validate fire service training materials for publication. These manuals are written by fire service and fire protection experts and reviewed by fire safety professionals from a variety of organizations. A unique validation process ensures the technical quality of this organization's products. Those interested in becoming a part of the IFSTA validation process can complete an application found on the IFSTA website at www.ifsta.org.

Federal Fire Protection Organizations

United States Fire Administration The United States Fire Administration (USFA) administers the federal data and analysis program and serves as the primary agency to coordinate arson control programs at the state and federal levels. This agency also administers a program concerned with firefighter health and safety.

National Fire Academy Located in Emmitsburg, Maryland, the National Fire Academy is part of the Federal Emergency Management Agency's office of training and its National Emergency Training Center. The National Fire Academy provides training programs ranging from fire service management to fire prevention. It is an excellent resource for fire-prevention-related topics as well as an outstanding educational institution. All fire service professionals should take advantage of courses and services offered by the National Fire Academy.

United States Forest Service The United States Forest Service (USFS) provides technical and financial assistance to state forestry organizations to improve fire protection efficiency. The USFS also provides fire protection for millions of acres of forests and grasslands.

Bureau of Alcohol, Tobacco, and Firearms The Bureau of Alcohol, Tobacco, and Firearms (BATF) is a branch of the United States Department of the Treasury. The BATF conducts arson investigations and provides fire investigation training and technical assistance to local and state law enforcement agencies as well as those fire departments responsible for conducting fire investigations.

Consumer Product Safety Commission Canada's Consumer Product Safety Commission (CPSC) collects data related to product failure and investigates injuries from products.

State and Local Organizations

State and local organizations will vary. The most common are local insurance providers, civic groups, and even large corporations. State fire marshal offices are located throughout the United States, with the exception of Colorado and Hawaii. Fire marshal's functions vary from state to state but can include:

- Code enforcement
- Fire and arson investigation
- Plan review
- Inspections
- Fire data collection
- Fire data analysis
- Fire legislation development
- Public education
- Fire service training
- Licensing

Every fire protection professional should know what fire prevention related services are provided at the state level.

State functions differ from those of local fire prevention offices since they must take care of the whole state. Typically state functions cover those parts of the state that are unincorporated or outside home-rule cities. For example, training may be provided for small outlying fire districts or departments that cannot afford their own training division or sections. The state facilitates this by providing resident and other courses throughout their state. Also, jurisdictions that do not have fire investigators typically can call upon the state to assist with or conduct an investigation, particularly if arson is suspected.

The staffs at state agencies generally are limited and their workload fairly intense. Like local jurisdictions, they must wade through the political peaks and valleys to obtain funding and resources; however, the problem of convincing legislatures most of the time is far more difficult and trying than having to deal with local elected officials or policy makers.

Summary

Codes are not new to the 21st century. They have been in place in some form or another since ancient times. The codes in place today have evolved as a result of many fire tragedies. It is important for the fire protection profession to understand the relevance of historical fire events. This lays the groundwork for how we got where we are today in the field of fire prevention. Many situations in fire prevention professionals' careers will require them to explain "Why do we need to do that?" or "What is the purpose or intent of this code requirement?" If they understand what led to the fundamental requirements in most model codes, they will be capable of explaining the purpose of or reasoning for code requirements.

The document *America Burning* as well as national conferences such as Wingspread have identified the fire problem in the United States and proposed alternatives to address our fire problem. Many issues identified over 20 years ago still need attention. Today's fire protection professionals face the challenge to move forward in addressing the country's fire problem and ensure we do not replicate the conditions that led to the tragic fires identified in this chapter.

Chapter 2 Review Exercises

2.1 How does learning about historical fires help an inspector do his or her job better? _____

_____

_____

2.2 How do tragic fires influence fire prevention? _____

_____

_____

2.3 What were some of the earliest established fire prevention rules? _____

_____

_____

2.4 What are the lessons learned from the Iroquois Theater fire in 1903? ___

_____

_____

2.5 What significant finding of the Triangle Shirtwaist Fire has become one of the principle exiting requirements in all of today's model building codes?

_____

_____

_____

2.6 What national fire protection publication was produced as a result of the Triangle Shirtwaist Fire? What was this publication later called? _____

_____

_____

2.7 What lessons were learned from Our Lady of Angels fire in Chicago?

_____

_____

2.8 What factors led to significant loss of life in the Beverly Hills Supper Club Fire? _____

_____

_____

2.9 Compare and contrast the Triangle Shirtwaist fire with the food processing plant fire in Hamlet, North Carolina. _____

_____

_____

2.10 What are the Wingspread Conferences? _____

_____

_____

2.11   What six basic issues of national importance were identified in the
        1996 Wingspread Conference? _____

        _____

        _____

        _____

        _____

        _____

        _____

2.12   Seven ongoing issues of national importance were listed in the
        Wingspread Conference of 1996. Rank them in order of importance
        and summarize why they are ranked as they are.

1.   _____

        _____

2.   _____

        _____

3.   _____

        _____

4.   _____

        _____

5.   _____

        _____

6.   _____

        _____

7.   _____

        _____

2.13   What is *America Burning*? _____

        _____

        _____

        _____

2.14   Name five key issues identified in *America Burning* and explain why
        each is important.

        _____

        _____

        _____

2.15 What is the Standard Test Fire and what is its use today? _____

_____

_____

2.16 What are some important areas of research that are being neglected?

_____

_____

2.17 What is the NFPA? _____

_____

_____

2.18 Name two fire testing laboratories. _____

_____

_____

2.19 Name five functions that state fire marshal's offices can provide. _____

_____

_____

2.20 Discuss how the United States Fire Administration works to better fire protection in America. _____

_____

_____

2.21 Discuss how all tragic fires are related and how the outcomes could be significantly altered. _____

_____

_____

NOTES

1. Pages from the Past, "Theater Was 'Fireproof' Like a Stove but 602 Persons Lost Their Lives," *Fire Engineering* (August 1977).

2. Ibid.

3. Paul E. Teague, "Case Histories: Fires Influencing the Life Safety Code," in Ron Cote, *Life Safety Code Handbook* (Quincy, Mass.: National Fire Protection Association, 2000), pp. 931–933.

4. Ibid.

5. Ibid.

6. Pages from the Past, "Flammable Decorations, Lack of Exits Create Tragedy at Coconut Grove," *Fire Engineering* (August 1977).

7. Chester Babcock and Rexford Wilson, "The Chicago School Fire," *NFPA Quarterly* (January 1959).

8. Richard L. Best, "Tragedy in Kentucky," *Fire Journal* (January 1978).

9. Richard L. Best, *Investigation Report on the MGM Grand Hotel Fire* (Quincy, Mass.: National Fire Protection Association, 1982).

10. International Association of Fire Chiefs, et al., The Fire and Emergency Services in the United States, Wingspread IV, October 23–25, 1996.

11. Ibid.

12. Arthur E. Cote and Jim L. Linville, *Fire Protection Handbook*, 17th ed. (Quincy, Mass.: National Fire Protection Association, 1991).

13. NCFPC, *America Burning: Report of the U.S. National Commission on Fire Prevention and Control* (Washington, D.C.: U.S. Government Printing Office, 1973).

14. Ibid.

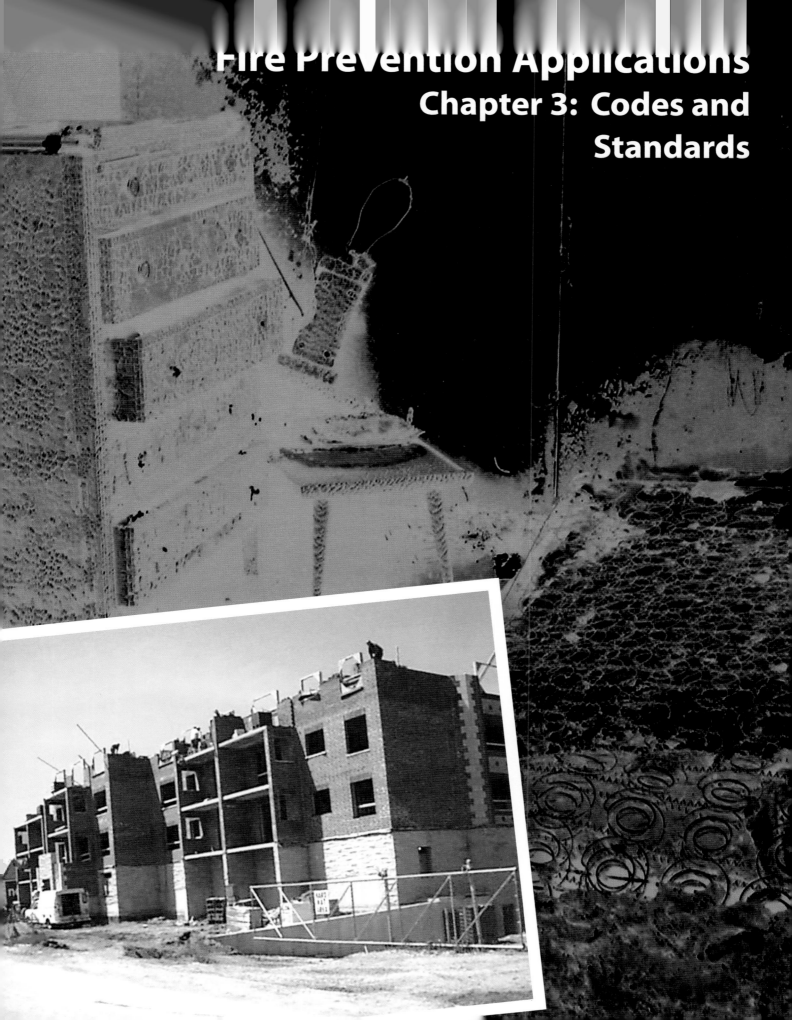

FESHE COURSE OBJECTIVES

1. Identify the laws, rules, codes and other regulations relevant to fire protection and the author authority having jurisdiction.*

2. Understand the difference between a code and a standard.

3. Identify public, federal, state, and private organizations related to fire prevention.

4. Understand performance-based designs and their impact on fire departments.

U.S. Fire Administration Objective

Chapter 3
Codes and Standards

What Are Codes?

Building and fire codes have existed a long time. Although the early codes' enforcement may have been a little stricter, their detail was not nearly as comprehensive as today's. The first well-known use of codes was recorded about 1800 B.C. The Code of Hammurabi was said to state, "If a builder builds a house for a man and does not make its construction firm and the house collapses and causes the death of the owner, that builder shall be put to death."

When we use the term *code*, we are referring to a body of law systematically arranged to define requirements pertaining to the safety of the general public from fire and other calamities. The purpose of codes is to establish *minimum* requirements for life safety. Codes provide a means of reducing hazards by regulating design and construction methods, controlling ignition sources and fuel arrangement. Codes are a shared responsibility between the public and private sectors.

A major shift in technical advancement started around the turn of the 20th century. Unfortunately, code development during that period stemmed primarily from disasters that had already taken place. After the disasters, changes would be made to prevent or mitigate the recurrence of the same situation. An example comes from the great Chicago fire of 1871. After that fire, Lloyd's of London, a large insurance underwriting firm, stopped writing policies in Chicago because buildings were being constructed so poorly. Other insurance carriers in the area also had great difficulty selling policies because they had to charge such high rates to cover their forecast losses. Even with those high rates, the insurance companies still lost more money in payouts than they gained through premiums because the fires grew larger even than initially feared. The reluctance to consider overall fire risk and design buildings accordingly led to substantial **community injury**, which we will define as including any significant loss of property or monetary value, as well as physical injury or death.

Just prior to the great earthquake in San Francisco, California, in April 1906, the National Board of Fire Underwriters (NBFU), now known as the American Insurance Association (AIA), published the first edition of its *Recommended Building Code*, which later would become the *National Building Code* (NBC)].[1]

✔ **code**
a body of law systematically arranged to define requirements pertaining to the safety of the general public from fire and other calamities

The purpose of codes is to establish *minimum* requirements for life safety.

✔ **community injury**
any significant loss of property or monetary value, as well as physical injury or death

This document provided uniformity in specifications that reduced the spread of fire by requiring construction of what it termed Class A buildings. These were basically fire resistive shells that could withstand substantial fire and exposure, likely losing contents but lending themselves to quick renovation and remodeling. These expectations were borne out in the conflagration that followed the earthquake. In that fire, 452 people were killed and 28,000 buildings were lost. The few buildings in San Francisco that were designed to the *Recommended Building Code*'s Class A criteria remained mostly intact and could be returned to service relatively quickly.

After various significant fires, larger communities began adopting recommended codes and standards. Insurance companies that were hard pressed to continue paying large amounts in claims endorsed many of these regulations, while local community governments forced other requirements. Keep in mind that large companies or corporations that have substantial properties in a community wield a great deal of power regarding fire protection for their locations and the surrounding areas. These big companies typically had property insurance carriers that had a strong vested interest in protecting their clients. Naturally if a large tire plant burned down, that loss would be difficult for a single insurance company to cover. To prevent significant incidents resulting in large loss, the insurers would exert tremendous pressure on their clients to use state of the art fire protection systems and administrative controls. In some cases, the pressure extended to the surrounding community, whose infrastructure may have been needed to provide water supplies, access, public fire protection, and other resources. In other instances, large insureds actually created their own internal fire departments to cover their risk because the surrounding communities did not have sufficient resources. Any number of these locations exist today, many of which provide supplemental protection as a service to their neighboring communities. The net result helped the entire community because everyone reaped the benefits of overall increased fire protection, not only from preventing the direct impact that a fire would have but also in avoiding the loss of jobs and economic instability that would have resulted.

Insurance Services Office

Another practice that significantly affected how fire protection was managed or mandated was **grading**, or **fire suppression rating schedules**. Slightly different than codes, these were basically methods by which the level of fire suppression capabilities was evaluated and credited to individual property fire insurance rates. This process was initially started by the NBFU and later adopted by the Insurance Services Office (ISO). Different revisions have been made over time, but the rating scales operate much the same way today. These schedules worked by providing an analysis of a given community's fire protection capabilities and grading them.

✔ **grading**
(fire suppression rating schedule)
method of evaluating fire suppression capabilities and crediting them to individual property fire insurance rates

The 1980 FSR Schedule gave relative weights of:

Water Supply	40%
Fire Department	50%
Fire Alarm	10%

These 1980 elements were further broken down in weighted subcategories:

Water Supply

Supplyworks, fire flow delivery, and distribution of hydrants	35%
Hydrants—size, type, and installation	2%
Hydrants—inspection and condition	3%

Fire Department

Engine companies	11%
Ladder companies	6%
Distribution of companies	4%
Pumper capacity	5%
Department staffing	15%
Training	9%

Fire Alarm System

Receipt of fire alarms	2%
Operators	3%
Alarm dispatch circuit facilities	5%

ISO sends a representative(s) to evaluate the community based on these elements and then determines a grading number of Class 1 through Class 10. Class 1 receives the highest rate recognition, and Class 10 receives no recognition.[2] This classification then is factored into the underwriting of various properties. Not all insurance companies use this schedule or grading, but it is still a common reference by which fire departments compare their level of service and protection to that of other agencies. Many experts believe that fire service accreditation will surpass the grading method as a means of properly evaluating a community's fire protection capabilities.

Many experts believe that fire service accreditation will surpass the grading method as a means of properly evaluating a community's fire protection capabilities.

What Are Standards?

When we talk about codes and standards some clarification can help. Is there a difference between the two? Yes. Codes typically are thought of as written documents that answer the questions who, what, when, and where concerning various requirements and their enforcement. **Standards** dictate how something is to be done. For example, the 1997 edition of the Uniform Fire Code requires that automatic fire sprinklers be installed throughout apartment houses

✔ **standard**
document that details how something is to be done in order to comply with the applicable codes

containing 16 or more apartment units. Assuming a municipality has legally adopted this code into law, we can break it down for discussion to see:

Who required it?	The authority having jurisdiction by reason of adopting the code into law
What is required?	Automatic fire sprinklers
When is it required?	When an apartment building has 16 of more units
Where is it required?	Throughout the apartment house

For guidance on *how* to install the automatic sprinklers, the Uniform Fire Code refers us to the Uniform Building Code Standards #38-1, which with minor modification is NFPA 13, *Standard for the Installation of Sprinkler Systems*. The standard answers the final question:

How do we do it?	According to UBC Standards 38-1

Codes are typically adopted by a jurisdiction or state and incorporated into the law that governs the community or state, such as a city charter, book of ordinances, or local or even state law. Standards are then adopted by reference through the adopted code.

An easy way to remember the difference between codes and standards is that codes tells you *what* to do and standards tell you *how* to do it. For example, throughout the 2000 International Fire Code are references to standards. It codifies (arranges in a logical order) these individual standards, lists them specifically, and declares them to be part of the code. Most model code standards are taken from other standards, such as the National Fire Protection Association standards. The model code publisher will either reference the standard it derives from or copy the standard verbatim, deleting or inserting specific elements, wording, or requirements, to meet the model code's particular needs. The new document is then numbered or named as a specific model code standard. It is important for jurisdictions to specifically adopt the relevant or desired standards they want to use and to list them in the code or in a separate ordinance or law. A jurisdiction never should assume that specific documents are referenced or included when it adopts a model code. The fire codes and standards written by the National Fire Protection Association are not even addressed in the model codes, and the municipality cannot enforce them unless they have been specifically adopted.

Jurisdictions must specifically adopt the relevant or desired standards they want to use and list them in the code or in a separate ordinance or law.

Appendices

Another important aspect of code language involves appendices. Appendices in model codes or individual standards contain a great deal of information ranging from background material, history, simplified tables or interpretations, to good fire protection practices. Time after time, jurisdictions have tried to enforce comments or elements contained within the appendix of a various code or standard; however, they cannot do this legally unless the material is specifically included and adopted. We recommend including the entire appendix or appendices in any state or local ordinance that adopts a code.

Federal Laws and Properties

Chapter 2 examined many federal agencies that have set forth regulations designed to ensure the safety of the public. These regulations cover a broad spectrum of activities and include such matters as employee safety, transportation of hazardous materials, patient safety in health care facilities, access issues for handicapped citizens, and minimum housing standards. The federal agency that sets the standards in any particular area typically is also responsible for enforcing them. However, in some cases, such as workplace safety laws, the state or county may choose to enforce federal regulations, as opposed to having the federal agency do it.

Generally, federal laws can be enacted to provide: (1) that all state laws on the same subject are superseded by the federal law, (2) that state laws not conflicting with the federal law remain valid, or (3) that any state law will prevail if it is more stringent than the federal law.[3] Examples of federal agencies include the Occupational Safety and Health Administration (OSHA), the Department of Health and Human Services (HHS), and the Consumer Product Safety Commission (CPSC).

In most cases, the local fire department is not responsible for enforcing federal regulations; however, we affectionately term those instances when the department is required to enforce federal or state requirements "Unfunded Mandates." In those instances where we do not have jurisdiction and we find hazards or violations, the department should know how and where to report them to see that they are corrected.

In comparing how local, state, and federal fire prevention laws work, we will contrast their applicability in a make-believe city of 300,000 people. The City of Make-Believe Fire Department has fire code jurisdiction over everything within the city boundaries. This means that the department adopts its own local fire code. It may either adopt one of the model codes as is or adopt a model code with local amendments or requirements.

Now the United States Postal Service decides to build a new post office in the middle of downtown. That facility must comply with federal fire codes, but it is not required to comply with the City of Make-Believe's local laws because federal property is exempt from local regulation (**Figure 3.1**). Out of courtesy, the federal government will likely ask the city organization for input on the plans, but the city has no obligation to comply. While Make-Believe has no legal authority to force the federal government to comply, it does have some motivational alternatives to exert pressure to gain a level of compliance or at least cooperation with local laws. Most municipal ordinances do not require the fire department to respond to all fires. Typically the language is such that the department has the authority (the right to do so if it chooses) to respond, but it does this at the chief's discretion. So, an interesting discussion to have with the Post Office representatives would be to ask them who will provide fire protection for them, should a fire occur? The Post Office's answer likely would be, "The City

Figure 3.1 Fire departments may lack inspection authority at federal buildings and have to rely on professional courtesy to accomplish their mission.

of Make-Believe." To negotiate compliance, the city might respond something like this: "I'm sorry, you are a federal reservation and, therefore, we have no responsibility to protect your installation. While we would like to provide that service as a good neighbor there are some issues that must be addressed. For our crews to perform this task properly and safely, we would need you to follow the same codes and standards all of our community follows, so that we can provide the best service and protection possible." This may provide a little incentive for the Post Office to cooperate. Is it "political blackmail"? Yes, but the issue is entirely political. We do not necessarily recommend going to this extreme, but it does provide an example of how jurisdictional games might play out among various entities and jurisdictions. We find it difficult to believe that there are jurisdictional or governing entities that are not concerned about the well being of their citizens. The issues are typically financial. When conflict arises, it usually involves determining what level of protection is "adequate." In utilizing a "systems approach," which is what we encourage throughout this book, this example shows how very important relationships and coalitions are to solving fire protection problems before they become exaggerated or emotional.

Territorial or jurisdictional differences do not exist solely to frustrate regulatory agencies or cause problems. Their intent is to allow certain levels of autonomy regarding various operations and responsibilities. It is important to remember that federal buildings within a local jurisdiction are not required to comply with local codes. In the past, the agencies that operated these buildings usually enforced their own fire protection regulations with the assistance of the General Services Administration (GSA). In recent years, however, the government has shown more willingness to follow local codes in community federal facilities. Relationships with the people responsible for extraterritorial properties should be fostered to ensure that fire protection is maintained at a high level, regardless of which code is followed.

State Laws and Statutes

In addition to enforcing selected federal laws, states are empowered to enforce state laws and statutes. A state government may also regulate specific fire inspection or code activities within its jurisdiction. For example, some states may specifically assign the duty to inspect nursing homes, schools, and daycare centers to the state fire marshal's office or another state entity. The local authority may be prohibited from enforcing any codes in these locations. Other states may assign particular jurisdictional powers to different agencies, such as a department of public safety or department of human services. States that have a state fire marshal typically reserve the responsibility for administration and enforcement of state laws that relate to fire and life safety as well as training. This often includes the authority and responsibility to investigate fires and crimes of arson and to enforce fire codes and some building codes.

The variations of duties and responsibilities among states are great. Some states have adopted codes that all local jurisdictions must enforce at a minimum. Others have mandated that state codes be used regardless of local desires. Many others have adopted some combination of the two, where state law will apply only if no other local regulation exists, or if there is a conflict the more stringent of the two laws shall apply.

State laws can also specify building construction and maintenance details in terms of fire protection and empower agencies to issue regulations. State labor laws, insurance laws, and health laws also have a bearing on fire safety and sometimes encompass fire inspection responsibilities.

Local Laws and Ordinances

Local laws and ordinances, although sometimes based on state laws, are more specific and tailored toward the exact needs of the county, municipality, or fire protection district. Typically, states allow local jurisdictions to adopt state regulations, either by reference or as enabling acts. To **adopt by reference** means that the local jurisdiction will follow the state laws exactly as drawn. Adopting them as **enabling acts** allows the local jurisdiction to use state laws as a basis but then amend them based on local needs or preference. Specifically how this is accomplished will vary from community to community and from state to state.

✔ **adoption by reference**
a local jurisdiction's formal decision to follow state laws exactly as drawn

✔ **enabling act**
method of adopting state regulations that allows the local jurisdiction to amend them based on local needs or preferences

General Principles of Fire Codes and Standards

Laws and ordinances should be kept current in order to meet growth and other changes in the community. Fire safety regulations generally fall into one of three categories:

Laws and ordinances should be kept current in order to meet growth and other changes in the community.

- Those that govern the construction and occupancy of a building when it is being planned and constructed

- Those that regulate activities conducted within a building once it has been constructed

- Those that govern the maintenance of building components

Fire departments should be involved in adopting codes that address all three categories; however, their degree of involvement in each will vary from jurisdiction to jurisdiction. Typically, the building code specifies how to construct a building to prevent the spread of fire by construction features or hazard arrangement, and fire prevention codes regulate the activities in a finished structure. The fire code, then, historically has been the code that details how to properly safeguard the activities or operations in the building, basically referred to as the **maintenance code.** While this

Figure 3.2 Fire prevention personnel are involved in all phases of the construction process. *Photos courtesy of the Mount Prospect Fire Department*

✔ **maintenance code**
code that details how to properly safeguard the activities or operations in a building

particular argument is still made in certain circles, we believe it does not apply today. Fire codes and standards are becoming extremely complex and technical with requirements that are far more relevant to the initial construction of facilities or processes rather than simply to their maintenance (**Figure 3.2**).

Tremendous amounts of information are being integrated into fire codes. This is a result of many factors:

- Highly skilled fire prevention staff (fire protection engineers)
- Improved technology
- Computer applications
- Web based communication
- Mission focus
- Budget constraints

This improved availability of information has allowed a variety of information to find its way into the fire codes and standards as never before. While fire codes of years past concentrated primarily on the building's use and occupancy classification, those today are integrating more and more detail into sections on hazardous materials, manufacturing or system processes, system operations, and the like. This makes the fire code integral to the initial construction of a facility.

Appeals Procedures

Code requirements from most jurisdictions may be appealed. The process is fairly straightforward but should be spelled out specifically for all to see and clearly understand. Basically if a code or standard requirement is imposed upon an individual or company, the individual or company should comply with it. However, in some instances the requirement may be viewed as overly restrictive or impractical. Most codes give the AHJ some authority to allow certain exceptions to the specific codified requirements. Granting an exception generally requires proof of need, substantial evidence that the lack of compliance will not cause more harm than the original requirement, and possibly an alternate means to accomplish the original requirement's goal. For those instances where an alternate means or substantial justification for relief from the code cannot be provided, a variance through appeal is justified.

Individuals or businesses that feel they are incorrectly being required to do something have the right to apply for a variance. To receive consideration for a code modification, the applicant generally must make a formal written request to the AHJ. The appropriate office then analyzes the request to ensure that the general intent of the code is being observed and that the public safety is maintained. The applicant receives a signed copy of this official's decision. Detailed records of the decision are generally kept available in the fire prevention office. **Figure 3.3** shows an example of a request for the modification of a fire code.

If the applicant feels that the enforcement officer reached an unfair decision or misinterpreted the fire prevention code, the applicant may file a request with

The process for appealing code requirements should be spelled out specifically for all to see and clearly understand.

the board of appeals. Most codes establish an appeals procedure with a board of appeals or other body empowered to interpret the code and issue a ruling. The board of appeals usually consists of three to seven members who have previous experience in the fields of fire prevention or building construction. The exact number of members and their professional qualifications are specified by the adopted code.

Fire inspectors need to understand the appeals process and the workings of the board of appeals. Some issues involving the appeals process and the board of appeals with which the fire inspector must be particularly familiar include:

- Can the fire inspector continue to enforce codes on the property during the appeals process?
- Can a victory by the property owner affect the way the fire inspector enforces the code or ordinance for other properties in the future?
- Is further action required? An example might be asking the board to clarify whether it has granted a general variance or a one-time variance.

CITY OF ______________________

FIRE DEPARTMENT

APPEAL for Modification of Fire Code

Address all communications to Department of Building

Meeting Date: ______________________

Petition must be on file at the office of the Board of Appeals ______________________
one week before meeting date.

Petitioner(s) must be present at meeting.

Approvals on proposed construction are null and void unless permit is obtained within 6 months.

Address of Job ______________ (No. Street) Legal Description: Lot ____ Block ____ Tract ____

Between Cross Streets ______________ and ______________

Owner's Name ______________________

Petitioner's Name ______________________

Petitioner is: ____ Owner ____ Contractor ____ Architect ____ Engineer

Address of Petitioner ______________ (No. Street)

______________ (Phone No. City P.O. Zone)

Status of Job: ____ Not Started ____ Under Construction ____ Finished

Permit No. ______________ Plan Check No. ______________ (If permit has not been issued)

Specific ordinance modification desired: ______________________

____

____

(Additional sheets or data may be attached)

Date: ______________ Owner: ______________________

(It is understood that only those points specifically mentioned are affected by action taken on this appeal.)

Plot on Reverse Side Required by Yard Modification

Figure 3.3 Most jurisdictions have a form for citizens to request a modification of a code.

A one-time variance is binding only for the particular circumstance and may not be directly applied to other similar situations. When the board grants a general variance by reason of equivalency, the fire inspector must apply this ruling to all future code enforcement. If the board of appeals rules that the code is too vague for enforcement, the fire inspector must take steps to ensure that the code is clarified.

Adopted code regulations usually specify a time limit within which the property owner must submit any appeal. Seven days from the time of the inspection is common, but this will vary in different municipalities. The board will then accept or reject the appeal and file an appropriate notice of denial or acceptance. Rules and regulations used by the board during its hearing generally are made public. A schematic of a typical appeals process is provided in **Figure 3.4**.

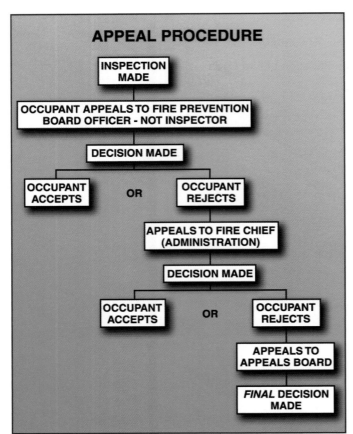

Figure 3.4 This chart shows a typical appeals process.

Today more than 50 percent of a building code usually refers in some way to fire protection.

Building Codes

The original purpose of building codes was to prevent collapse. Later changes added protection from ravages by fire or other natural disasters. Today building codes dictate how we construct buildings to resist wind, earthquakes, floods, fires, snow, and ice, as well as to avoid problems with sanitation, ventilation, loss of energy, and contamination. Not too many years ago, up to 80 percent of code content dealt with fire and life safety. Today more than 50 percent of a building code usually refers in some way to fire protection.[4] Due to this large fire protection component in building codes, some communities have designated the fire department to manage the building department along with its usual fire prevention functions. Considering the intent of the building codes and their impact on a community's fire problem, more communities might consider this approach.

Building Departments

Local building departments or agencies typically enforce building codes that designate a building official as the manager. The building official is the AHJ with regard to building requirements, just as the fire marshal is the AHJ with regard to fire prevention requirements. Building departments are organized much like fire prevention divisions in that they likely will have staff filling the following positions:

- Plans examiners
- Inspectors
- Support staff (issuing permits, licenses, enumerations, etc.)

Depending upon the jurisdiction, building departments may be staffed with public works staff (engineers, inspectors, etc.), planning staff (planners, zoning inspectors, hearing officers, etc.), flood plain managers, and a host of others involved in the development and construction process. In some jurisdictions, these interrelated functions may all be housed in a "one-stop shop" or in different locations with plans and meetings moved from office to office. Each community generally tries to provide the most customer-oriented process and organization it can with regard to performing the various tasks efficiently.

More often than not, it is the building official who recommends which model code to use. The building official is responsible for reviewing and inspecting every construction-related plan that comes through his/her jurisdiction. For this reason, he/she must provide the best recommendation for code compliance, use, and consistency. While the building code is the principle code regarding construction, others (fire, mechanical, plumbing, etc.) are viewed as companion documents. In order to maintain consistency, the appropriate companion documents or codes should accompany the model code of choice.

This provides the best overall fire protection and code management. Some jurisdictions do not have good relationships with their building departments and have adopted other codes in lieu of the companion documents referenced by the model building codes. While this can work, it gives rise to many conflicts and interpretational issues that confound designers and regulators alike. We strongly recommend using companion documents for ease and consistency in the implementation and enforcement of fire prevention codes. As you go through this text and learn of the importance of coalition building, you will see that no relationship is more critical than that of the fire official and the building official. We find that in many jurisdictions, fire marshals and building officials do not relate well. This is not a productive environment. These officials should make every effort to develop good relations. (This will become even more apparent as you read Chapter 8, "Construction Document Review.")

The appropriate companion documents or codes should always accompany the model code of choice.

Model Code Organizations

Most communities or fire protection districts adopt a code from one of the four major model fire code organizations:

- *National Fire Codes* (published by the National Fire Protection Association (NFPA)

- *BOCA National Fire Prevention Code,* published by the Building Officials and Codes Administrators International (BOCA)

- *Uniform Fire Code*, published by the International Conference of Building Officials (ICBO)

- *Standard Fire Prevention Code,* published by the Southern Building Code Congress International (SBCCI)

We have listed these four model code groups because many jurisdictions still reference these organizations and codes. However, as of the new millennium, a huge national code consolidation effort produced two new codes:

- *International Fire Code*

- *National Fire Code,* National Fire Protection Association (NFPA)

These two principle codes soon will be the only two American codes available. Only outdated versions of the model codes will remain. All of these codes are relatively good, but each has a little different flavor, if you will, that was principally designed for different parts of the country. While almost all of the fire codes from each of these model organizations are nearly identical, their parent codes or building codes have slight differences. The *Uniform Building Code* is principally used in the western United States and was first printed in 1927, at the same time as the *Building Exits Code* (later the *Life Safety Code*). The *Uniform Building Code*'s format deals more with issues concerning the western United States, such as earthquake prevention systems and installations. In 1940, the Southern Building Code Congress International (SBCCI) was formed. Another group, the Building Officials Conference of America (BOCA), already had been founded in 1915. Its members were from large East Coast cities that wrote their own codes or from smaller communities that used the National Board of Fire Underwriters' *National Building Code*. BOCA codes have been around in some form or fashion for a number of years, with the *Basic Code* printed in 1950. The acronym has been modified from its original name to Building Officials and Code Administrators and then to the current title of *BOCA National Building Code*.

BOCA'S principle target audience is the Midwest and northeastern United States. It does a very good job of addressing snow loading and heating systems. SBCCI, as its name implies, targets the southern United States. It covers many issues related to wind loading as would be expected from hurricanes that are typical along the Gulf and the East Coast.

How NFPA Codes Are Developed

Fire codes are typically developed through input from special interest groups or through consensus. Usually, proposals are sought from various individuals or organizations, reviewed by various technical committees, and then discussed in open meetings. Revisions or new drafts are provided for additional votes and comment. Once sufficient discussion has taken place, votes are cast and decisions rendered.

Most codes are developed and created in a similar fashion. The very specific rules and procedures used by all code groups are far too detailed to print here. However, in a very general sense, codes are written as follows. Technical committees or groups formulate drafts of new codes as requested. A Standards Council or other similar group generally issues the approval for certain codes or standards to be drafted and or revised if it is not already on a set printing schedule. Technical committees also may hear numerous appeals throughout a given code cycle. Once the assigned committee or group makes drafts or revisions, the drafts are then put out for public comment. The technical committee receives the comments and then makes changes. In some cases, staff makes these changes rather than a technical committee. The revised proposal is then republished for public comment. Often, hearings are held to discuss the proposals and potentially to receive comments from the floor. In other instances, residents submit comments again and the technical committee makes one last revision. The code is then ratified, accepted, and printed.

The intent is to make sure that the code development process is fair, equitable, and representative of the interested people. Codes or standards can be very time consuming and expensive to make. The process is very involved and technical and requires tremendous collaboration and interpersonal skills. We strongly recommend that anyone who is making a career of the fire service should try to get on a code committee. There is no better way to shape your knowledge of codes and the overall process of how they are made.

> Anyone who is making a career of the fire service should try to get on a code committee. There is no better way to shape your knowledge of codes and the overall process of how they are made.

Model Codes and NFPA Codes

Most code renewal cycles repeat approximately every four years. Standard renewal or revision cycles occur at about the same frequency. The important thing to glean from this is that while technology, processes, and products advance, the codes are typically outdated. Even if you are using the most current version of a code, the discussion and committee vote on that code typically occurred one to two years prior. This is a slight disadvantage to industries or designers who are on the cutting edge because frequently there can be gaps in available knowledge to judge the safety of a particular design or product.

The Reality of Fire Codes

Although fire code development has progressed significantly in the last decade, many problems remain. Insufficient research, which was pointed out in *America Burning,* still delays these documents' advancement, and other issues unfortunately still leave much of the progress to result from experiential data derived from case studies of actual fires. These experiential data make it much easier to address arguments against code provisions since past history already shows the issues are relevant and dangerous, but "averaging" requirements in a "one-size-fits-all" approach makes them inequitable for many.

Performance-Based Codes

A new breed of codes quickly coming into play is called **performance-based codes**. Performance-based codes are currently used in various countries such as New Zealand and Australia. These codes, while very labor intensive to work with, provide a designer with an opportunity to design something quite out of the ordinary, so long as it meets appropriate goals and objectives for fire and life safety. This is much like what the National Aeronautic and Space Administration (NASA) does today. They are embarking on new and different technology almost daily. They have no codes or standards for reference and therefore must create adequate engineering designs based on the desired outcomes and potential risks. Such is the objective of performance-based design.

✔ **performance-based code**
code that allows designers to determine how best to meet an individual building's unique fire protection needs

Current building and fire codes for the most part are prescriptive. As we have already discussed, the codes define exact requirements based on the occupancy classification of the building. A **prescriptive code** specifies the number of exits, fire separation requirements, construction type (what the building is made of), and fire suppression (automatic sprinklers) requirements. The authority having jurisdiction applies the code requirements during the construction document review process.

✔ **prescriptive code**
code that lists specific design requirements, such as number of exits, fire separation, construction type, and fire suppression systems

This prescriptive approach works well to meet the needs of the owners of and architects for most structures. However, there are situations where applying these types of codes may not be practical—for example, a large irregularly shaped facility with complex industrial processes or a building with highly sensitive operational requirements. In these situations, prescriptive codes will not always address all of the concerns of the building owner, the architectural design team, or the AHJ. For example, the occupancy-related or prescriptive codes may not address all of the fire resistive requirements needed for a given fire scenario that could occur in facilities such as these. A larger than normal heat release rate may be generated, or longer travel distances to the exits may be necessary because of the structure's shape and associated processes.

These difficulties lend themselves to a unique opportunity to use an alternate method—performance-based design.

Along with such opportunities, however, come additional responsibilities to ensure that the scope of the fire safety problems being addressed is well understood, that the tools and methods being used are applied properly, and that the resulting designs and levels of safety afforded are tolerable to society.[5] American performance-based codes, which have yet to hit the market, will not be nearly as thick or comprehensive as the prescriptive codes we use today.

The concept of performance-based codes is to design fire protection measures to a level of safety that the owner, the designers, and the AHJ all agree upon. This concept has also been referred to as a quantitative assessment or an engineering approach. Even though this type of design references a performance-based code, it is actually performance-based design. The latest editions of the model building codes now include provisions to allow performance-based designs. The difference in application is that the prescriptive requirements in the code are not followed under a performance-based design approach. When the model codes permit this design alternative, the term *performance-based code* is used.

Performance-based designs use scientific theories, carefully weighted assumptions, empirical formulas, and mathematical calculations to determine the probable outcomes of a fire scenario. Typically this is accomplished through the use of complex computerized fire modeling performed by a fire protection engineer. The performance-based design approach identifies specific hazards and methods to protect them. It considers the entire building's features in relation to the assumed occupants' behavior and addresses the unique building features that have triggered the need for performance-based design. When done correctly, the performance-based design will provide a comprehensive fire protection plan that addresses the uniqueness of the structure based on its anticipated conditions.

The use of performance-based codes will necessitate the religious use of all forms of human communication among fire officials and the design team. Failure is all but certain unless everyone involved understands, communicates, and decides upon all aspects of the project. Interpersonal skills will play an important part in the overall process since we will be forced to meld engineering science with practical fire fighting tactics. The accuracy of this blend is all that will stand between success and failure of a system.

In order to provide good performance-based design reviews, a fire prevention division will need to have either its own technical experts in fire protection engineering or a fire protection engineer on contract to evaluate proposed designs and models. Computer modeling will be an essential part of this practice, and as with any models, the model is not necessarily as important as the assumptions plugged into it. The fire service needs to be very careful in its approach to this process. It is a far cry from the old days of rubber-stamping plans with the comment, "Hydraulic calculations are the responsibility of the designer." The responsibility of a good fire safety design rests not only with the design or project engineer but also with the fire department plan examination staff. All must engage in dialog about risk, expectations, and outcomes. Otherwise disaster is a very real possibility.

The future of performance-based codes desperately requires the fire service's participation. While these codes can be beneficial and very flexible, a very significant pitfall awaits. If a particular building is designed for a given occupancy and all of the assumptions, modeling, and design is done to accommodate that specific occupancy, then what happens 20 years down the road when the occupancy changes? Remember that the fire service is responsible for buildings during the entire time they remain standing. Questions that beg to be answered are:

- Will we know if the occupancy changes?

- What impact will various changes have on the original performance-based design?

- How will the occupancy changes impact the performance of the life safety and fire protection systems already installed?

- Can a given building, designed under a different premise, be modified to accommodate a new occupancy at a reasonable cost?

- What role do we have in accommodating all of these changes?

- How do we inspect a building that changes from one performance-based design to another, and what skill level will an inspector need to accomplish this?

Many disconcerting issues surround performance-based designs. We must keep a proactive approach and thought process focused on this change and make certain we keep abreast of changes as they occur. Change is generally good; however, it remains to be seen if the fire service can adjust fast enough to this dynamic design process.

What does this mean to the fire protection professional? The use of performance-based designs requires the local fire marshal or his/her staff either to obtain the technical training and education to review performance-based designs or solicit the expertise of someone who already has it. It also means the fire official must have obtained sufficient data for fire inspectors who conduct inspections later to verify that conditions used in the performance-based design have not changed to alter the outcome of a fire. Ongoing fire safety management must be carefully monitored in facilities designed and constructed with a performance-based design. The local AHJ must understand the complexity of performance-based designs and establish a method to review them before one lands in his/her in-basket. Secondly, the AHJ must have a method to retain the supporting documentation of the performance-based design for future fire safety management.

Ongoing fire safety management must be carefully monitored in facilities designed and constructed with a performance-based design.

Summary

Building and fire codes have existed for some time. The codes themselves provide minimum requirements. The use of codes in the United States was developed from pressure of the insurance industry to provide a method for quality construction. Codes are rewritten through a process that permits input from the public. Because of rapid technological changes and the time it takes for the code revision cycle to be completed, codes are never current.

Today the different model codes throughout the country are somewhat consolidated resulting in two major codes related to fire protection. They include the National Fire Protection Association Building Code and the International Building Code. Most codes are referred to as prescription based codes. They tell exactly what is required. Today the codes permit a performance-based approach that allows for an engineering analysis to determine what is required.

Codes differ from standards. Codes typically cover the who, what, and when concerning their requirements. Essentially codes tell you what you have to do. A standard will tell you how to do it. The enforcement levels of the adopted codes range from the local level to the state level and the federal level. In most cases the local authority cannot enforce local codes on federal facilities. In recent years, however, the federal government has worked with local municipalities to meet their requests for compliance.

Chapter 3 Review Exercises

3.1 What are some of the historical issues or events that caused codes to be developed? _____

_____

_____

3.2 What is a code? _____

_____

_____

3.3 What is the function of the ISO? _____

_____

3.4 What is the best ISO rating that your community can receive?

_____

3.5 What total percentage can Fire Alarm System grading provide to your overall rating? _____

3.6 What is a standard? _____

_____

3.7 Explain the difference between a code and a standard and give an example of each. _____

_____

_____

_____

_____

_____

3.8 What is significant about appendices to codes or standards? _____

_____

_____

3.9 What are the three categories of fire safety regulations? _____

_____

_____

3.10 What do building codes govern? _____

_____

_____

3.11 What were the four model codes prior to their consolidation?

_____ _____

_____ _____

3.12 Identify the reasons for model code consolidation. What two codes evolved from this consolidation? _____

_____

_____

3.13 What is a performance-based code? _____

_____

_____

3.14 When are performance-based codes used? _____

_____

_____

3.15 What are the advantages of performance-based codes? _____

_____

_____

3.16 What are the disadvantages of performance-based codes? _____

_____

_____

_____

_____

_____

3.17 Explain the code development process. _____

_____

_____

_____

_____

_____

_____

_____

_____

3.18 What determines when codes are changed or modified? _____

_____

_____

3.19 Can a local jurisdiction mandate a federal institution to comply with local code? If so, how? _____

_____

_____

3.20 Which legal authority has more clout: state or local? Explain your answer. _____

_____

_____

3.21 Develop and explain a general board of appeals process. _____

_____

_____

_____

_____

_____

3.22 Who has more authority: a building official or a fire marshal? Explain your answer. _____

_____

_____

3.23 Explain why codes are not necessarily current. _____

_____

_____

_____

3.24 What is the AHJ? _____

_____

_____

Fire Prevention Applications
Chapter 4: Development and Implementation of Fire Prevention Bureaus

FESHE COURSE OBJECTIVES

1. Discuss training programs for fire prevention.*

2. Recognize the need, responsibilities, and importance of fire prevention organizations.*

3. Recognize the need, responsibilities, and importance of fire prevention as part of the overall mix of fire protection.*

4. Understand the changing work environment of the 21st century and the impact on fire prevention organizations.

5. Identify potential methods to retain and motivate fire prevention personnel.

U.S. Fire Administration Objective

Chapter 4

Development and Implementation of Fire Prevention Bureaus

Fire Prevention as a Public Business

No other function within the fire service is more like a business than the fire prevention bureau. We have as many contacts with our public as the emergency operations division, if not more; we perform more problem solving activities than any other division; we deal with irate customers; we solve problems for customers; we assist with complex designs of processes and facilities; we handle complaints among neighbors and landlords, and for that matter just about anybody. We also collect money in the form of revenue from permits, but we do not do taxes. Yet.

In an article on the fire service, as opposed to the fire business, Ronny J. Coleman wrote, "If business were the answer to all of our problems, by now we would have eliminated all but a few essential services from government. If government were the key to solving all of our ills, by now we would have eliminated all but a few major industries from the private sector and nationalized them." Coleman's points are on the money. Fire protection requires a balancing act between the public and private sectors.

Fire prevention bureaus must be empathetic to their clients. They must rigorously enforce codes and standards to protect lives and property but on the other hand must be professional and diplomatic in meeting the needs of the customer (**Figure 4.1**). As fire protection professionals we must remember that doing our job in fire prevention does not make us the heroes who ride the big red trucks. We generally aggravate people because we cost them money by pointing out their problems. However, this only increases the importance of establishing a relationship with the customer and sometimes serving in a consulting role.

The thing to remember is that fire prevention is the most important job that the fire service can perform. When our efforts prevent a fire from happening or keeping it as small as possible, we protect not only our community but also the

> No other function within the fire service is more like a business than the fire prevention bureau.

Figure 4.1 Fire prevention personnel must work with their customers no different than any other business.

> Fire prevention is the most important job that the fire service can perform.

heroes, our brothers and sisters we send to respond. Our job is sometimes the toughest and most often the least thanked, but it should be one of the most important nonemergency functions a fire department performs. However, the importance of fire prevention services and the associated staffing are easy to overlook when trying to balance a fire department's budget. One of the greatest challenges the manager of the fire prevention bureau faces is having sufficient staff to carry out fire prevention services.

Figure 4.2 Fire departments in the 21st century provide a number of services because of the incidents they are forced to handle.

In times of economic growth as well as during economic downslide, the ability to effectively address staffing issues will play a critical role in the organization's operational success. This is true whether the organization is private or public. Today, both the public and private sectors are struggling to do more with less. To address the dynamics of a changing work environment, all types of staffing options must be considered, even outsourcing the service. In the future, fire departments will continue to face the need to do more with less. The reduction of funding for fire suppression activities will likely become common in many areas of the country. Well-staffed fire prevention bureaus will likely play a more significant role in providing fire protection services along with encouraging more built-in fire suppression systems. The escalating costs of fire suppression activities combined with the direct and indirect loss from fire will continue to force fire departments to place a greater emphasis on active and passive fire protection systems. Though we stress prevention's importance, a large portion of many fire department's budgets are allocated to suppression activities. A common distribution is around 3–5 percent for prevention and 97–95 percent for the rest of the department. Staffing and equipment costs continue to rise, in turn increasing the expense of mitigating a variety of situations with which fire departments are now forced to deal (**Figures 4.2 and 4.3**). Salaries and benefits are the most expensive element in a fire department's budget (excluding all-volunteer departments). In fact, studies have shown that the costs of wage and benefit packages are outpacing the consumer price index, which could easily lead to a future when departments simply cannot afford to continue staffing as they do today. This should alert administrators and firefighters alike. If we do not start thinking about cost effectiveness, we will be putting ourselves out of a job.

Figure 4.3 Many fire department services are not directly related to fire suppression activities but instead have evolved out of need for resource justification and economies of scale.

Just a few years ago, the need to deal with the effects of terrorism was not a significant factor in most fire department budgets. Now due to the war on terrorism, fire departments face the need to provide still another service, homeland defense. That task will place yet undetermined demands on service delivery and budget.

Government entities at all levels have been portrayed frequently as overstaffed and underworked. The need for exploring a variety of staffing options was not always the case with government organizations in years past. Many elected officials have taken staffing and cost criticism seriously, seeking ways to perform services at maximum, sometimes excessive, levels with minimum staffing and at a reduced cost.

Only the future knows what budget limitations and other venues may bring changes. In the State of Colorado, for example, functions of many building departments, which in most jurisdictions are city- or county-run regulatory agencies, are operated regionally. The building departments are enterprises run autonomously through intergovernmental agreements between cities and/or towns, generally a county, and the enterprise itself. On its inception, this was actually quite resourceful. It was created to maximize cost efficiencies within local area governments, benefiting all the government entities by allowing for a staffed building department without the total burden of the cost.

Unfortunately, things do not stay the same. As communities grow, so does the workload and so does this regionalized machine. In many locations regional departments have grown so large that without proper oversight and regulation they become autonomous organizations that may or may not serve their clients to the best of their capability. They maintain their existence simply through the financial need to sustain themselves.

Some years ago, the State of Colorado passed a Taxpayers Bill of Rights (TABOR) that limits the amount of tax and other revenue a city can keep. While a good idea on the surface, this puts local government at risk of possibly having to return money to taxpayers unless a specific election is held allowing the government to keep the money.

Example: The fire prevention bureau collects $150,000.00 in revenue from permits for the first half of the fiscal year. Unfortunately, the overall city budget has hit the revenue cap established by TABOR. This means any additional money collected by the fire prevention bureau is going to count against the cap (along with any other city revenue). This leaves the fire marshal the following choices:

- Continue to charge for permits only to spend money later figuring out a way to refund the excess collected above the cap

- Stop charging for permits but continue doing the work

- Stop charging for permits and stop doing the work

The benefit to an enterprise in this situation is that it is not a governmental agency and therefore any revenue it generates in accordance with its IGA does not count against the cap. So, the regional operation can continue unimpeded by the TABOR law, whereas, the city must find alternate ways of doing its job.

This may in the future force the fire service to be very creative in its way of doing business. Not long ago many cities and counties in California went bankrupt. Privatization of fire prevention bureaus has not been typical to date, but it could easily be the way of the future if governments and the departments they operate do not pay more attention to how they do business. We will explore the use of private companies to perform municipal fire prevention bureau services later in this chapter during our discussion of staffing fire prevention bureaus.

A variety of fire prevention staffing options is available to meet the needs of the community. Identifying the best staffing option and developing the organizational structure of the fire prevention bureau is not easy. Doing so requires managers to consider a number of factors. Even though fire departments throughout the United States provide similar services, how they provide those services and the level at which they provide them will vary throughout the country. The fire prevention bureau manager, fire marshal, or fire chief must consider several critical elements in order to lead the fire prevention bureau in the right direction. These elements serve as guidelines in creating organizational structure and developing staffing options. The following steps do not include all of the tasks needed to develop the framework for a fire prevention bureau but are merely a road map for getting there.

- Ensure the organization's mission statement includes the fire prevention bureau's primary function.

- Ensure fire prevention is part of the fire department's strategic planning process.

- Adjust the organization as needed while monitoring the environment for internal and external changes and opportunities.

Ensure the Organization's Mission Statement Includes the Fire Prevention Bureau's Primary Function

The first step in staffing a fire prevention bureau or similar division of an organization is to evaluate where its function fits into the entire organization's goals and mission statement. We must create or reevaluate our mission statement. It should be on track already, but if it is not, involve the team in recreating it to spell out the things you should be doing. After that, do the same thing with vision and values statements. The **vision statement** should be a brief description of how the fire department, or more specifically the fire prevention bureau, will operate. The **value statement** should reflect ethical priorities for everyone's behavior when working on the mission. Some departments may build on this and create a code of conduct. In any case, it is important for people to be able to see how they will do what they need to do.

Mission statements should describe the purpose of the organization. These vary from being exceptionally brief to very comprehensive. Regardless of length, a major component should specifically spell out fire prevention functions. Remember, the fire service fights fire in two ways: (1) prevention and mitigation, or (2) emergency response. Why would we want to serve our public only after a bad thing happens rather than stopping it from happening

✔ **vision statement**
a brief description of how the fire department, or more specifically the fire prevention bureau, will operate

✔ **value statement**
a summary of the ethical priorities for everyone's behavior when working on the mission

✔ **mission statement**
a description of the purpose of the organization

in the first place? Would we ever buy a car and never change the oil or add any until the engine seizes and then just replace the whole car? Changing the oil regularly prevents and certainly mitigates the damage that can and will occur to an expensive engine without adequate fresh oil. Prevention is a critical function of the fire service and must be included in the department's overall mission.

When the mission statement of a fire department clearly establishes the role of the fire prevention bureau, it informs the entire community (the customers) as well as the fire department of the fire prevention bureau's significance. The fire prevention bureau must not be structured to function independently within the fire department but to function with the other divisions of the organization. The fire prevention bureau must understand the other divisions' goals as well. Conversely, other divisions within the organization must be capable of identifying the organization's fire prevention focus. Each division must share the mission of the fire department and understand all of the divisions' roles to carry out the mission.

Fire department mission statements may be common in many areas of the country, but this was not always the case. Like many other management issues, looking to the private sector for management models has not been widely accepted as a useful tool.

The mission statement should answer the following questions[1]:

- Who are we? This simply identifies the organization and sometimes its service; for example, fire department, fire and rescue, fire and emergency medical services, or public safety.

- In general, what basic social or political needs do we exist to meet, or what basic social or political problems do we exist to address? The answers to this question frequently address the community's risks and how the organization will address them; for example, "Reduce the number of children and senior citizen fire deaths through extensive fire safety education." Focus on the community's needs and the fire department's capabilities to address those needs.

- In general, what do we do to recognize, anticipate, and respond to these needs or problems? That is, how do we identify problems and what actions will we take to address them? In other words what justifies our organization's existence?

- How do we respond to our key stakeholders? The question simply asks, "What are we going to do?" The answer: provide fire, rescue, special teams, and fire prevention services. The stakeholders are the citizens, or customers.

- What are our philosophy, values, and culture? This simply determines our attitudes and beliefs, or what type of people make up our organization.

- What makes us distinctive or unique? The business world or private sector may refer to this as a niche. Why are we better than the rest? What

> When a fire department's mission statement clearly establishes the role of the fire prevention bureau, it informs the entire community (the customers) as well as the fire department of the fire prevention bureau's significance.

do we do that makes us stand out compared to similar organizations? Possible answers might include, "We are all volunteer"; "We are cost effective"; or "We provide a quality service."

These are the guidelines for developing a mission statement for the entire fire department. The challenge is to answer the questions to include the efforts and needs of the fire prevention bureau. Remember, this is the framework for why the fire department exists—the "why are we here?" The individuals learning and applying the mission statement are not just those assigned to the fire prevention bureau. They include every person employed by the fire department. The desired outcome of incorporating fire prevention in the mission statement is to make it everyone's responsibility. With that in mind, one person or one division cannot develop the mission statement (**Figure 4.4**).

If a fire department does not consider input from the local government, it may create a mission statement to address a problem its governing body does not consider significant. Keep in mind, the mission statement should not be so complicated that the average citizen does not understand it. The citizens are your customers or stakeholders, and your mission statement should have the power to become one of your fire department's best public information tools.

Here are some examples of mission statements from a variety of fire departments:

Figure 4.4 Organizational meetings are very important for keeping the focus on the mission and accomplishing goals and objectives.

- Colorado Springs Fire Department: "To mitigate the threat to life and property from fire, medical and other emergencies through education, prevention, community preparedness, emergency response and recovery programs."

- Mount Prospect (Illinois) Fire Department: "The mission of the Mount Prospect Fire Department is to eliminate injury and loss of life due to the causes of fire and to reduce and control fire losses to property through comprehensive programs of fire prevention, public education, fire suppression and rescue, within the scope of the resources provided."

- Colorado Springs Fire Prevention Division: "To promote a safer community through hazard mitigation, fire prevention, fire code development and enforcement, fire investigation, public education and injury prevention, hazardous materials regulation, and wildland fire risk management."

Ensure the Fire Prevention Bureau Is Part of the Fire Department's Strategic Planning Process

Fire departments are proud of their local tradition and heritage. If you ask why a department does something in a certain way, a common response is, "We have always done it that way." One thing is certain; the fire service today is not the same as yesterday. The entire world around us is constantly changing. Consider the evolution of the computer, the rapidly changing diversity of our culture, demographic changes, state and federally mandated compliance, not to mention a sometimes volatile economy that can literally change overnight. Not too long ago one big change in the fire service came with the development of the National Fire Protection Association (NFPA) Standard 1500, *Occupational Safety and Health for the Fire Service.* This standard impacted not only the way we fight fires but the way we sleep, the way we get dressed, the way we do laundry, and the way we go to the fire. In the early 2000s, fire departments face the new challenge of compliance with NFPA 1710, *Standard for the Organization and Deployment of Fire Suppression Operations, Emergency Medical Operations and Special Operations to the Public by Career Fire Departments.* This document is not only causing tremendous heated controversy on the topic but will likely require communities to spend hundreds of thousands or even millions of dollars as they strive to provide consistent expectations for response times, station locations, and resources. Biological weapons and terrorist training are now national, state, and local priorities. Fire departments that want to survive and be adequately trained must be willing to respond to all of these developing changes.

If we go from an anecdotal explanation to a more scientific statistical analysis, the call distribution for most of the U.S. fire service is comprised mostly of medical incidents. The frequency and volume of fires are gradually declining or remaining mostly steady. In fact, the typical urban fire department is seeing a decline of roughly two percent annually in population-adjusted fire incident rates.[2] Examining various fire departments throughout the country in light of this trend, we can see that the decrease is commensurate with an increased involvement in fire prevention activities, such as plan review, inspections, and risk management. This too is substantiated in a survey conducted by the Colorado Springs Fire Department. Looking at what urban fire departments are doing to reduce their overall increasing workload, fairly recent programs aimed at fire prevention appear to be having a dramatic impact:

- Proactive education programs at nursing homes
- Low-hazard inspections reduced from annually to every five years
- Fewer vehicles responding to selected types of incidents
- Public education programs for EMS
- Smoke detector blitzes in key areas like housing projects
- Aggressive inspection programs
- Public education and awareness programs
- Ambulance service providers taking nonemergency medical calls[3]

Five of the eight functions in this list are related directly to fire prevention. In fact, one of them showed an adjustment to the historically significant fire prevention function of low-hazard fire inspections. This adjustment is possible because we are better targeting our efforts and able to quantify the net results of our efforts. For this reason alone, a fire chief would be foolish not to include fire prevention activities as a major part, if not the most important part, of strategic or long-range planning.

The best way an organization either public or private can cope with constant changes is to think strategically. The best tool to accomplish this is strategic planning. A number of books and courses available at the National Fire Academy address strategic planning. Fire prevention bureau managers should learn as much as they can about strategic planning and take an active role in the fire department's strategic planning process. It is beyond the scope of this text to go into great detail about the strategic planning process; however, since it is so important, we will provide a rough template that could serve as a starting point. Remember, though, Fortune 500 companies spend vast amounts of money and time on this very task. It is not easy, nor should it be taken lightly, but it is possible and can be accomplished at any level.

> Fire prevention bureau managers should learn as much as they can about strategic planning and take an active role in the fire department's strategic planning process.

Strategic planning produces a number of benefits to the organization. The most obvious is the ability to think and act strategically. A benefit of taking part in the strategic planning process is having input into the plan and its implementation. It is here that fire prevention becomes crucial to the organization. When the fire prevention bureau is involved in the strategic planning process, it has the opportunity to communicate the challenges it expects to face. Keep in mind, one of the outcomes of the strategic planning process is to make a cohesive plan that addresses the challenges of the entire fire department while producing a number of other benefits. For example, strategic planning:

- Defines the purpose and objectives for specific hazards based on your organizational mission and values

- Creates an environment where your entire department has ownership

- Creates synergy by pushing everyone to be his or her best all at the same time

- Communicates goals and strategies to your clients and the policy makers

- Helps make sure you are using your department's resources to their fullest

- Provides a benchmark or baseline from which to measure progress

The results of the strategic planning process will most likely last into the future and benefit the fire department for many years to come. For example, a fire department in the late sixties or early seventies may have included new approaches involving a paradigm shift, such as beginning delivery of emergency medical services or starting a fire safety education program (**Figure 4.5**). Today

Figure 4.5 Fire and life safety education is a critical service provided by fire departments.

we look at these as obvious functions of most fire departments. However, fire departments at that time did not commonly provide these services.

Conducting strategic planning effectively is not easy or quick. The process should not be undertaken if the developed strategic plan is not likely to be implemented. Planning takes time and resources. To develop a plan for addressing identified problems, it is imperative that the organization have the ability to collect and interpret data to identify the problems it faces. You cannot begin developing a strategic plan if you cannot identify your problems or challenges. With the proper information, the strategic planning team will be better equipped to arm the fire chief with the data to fight for the resources and to implement the solution to the problem. At some point, the fire chief will need to bring the strategic plan forward for implementation. Most likely this will require resources, either in the form of personnel or equipment. One step to help ensure the governing body will endorse this endeavor is to get their support before you begin the planning process. In fact, they may have challenged the organization and be anxious for a plan to be implemented.

> Getting the governing body's support before you begin the planning process will help ensure that it will endorse this endeavor.

There are a number of strategic planning models to choose from. Almost every strategic planning model includes the steps of developing the mission statement, creating the vision, and developing strategic goals. Developing strategic goals can generate in-depth discussion. Keep strategic goals specific enough that there is no question about what you are tying to accomplish but vague enough that you do not get bogged down in the strategies for accomplishing the goals. For example, the Bureau of Alcohol, Tobacco, and Firearms (ATF) has the following strategic goal:

Effectively contribute to a safer America by reducing firearms, explosives, and arson related violent crimes.

This is specific in that it states the desire to create a safer country by reducing firearms, explosives, and arson as a weapon.

The ATF's strategic goal does not go into detail on how it is to be accomplished. That comes in the next planning phase, which is the development of strategies. ATF's strategic initiatives are to:

- Safeguard the public from arson and explosives incidents
- Deny criminals access to firearms
- Remove violent offenders from our communities
- Prevent violence through community outreach

Each of these elements is a specific strategy that the bureau will use to accomplish its strategic goal. Individual groups can then subdivide each of the strategies further to focus on specific tasks or missions. Easy, isn't it?

The last but very important step is to document your plan. Put it in a format that is easy to read and that can be distributed to everyone. Some organizations have put their plans in the form of a contract; do whatever you feel is comfortable to your group, but then have the members sign it. All of the team signs the document affirming their commitment and understanding as they helped create it. Then all you have to do is implement, evaluate, and correct. You have just completed your first strategic plan.

Determine the Level of Fire Prevention Services

Given that the mission of the fire department must include fire prevention, the question that remains to be addressed is what level of fire prevention service to provide. The mission of the fire department commonly includes an element of fire prevention such as reducing the number of fire deaths or reducing the fire loss. Achieving this is not an easy task. The level of commitment to meet these goals must begin with the governing body of the fire department. This may be the most critical element in the establishment and management of a fire prevention bureau. It creates the foundation for staffing levels and for the fire prevention bureau's organizational framework.

The level of commitment to meet fire prevention goals must begin with the governing body of the fire department.

These services will vary considerably from department to department. In some jurisdictions, fire departments or fire districts may provide services for several communities or municipalities. This may require the department to perform different types of plan reviews or inspections depending upon each locale's preference. As an example, one town's building department may do all of the new construction plan reviews and inspections while leaving the routine fire inspections to the fire protection district. Others may want the jurisdiction to handle all plan review activities and inspections. These differences can be challenging as staffing and resources can be difficult to manage and juggle. Service delivery should be determined and agreed on through an intergovernmental agreement (IGA), a contract, or at least a memorandum of understanding (MOU). We strongly recommend that these agreements lock in time frames for service delivery and also include service performance criteria. They should contain a clause or phrase that spells out periodic discussions among the various clients and the jurisdiction to facilitate proper planning and prevent any surprises.

Another method of determining what level of fire prevention services to provide is through strategic planning. If you conduct a thorough strategic plan and your elected officials, board, or governing authority approves the plan, they have in effect bought in. They are then committed as best they can to support and further your mission and direction. This is an excellent mechanism that can provide a great many resources without the continual inconveniences and distractions of having to come back time after time to ask for approval.

Retain and Motivate Staff

While family demands spur employee's desires, highly qualified people still give great weight to salaries. However, studies have shown that salary alone is not a key factor to motivate or retain employees. Smaller fire departments probably have a greater need for higher quality work, as they do not typically have numerous local experts in every field, such as fire protection engineering. Ironically, these smaller departments typically cannot afford the salaries needed to attract quality (highly trained) staff, let alone retain them. Upward mobility in the organization is another problem. Some departments that staff their bureaus with sworn personnel may attract individuals based on promotional opportunities. Using promotional opportunities to attract individuals into the fire prevention bureau is a sound concept. However, the cost of those promotional opportunities may increase the budget. These organizations will soon out-price themselves and be forced to find different avenues of attracting and retaining personnel.

Fire departments that use civilian personnel have the opportunity to do a better job of recruiting and retaining employees because these individuals choose and are selected to do a specific job, as opposed to being rotated in from fire suppression for a year or two and then being sent back (**Figure 4.6**).

Whether the fire department uses civilians, sworn personnel, or outsources its staff, it definitely needs to attract, motivate, and retain fire prevention bureau personnel. Nothing is more frustrating to a fire prevention bureau manager than having a good employee spend two years in fire prevention and then go back to suppression or, in the case of a civilian, leave for another department. The bureau has spent considerable time training the individual and now must start the process all over again, raising costs and lowering productivity.

Studies have shown that salary alone is not a key factor to motivate or retain employees.

Figure 4.6 Rotating suppression personnel to the fire prevention bureau requires the manager to continuously train new staff.

According to the Employment Policy Foundation, the work force is changing. In the last fifty years, the traditional workforce of "stay at home mom" and "working husband" has declined. Married couple families in which both spouses work represent 70 percent of married families and one-half of all families. With job demands forcing more parents to be away from their children, employees focus more on quality of life than on pay. Earnings alone do not play as important a role in job satisfaction as they once did. The increased demands on the working parent filter over into the workplace. Employees need flexible enough conditions to balance the needs of their families with the demands of their jobs.

In 2000, the International Personnel Management Association identified the top eleven trends in human resource management. Work life issues such as family leave, flextime, telecommuting, and humanizing the workplace ranked fifth. Shifting demographics such as labor pool shortages and shorter tenure of workers ranked sixth in the survey, while implementing compensation packages to include an alternative rewards program ranked eighth. Part of the change in compensation packages can be attributed to an increased number of men sharing more of the child-rearing tasks. This in turn demands more of their time. Some private sector companies are using formal policies such as flextime, paid leave, and unpaid leave to address the unique pressures faced by working fathers.

Work scheduling has changed significantly in recent years and continues to do so well into the 21st century. Alternatives to the five-day, eight-hour work schedule come in a variety of forms. Alternative schedules commonly known as flextime and compressed workweeks may soon become more prevalent in public agencies, such as fire prevention bureaus. Flextime has been in the workplace since the 1970s and consists of allowing employees to choose their work hours within limits established by the employer. The band of start and stop times may vary by as little as fifteen minutes; some situations allow employees to periodically balance shorter and longer days over a week or more. The government and the private sector offer a similar extent and variety of flextime programs.

The Bureau of National Affairs indicates many employees value flextime because it allows them to adjust their work schedule to meet family obligations and other personal responsibilities. Flextime can allow employees to avoid rush-hour traffic, accommodate childcare schedules, coordinate with public transportation, and fit the work schedule of the employee's spouse. Many employers have argued that problems such as scheduling meetings and the lack of supervision can arise from a flextime policy. Flextime also can involve legal issues, such as meal periods, timekeeping, and state overtime/maximum-hour requirements.

Another scheduling alternative is the **compressed workweek**. This arrangement is increasing among employers interested in helping employees manage family and work demands. A compressed workweek schedule permits full-time employees to perform the equivalent of a week's work in fewer than five days. Compressed work weeks can achieve many work scheduling objectives, such as improving recruitment and decreasing turnover, increasing employee

✔ **flextime**
scheduling system that allows employees to choose their work hours within limits established by the employer

✔ **compressed workweek**
scheduling system that permits full-time employees to perform the equivalent of a week's work in fewer than five days

loyalty, extending customer service hours, improving scheduling flexibility, reducing work and personal conflicts, and increasing the opportunity for the employees to further their education. As with any policy, the compressed work week does have some disadvantages. These include problems accounting for holidays, the impact on other employees, and legal considerations, such as the Fair Labor Standards Act and record keeping requirements. Because the compressed workweek means working fewer but longer days each week, employees may become tired and less productive at the conclusion of those longer days.

Even with the disadvantages of work scheduling alternatives, they can offer many benefits to a government entity, such as a fire prevention bureau. The bureau can use scheduling alternatives to attract and retain employees. The variety of staffing options available for the fire prevention bureau may include individuals used to the traditional fire department schedule of working 24 hours and being off 48. Even if they are still sworn members of the fire department assigned to the fire prevention bureau, the change in scheduling a 40-hour workweek may affect the individual personally. One disadvantage of the 40-hour workweek usually associated with fire prevention is that it lacks the scheduling flexibility offered to sworn or shift personnel.

The nonprofit sector is examining retention strategies to counter the corporate world's incentives for potential and current workers. Many non-profit employers, such as fire departments, are realizing they cannot match for-profit organization's cash. Still, it is important that fire prevention bureaus are staffed with the best-qualified individuals. Those individuals may or may not be sworn members of the fire department. Having something that may entice them to join the fire prevention bureau can benefit recruitment as well as retention of that individual for an extended time. Work-life benefits and flexibility are two ways for nonprofit organizations to retain employees (**Figure 4.7**).

The fire department should not focus just on benefits as a method of retention but also on programs within the department that address the needs of the work force. They can start by focusing on the same human resource programs as the private sector. For example, for a number of years the private sector has been successful using mentoring programs for employees. Mentoring programs provide the opportunity for the new employee to learn from one of the more seasoned or veteran employees. The concept is to provide an atmosphere conducive to continuous learning. Also, the new employee has a person he or she can trust and ask questions. This benefits the company as well because an individual who is winding down his or her career can find a new sense of self-worth by being needed to train the newer employee. Hopefully the veteran employee's guidance can keep the new employee from getting frustrated and possibly leaving the organization.

> The fire department should not focus just on benefits as a method of retention but also on programs within the department that address the needs of the work force.

Figure 4.7 Nonprofit organizations can use work-life benefits to compete with the higher pay offered by private employers.

Why not use this concept in a fire department to retain employees and provide an opportunity for a veteran firefighter or inspector to teach the rookie what has been learned over an entire career? This is exactly what McHenry Township Fire Protection District did. McHenry Township Fire Protection District is an extended suburb of Chicago, Illinois. The fire department is comprised of 151 volunteer members who protect an area of 56 square miles out of three fire stations. One of this volunteer department's unique aspects is that 38 of its 151 members are also full-time career firefighters on other fire departments. In this fire department, the seasoned or experienced firefighter may not necessarily be the most senior or the oldest firefighter.

The fire department has been using what they referred to as a big brother/big sister program for over 25 years. Essentially this was their mentoring program. Each candidate, or rookie, was assigned a big brother or big sister. The intent of the program was to provide a contact person for the new candidate. Although the program had been successful, the department began to experience a significant turnover rate among new recruits. This turnover rate forced the fire department to evaluate the existing mentoring program. The department formed a committee and formalized the existing mentoring program to include a candidate's booklet that serves as a tool for the new candidate and the mentor. The booklet explains many of the fire department's operations, procedures, and policies. It also provides the big brother or big sister with topics to discuss one-on-one with the candidate (**Figure 4.8**). The big brother or big sister is the contact person for the candidate and serves as the candidate's liaison to the department.

Since the McHenry Township Fire Department began using their revised mentoring program and candidate's booklet, they have been able to retain their candidates. Most all of the candidates have exceeded training expectations and continue to achieve high test scores on the State of Illinois' written certification exams. Many of the candidates have excelled to the point where they are taking on additional roles in fire and life safety education and as apparatus engineers.

This is a great example of adapting a human resource program from the private sector to the fire department. This type of program easily could be applied to train and retain fire prevention staff.

Figure 4.8 Mentoring can serve as an excellent means to ensure new fire fighters or fire prevention personnel have a contact for questions and method for continuous learning. *Courtesy of McHenry County Fire Protection District*

Adjust the Organization as Needed While Monitoring the Environment for Internal and External Changes and Opportunities

One thing is certain; nothing remains the same. As fire protection professionals we must be able to change the way we do business to meet the needs of our customers while mitigating the risks of the community. Just like many businesses, our customers can change. In fire prevention, the community may undergo demographic changes that create a new target audience for fire and life safety education. For example, if a large senior citizen housing complex or development was constructed in a small community, the community would have a significantly increased senior population that required a different approach to fire and life safety education. The number of citizens in the high-risk group for fire deaths also has increased. Another change that fire protection professionals may have to accommodate is reduction in staff and or funding; the fire prevention bureau will have to refocus its efforts. Or conversely, the fire prevention bureau may be approved to hire additional staff because of the new development, or it may have received a large grant for fire prevention programs. The following list of some basic principles about change comes from a presentation entitled "The Human Side of Change with Russ Linden, of Russ Linden and Associates":

- Change is inevitable. One of your jobs is to help people realize this truth: It's not whether we change; it's how we deal with the inevitability of change.

- Most organizations are good at "waiting them out" and "wearing them down." Therefore, your persistence is critical. (However, persistence alone is not enough. You need to include the other points that follow below.)

- Most people, when told of a major change, ask (in their heads if not out loud):

  — Why? Why this change?

  — What's in it for me (WIIFM)?

- Change leaders must provide answers to these questions, directly, early.

- These are cynical times. Therefore, your credibility is absolutely essential. Be sure that you are honest with people. Always. As Mark Twain once said, "Tell the truth and you don't have to have nearly as good a memory."

- Most people treat change as a loss. Thus people must be allowed to go through the stages of loss. Dr. Elisabeth Kubler-Ross learned in her work with dying patients, the stages people go through are fairly predictable:

  — Shock, denial ("It can't be me")

> Fire protection professionals we must be able to change the way they do business to meet their customers' needs while mitigating the risks of the community.

— Anger ("Why the hell is it me?")

— Bargaining ("If only this could be put off until _____ happens")

— Depression (the loss of all hope)

— Acceptance

- Most change is pain driven. Most of us continue doing what we do until we become dissatisfied with the status quo. Thus, leaders must help people articulate the "pain," or cost of continuing to do business the same way.

- Most people are supportive of changes they help to design. Thus, involvement is a key to successful change.

- During major change, you can never communicate enough. Most of us don't hear the message the first time (or second, third either!). Leaders must continually discuss the goal, rationale, and impact of the change on others.

- More important than leaders' words are their actions. Those actions must be consistent with the goals of the change.

- People need hope, a reason to believe that this time it will work. Early successes' visible proof of change helps others get past their skepticism.

No matter what is causing the change, fire prevention bureaus must manage the change and the change process. Those involved in the change will react to the change. Reaction to change is a normal part of the process. The challenge to the change manager is to make the most of the positive reactions and minimize the consequences of the negative ones. Individuals either will accept and support the change, comply in action without actually supporting the change, or just be as resistant as possible.

> The key to the success of any change is in communicating it to all those involved while giving them the opportunity to offer feedback.

The key to the success of any change is in communicating it to all those involved while giving them the opportunity to offer feedback. This communication needs to be continuous. If the change is directed from the top of the organization down, then there must be a means to communicate back to the top of the organization. Communication is the most important aspect of dealing with change. A survey conducted by Wake County, North Carolina, during a major reengineering effort asked employees what communication medium worked best. Most employees favored direct face-to-face communication from the supervisor, with written notes or communications next, and what we will term as the grapevine last. No means of communication, however, is more difficult than face-to-face. It takes time and can be very laborious but achieves the best results. The key is not for the "Big Guy or Gal" to come around with the message; the troops would much rather hear from their supervisor. That supervisor is the person with whom they must deal, whom they must believe, and with whom they generally have the best rapport. If the supervisor has bought in, the troops generally will, too.

Fire protection professionals must also keep in mind that they, too, are agents of change. In many situations they are actively trying to cause change. Sometimes they may wait to take advantage of either the political climate or a pertinent event before they begin the change process. Remember our previous discussions of code changes that resulted from tragedies? The individuals responsible for those changes initiated them when the climate was conducive. They were monitoring their environment for change opportunities.

Causing change is not always an easy task. The fire inspector may be trying to change how an industrial operation stores flammable liquids, or the fire and life safety educator may be trying to modify the behavior of adults who do not see the importance of testing smoke detectors or practicing a home escape plan. Fire protection professionals are definitely agents of change, and while effecting changes, they should keep these simple guidelines in mind:

- Help people let go of the old stuff before we expect them to grab onto the new stuff.

- Remember Einstein's quote: "Thinking as we are has brought us to where we have already been. In order to go somewhere else, we must think in a different way."

- Identify your steps (beginning, middle, and end). People like closure and want to know the status of ongoing processes.

- Remember that change generally involves some type of loss or failure.

- Let people have feelings. They do not necessarily need to act on them but they should have them.

Summary

Fire Prevention is one of the most important functions that a fire department performs. While in America it typically garners only 3–5 percent of a fire department's total operating budget, it is probably the most important loss control function the department can provide.

The cost of providing fire protection services is constantly increasing. In fact, it could easily be argued that the cost is outpacing most communities' ability to pay for it. For this reason, fire prevention—mitigating and preventing incidents before they occur—is truly the best bang for the buck.

In addressing service delivery, fire departments must work harder at trying to be competitive both in costs, price, and service delivery. The construction industry has essentially moved to an all fast-track approach. This means a fire prevention bureau that is involved in new construction plan reviews and inspections needs to respond to quick changes in economic conditions affecting construction and building permit activities. This means as a fire service we should be more empathetic to designers and contractor's needs as well as being capable of providing technical resources and assistance to many people who are not typically capable of staying current on fire code issues. This may also involve dynamic solutions for staffing options. Providing good technical services necessitates adequate resources and funding.

In staffing a fire prevention bureau, many issues must be considered. Some jurisdictions may prefer to staff the bureau with sworn personnel while others may prefer to use civilians. There are pros and cons with both.

Mission statements are critical to fire department administration, but it is imperative that fire prevention bureaus have clear and concise mission statements regardless. Early and regular involvement in short-range planning and particularly in long-range strategic planning, especially at a high level within the organization, will assist in keeping employees focused on their jobs. It will also allow managers to hit their target and assist the entire department in doing a better job of saving life and property.

Another important consideration for utilizing well-managed fire prevention programs is the overall impact on response time standards. Good fire prevention and injury prevention programs can drastically reduce call volume, which in turn can reduce response time to alarms. This occurs because the more companies a department can keep in service, the less the demand upon adjacent still districts to cover particular alarms. Basically, if a company is in quarters more often, it is available to run on calls. If it is exceptionally busy, other companies from outside the district will have to cover overlapping calls, which increases overall response times. This will become more of a factor as NFPA 1710, *The Standard for the Organization and Deployment of Fire Suppression Operations, Emergency Medical Operations and Special Operations to the Public by Career Fire Departments*, becomes more widely recognized.

Managers must remember that their most important asset is their employees. Do all you can to provide promotional opportunities and stay abreast of changes in your overall environment. These changes may be internal or external. Either way, change is hard for everyone. Be prepared and prepare your staff. Change is inevitable and if done right, will keep your operation on the cutting edge.

Chapter 4 Review Exercises

4.1 Explain some ways in which the fire service can be more customer friendly. _____

_____

_____

_____

_____

_____

4.2 What percentage of a fire department's overall budget is typically allocated to fire prevention? _____

4.3 Why do fire prevention bureaus need to consider staffing options?

_____

_____

_____

_____

4.4 Name some ways a fire prevention bureau may be alternately funded and staffed. _____

_____

_____

4.5 Why would developers want to privatize a fire prevention bureau? Is this a good thing? Why? _____

_____

_____

_____

_____

4.6 What is the best method to staff a fire prevention bureau? Why? _____

_____

_____

_____

_____

_____

4.7 What are the advantages of having sworn fire inspectors? _____

_____

_____

_____

4.8   What are the disadvantages of having sworn fire inspectors? _____

      _____

      _____

4.9   What are the advantages of having civilian fire inspectors? _____

      _____

      _____

4.10   What are the disadvantages of having civilian fire inspectors?

      _____

      _____

      _____

4.11   Other than pay, what are some methods to attract and retain fire inspectors? _____

      _____

      _____

4.12   Why do fire protection professionals need to be concerned with change? _____

      _____

      _____

4.13   Give three examples of how fire protection professionals can cause changes that will benefit the community. _____

      _____

      _____

4.14   Name six questions that a fire department mission statement should answer. _____

      _____

      _____

      _____

      _____

4.15   Create a mission statement of your own, addressing the six important points. _____

      _____

      _____

      _____

4.16 Why is it important for the fire department to include the fire prevention bureau in its strategic planning process? _____

_____

_____

_____

4.17 Name five ways that fire departments can utilize fire prevention programs to reduce their workload. _____

_____

_____

_____

_____

_____

4.18 Name four reasons why strategic planning is important to fire prevention activities. _____

_____

_____

_____

4.19 Are promotional opportunities important to fire prevention staff? Why or why not? _____

_____

_____

_____

4.20 Is change good or bad? Explain your answer. _____

_____

_____

_____

_____

_____

NOTES

1.   Adopted from John Bryson, Strategic Planning for Public and Non-Profit Organizations: A Guide to Strengthening and Sustaining Organizational Achievement, rev. ed. (Hoboken, N.J.: Jossey-Bass, 1995). This is a must read for fire service personnel!

2.   William H. Wallace, Colorado Springs Fire Department, Summary of Survey Responses, page 25, January 3, 2003.

3.   Wallace, p. 11.

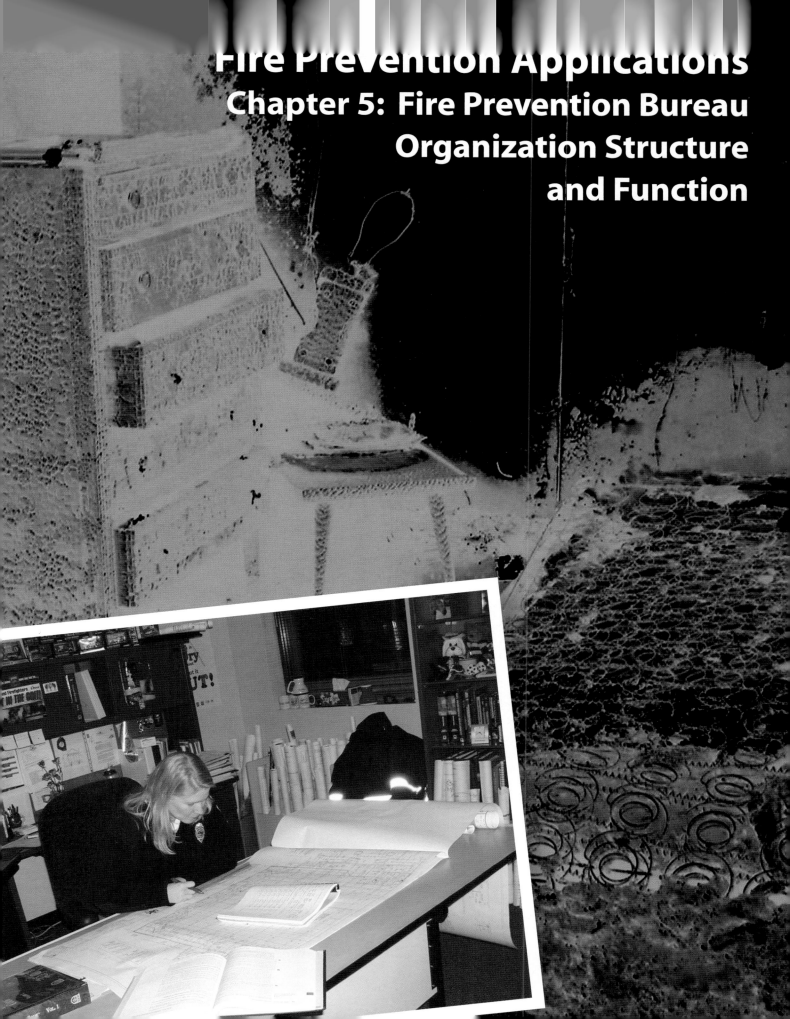

Fire Prevention Applications
Chapter 5: Fire Prevention Bureau Organization Structure and Function

FESHE COURSE OBJECTIVES

1. Review minimum professional qualifications at the state and national levels for fire investigator, fire inspector, and public educator.*

2. Identify the functions of a fire prevention bureau.

3. Identify the duties and responsibilities of fire prevention.

4. Identify staffing options for fire prevention bureaus.

5. Understand the advantages and disadvantages of the various fire prevention staffing options.

*U.S. Fire Administration Objective

Chapter 5

Fire Prevention Bureau Organizational Structure and Function

Administration

Fire prevention bureaus can have many variations in configuration and organizational layout. Some bureaus report directly to the chief, while others report to some other chief officer and in some cases may be completely outside the fire department organization. In this chapter we present the organizational designs that have provided the best results in accomplishing a fire prevention and mitigation mission. We provide an overview of fire prevention bureau functions here. Details of specific fire prevention functions are examined in following chapters.

As with any loss control function, whether for a large industrial company or a municipal fire department, the head of the fire prevention bureau can function best when the position reports directly to the chief executive officer or, in the case of the fire service, the chief of the department. This direct communication is important not only for the functions of the bureau but also the needed communication with top administrative officials. The head of the bureau is typically an assistant chief or battalion chief. However, depending upon the size of the department, the position may be a captain's or any rank as determined by that jurisdiction. The position may in fact be filled by a civilian rather than from the ranks.

If you plotted the head of the fire prevention bureau on the organizational charts of similar sized departments offering similar services, the position would be at roughly the same administrative level. The fire marshal is basically an agent of the chief. Most fire codes typically assign all responsibility for enforcement and action to the chief, who generally will delegate that responsibility to the fire marshal, also known as the authority having jurisdiction (AHJ). We cover more specifics later, but having established who is in charge, we will next discuss some of the organizational structure's functions and layout.

Explanation and Scope

The head of the fire prevention division or bureau shoulders the responsibility for planning and implementing the "three Es" (education, engineering, and enforcement). This person may wear many hats (**Figure 5.1**). In fact, in smaller departments or districts, he or she may do all the fire prevention functions or

> The head of the fire prevention bureau can function best when the position reports directly to the fire chief.

> The head of the fire prevention bureau is responsible for planning and implementing the three Es: education, engineering, and enforcement.

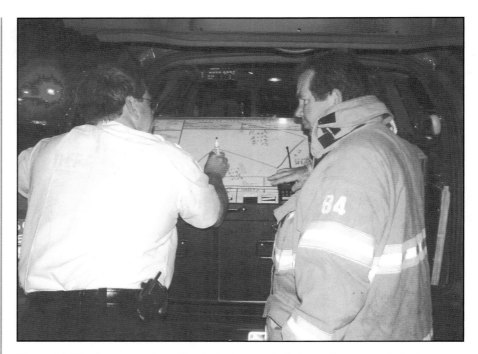

Figure 5.1 The fire prevention officer's duties may include serving as a technical resource to the incident commander during an incident. *Photo courtesy of the Mount Prospect Fire Department*

activities. In reading this chapter, consider how you may be positioned within an organization and what functions you may be charged with performing before you launch into doing exactly as we say. Remember, our discussion focuses on the "typical" department—one that is comparable to a larger department with an experienced staff and dedicated resources. Modifications are certainly acceptable, as our intent is to communicate concepts to you, not a rigid layout or blueprint.

Fire prevention and the related functions can easily be argued as being the single most important fire protection mission in any department. This runs contrary to some views, so prepare your argument before you engage. Remember that as fire service professionals we deal with hostile fires in two principle ways.

- We mitigate, control, or prevent fires from occurring (best).

- We respond to fires and try to put them out when prevention fails (better than none).

If we've heard the saying once, we've heard it a thousand times, "Big fires will eventually go out no matter what we do." Since the publication of *America Burning* in 1972, strong emphasis has been placed on fire prevention activities. It is no secret that we must continue to expand the resources allocated to all fire prevention activities. We must embrace technological advancements in systems, research, planning, education, investigations, legislative and code development, and the creation of dynamic programs to support and facilitate all of these elements. Progressive fire departments must foster progressive prevention programs that nurture strategic partnerships with designers, builders, regulatory agencies, manufacturers, and ordinary citizens. Communication

Progressive fire prevention bureaus must nurture strategic partnerships with designers, builders, regulatory agencies, manufacturers, and ordinary citizens.

continues to be our downfall here. Nurturing these relationships will help us to surmount many of our current shortcomings.

We must also acquire a much broader view of our political obstacles. Some folks may believe parks and recreation are more important than fire trucks. Others may think police protection is a higher priority, or maybe pot holes and transportation are in worse shape than the fire department. We live in a world of "Nothing is burning now, so what's the emergency?" The many competing needs in any community must be funded from the same limited resources. Politics is a fact of life and the very core of the bureaucratic society in which we live. We cannot obtain resources without political support. We cannot enable the will of the people without political capital. Our quest must be to balance all of these factors for the good of our communities and the good of the taxpayers, the ones we support and work for, as volunteers or paid professionals.

Let's look at some common fire prevention functions and methods to perform those functions. Not every department may perform all of these functions. Other departments may have one person perform them all, or they may be performed under a different title. Yet other departments may have positions not even mentioned here. In any case, the field is varied and the competencies many. This chapter will explain what *tasks* fire departments should perform, and not necessarily what positions should be filled. Our objective is to provide guidance, but not to pretend we have every answer for every situation. Different jurisdictions may have different needs that require different arrangements. Any combination is acceptable as long as it meets your objectives.

Identify the Staffing Levels to Provide the Desired Level of Services

Before we can consider the staffing levels of the fire prevention bureau, we must examine some critical points. For example if the elected officials or governing body have indicated it is important that all occupancies are to be inspected once a year, then you should begin structuring your organization based on the number of properties to inspect. Assuming the inspector's only task is to conduct fire inspections, you can estimate how many hours he or she works a year. (Remember to deduct hours for conferences, vacations, holidays, and sick time.) When you have determined the number of hours available, you can then factor in the number of inspections required. A difficulty can arise, though, because some inspections take longer than others, and many require reinspections to achieve compliance.

Accordingly, to address overall staffing levels, we need to look at every function of the fire prevention bureau and correlate them to the level of service the community has determined we should provide. Then we decide the total number of individuals needed to provide that level of service. Keep in mind, we will be asking the elected officials for appropriate funding. This is the same government entity we asked to establish the levels of service it wants us to provide. Often the request for resources will not match the required workload.

When we consider the staff needed to provide the determined level of service, at some point we need to examine support functions. These can include clerical support, training, and vehicle maintenance. If the fire department is large enough to have a substantially sized fire prevention bureau, vehicle maintenance alone, not to mention all of the other necessary support issues, can greatly impact the organization. Remember that when creating an organizational framework you must include the fire prevention bureau in the fire department's strategic planning process. This is when other divisions become involved in determining additional staffing department-wide. Examples could include (**Figure 5.2**):

- Information technology support (how many computers and computer fixers)

- Number of vehicles (trucks, cars, four-wheel drives)

- Training staff for inspector training

- Staffing or enhanced software for bigger payroll

- Geographical information systems support

Figure 5.2 Constant technical training, knowledge, and management interaction are a staple of modern fire prevention bureaus.

In most cases the supervision of fire prevention personnel is dependent on the size of the bureau as well as the makeup of the other fire division's supervisory levels. For example, an engine or truck company may be comprised of a crew of four. One of the crewmembers is the officer, or supervisor. This gives a span of control over three people. Another individual may manage multiple companies or engines in a station. The next level may manage a group of stations in a district or in the entire community. As a rule, many documents speak of a span of control not exceeding seven subordinates to one manager or supervisor. If you follow that rule in light of how your organization staffs the emergency response side of the house, you can get a fairly accurate idea of the type of supervisory or management structure that should be in place.

Determine the Optimum Organizational Framework for the Staffing Levels to Provide the Desired Level of Services

The design and implementation of an optimized organizational framework is dependent upon the tasks required. Basically, you should try to provide the number of resources necessary to provide the best possible service.

To save you a little guess work, we will consider one organization's estimate of how many inspectors and plans examiners are needed to process a particular work load. This example is based on a workload study performed in the Colorado Springs (Colorado) Fire Department's fire prevention division. The study provides an approximate number of inspections and plan reviews that could be expected from each staff member. It is important to note that this number includes a typical number of reinspections and resubmittals of plan reviews. This gives a fairly accurate representation of "typical" inspection and plan review functions. An inspector could be expected to perform 900–1,000 inspections, and a plans examiner could be expected to perform 900–1,050 plan reviews annually.

These represent average totals of inspections and plan reviews defined as follows:

- *Type of inspections:* New construction, existing, occupancy, fire detection and alarm installations, fire suppression system installations, hazardous materials, complaints, and referrals.

- *Plan reviews:* Development, new construction, detection and alarm plans, fire protection systems, water main, hazardous materials, and miscellaneous permit-required drawings or sketches.

The numbers allow the manager to determine roughly how many staff members are required to perform these functions. Obviously if you are from a small department, one person may be able to split the duties handling around 1,000 total inspections and/or plan reviews. Larger departments may need a larger complement of staff divided into different sections as shown in **Figure 5.3**.

> The basic goal of designing and implementing an organizational framework is to provide the number of resources necessary to provide the best possible service.

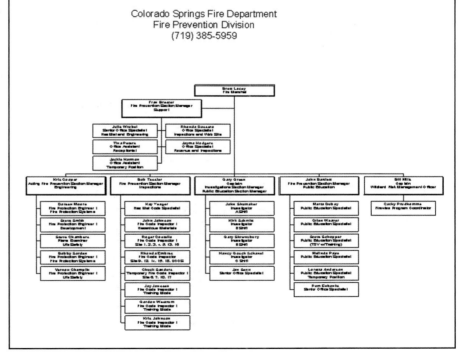

Figure 5.3 The Colorado Springs (Colorado) Fire Department's organization chart shows one way of organizing a larger fire prevention division.

To determine the other staffing levels for other bureau functions, the process may not be as straightforward, as the tasks can be quite varied and nonspecific. For example, the division should have enough fire investigators to handle the number of fires to be investigated. This forces the division to make decisions and implement policies such as:

- Do you investigate all vehicle fires?

- Do you investigate all fires regardless of dollar loss?

- Do you work 24-hour shifts or FLSA 43-hour work weeks? (The Federal Labor Standards Act requires that firefighters who are sworn police officers acting in that capacity as fire investigators must be considered as police officers and must receive an overtime rate after a maximum 43-hour work week.)

- Do you have one vehicle per investigator?

- Do the investigators take vehicles home?

- Are investigators on call?

- Can your budget handle on-call and standby pay?

- How many fires per year require investigation?

Once you have answered questions like these completely, then and only then can you begin to address workload and staff requirements. There are so many variables based on case load, cooperation with the district attorney, and so forth, that we have no rule of thumb for the number of investigators vs. the number of cases. This is a very specific issue based on the local jurisdiction and the enacted policies and procedures. However, the example should give you an idea of what to consider in determining your own department's optimum number of fire investigators.

Life Safety Educator

The life safety educator's position is very hard to quantify, particularly if you follow our recommendations in the following chapters. Specific work tasks and objectives will be required, and you will have to complete specific time studies to make any reasonable estimate. Conferring with business consultants may be appropriate, as these positions generally conform to a typical professional business functions and applications model more than do the other, more technical positions.

Fire Protection Engineers

Fire protection engineers' positions can vary. If their functions are similar to those of plans examiners, the numbers discussed above will work. However, a wise fire marshal will use these positions to perform higher-level applications such as fire modeling, risk analysis, and higher level technical studies and process management. Again, these positions can be closely aligned with a standard engineering business model that is easily time tracked. However, doing this requires a specific set of performance expectations in order to construct an accurate evaluation model. If you define exactly what you expect fire protection engineers to do, evaluating the model is easy.

Staffing Options for a Bureau

Many successful managers have stated time and time again that the greatest asset a company has is its personnel. This is especially true for a service organization such as a fire department. Fire departments do not mass-produce products for distribution. The product they sell is service. The service is provided to the citizens of the community. The citizens and business community are in fact the customers of the fire department.

Fire departments are really no different than the business community when it comes to selecting the people best fit to do the job. Both want to select the most qualified person for the job. In fact, more than that, based on increasing demands and fiscal reductions, we propose General Colin Powell's approach: "Look for intelligence and judgment and, most critically, a capacity to anticipate, to see around corners. Also look for loyalty, integrity, a high energy drive, a balanced ego and the drive to get things done."[1] What can differ between fire departments and the business community is the process of selecting the individual for the position.

In years past, some fire departments would use the fire prevention bureaus as dumping grounds for poor performing or injured personnel. They were not always assigned to the fire prevention bureau by choice. In fact, in some fire departments, people who were hired but then did not "fit the mold" as a firefighter were sent to the fire prevention bureau. An old phrase labeled fire prevention as the depository for the sick, lame, or lazy. Instead of receiving a disability pension, injured fire fighters have been sent to the fire prevention bureau to finish out their careers. This in itself is not bad, but typically the bureau is the last place these individuals wanted to work. They hired on to be firefighters, not desk jockeys. Significant problems can result from forced transfers or promotions into the fire prevention bureau. They might include increased turnover, job dissatisfaction, poor work attitudes, apathy, and most obvious, poor performance.

Poorly motivated or ill prepared individuals face considerable challenges if they are suddenly thrust into a performing fire prevention bureau. There have been considerable advances in construction materials, engineering, building techniques, and in the codes themselves. New buildings, combined with the rapidly changing technology, make it difficult for just anyone to work productively in a fire prevention bureau. Technically complex fire suppression and alarm systems are becoming more and more prevalent (**Figure 5.4**). Most fire departments adopt ordinances making significant local amendments to the nationally recognized codes. The many activities required of the fire prevention professional in the 21st century have placed fire prevention positions among the most professional and technically challenging assignments in many fire departments. Fire prevention personnel

> The greatest asset a fire department has is its personnel.

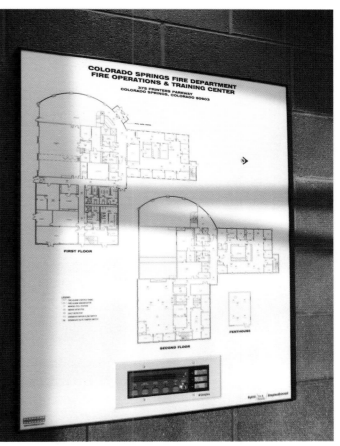

Figure 5.4 Complex and technical fire alarm panels are becoming more and more common.

in the 21st century will be some of the most technically trained people in the fire department. Using the sick, the lame, and the lazy will no longer suffice. To provide the best, most technically proficient service available, filling these positions with educated, qualified, and technically proficient individuals will be a must. We have long since left the age of just doing inspections.

As an example, fire departments amend requirements for sprinklers and fire alarms. It is not unusual to require automatic sprinkler protection in all new construction regardless of square footage or occupancy classification. Whether in a home or a convenience store, sprinkler protection is required. Sprinkler installation has even started to expand into residential applications. The complexity of sprinkler and fire alarm systems has increased so much that newer and more effective sprinkler or fire detection devices are always available. From 1955 to 1981, the choice of which sprinkler to install was simple; there were only three types, an old style, a pendant, and an upright.

In 1981 sprinklers were manufactured and tested by approving agencies to be used in specific occupancies (hazards) rather than in a one-sprinkler-fits-all-situations approach. Until 1991, automatic sprinkler systems were permitted to be installed based on what is referred to as the "pipe schedule method." The pipe schedule design based the size of the sprinkler piping on the occupancy hazard of the building and a predetermined number of sprinklers supplied by the piping. To evaluate the design, the construction document reviewer would count the number of sprinklers on the sprinkler piping and then refer to a table in a code book to see that the system was designed properly. Today pipe schedule sprinkler designs have little use and are a permitted design method in only limited applications, such as preexisting installations. Sprinkler systems today are hydraulically designed. This type of design was developed as a means to reduce the cost of sprinkler systems. The size of the sprinkler piping is not based on the number of sprinklers the piping supplies but on the amount of pressure and gallons per minute available for the system to operate. The size of the pipe is limited basically to a mathematical proof of how much water will be available at how much pressure. This is much more complex than the pipe schedule method and requires significantly more training and expertise to verify.

Similarly, fire alarm and detection devices are changing as fast as the electronics and computer industries. Fire alarm panels as well as the detectors themselves change as fast as computers.

Fire codes have not changed just in the area of sprinkler and fire alarm design and installation. Until recently, most fire and building codes used what are referred to as prescriptive codes. Prescriptive codes prescribe, or dictate, specific requirements or combinations of requirements, much like a "cookbook" approach. As an example, a common prescriptive code requires a typical stairway be constructed with a minimum width of 44 inches. Using this type of approach, prescriptive codes permit very little flexibility in the design and construction of a building.

Today, most building codes have begun including an alternative to the prescriptive approach. Alternate means and methods, or performance-based design approaches, are now permitted in building codes used throughout most of the world. The performance-based design option was included for the first time in the 2000 edition of the *Life Safety Code*.

Performance codes detail objectives and establish criteria for determining if they have been met; thus the designer and builder are free to select construction methods and materials as long as they can be shown to meet the performance criteria.[2] The methods to achieve the objectives or goals are proven by a sequence of complex calculations and computerized fire modeling based on assumptions agreed to by the designer and the AHJ. The computer fire modeling calculates the effects of a fire in a particular room or space. Additional modeling indicates the potential effects on the occupants. The overall outcome of the fire modeling will determine the construction requirements for the building.

The design engineer and architect may reduce the cost of the prescriptive code requirements by using the performance-based design option. If the designer can show the authority having jurisdiction that the design can meet the goals for the level of safety, the prescriptive code requirements do not have to be met. This forces the AHJ to assure that the engineer and architect are accurately representing a computerized fire model and sequence of calculations. The major stumbling block of this process is that the parameters of the design of the building must remain constant for the life of the building. The calamity is that buildings never stay the same. After a building that incorporates a performance-based design is constructed, the long-term maintenance of the design becomes a significant factor during the inspection of the building.

Performance-based designs require the authority having jurisdiction not only to grasp the design method but to ensure that the design parameters are maintained (**Figure 5.5**). This has propelled the authority having jurisdiction into a realm of higher technical expertise that requires extensive education, training, and experience. If the AHJs themselves do not have this training, they likely will or certainly should have staffs who do.

Many smaller fire departments throughout the country will not have an individual on staff capable of reviewing and inspecting performance-based designs. Some fire departments are not convinced that performance-based designs are a reality or a probability, and subsequently they are not prepared to handle them.

> Performance-based designs require the authority having jurisdiction not only to grasp the design method but to ensure that the design parameters are maintained.

Figure 5.5 Fire protection engineer conducting a typical plan review.

Staffing with Sworn Personnel

Many fire departments staff the fire prevention personnel with assigned fire-fighters, also known in many jurisdictions as sworn personnel. Typically, sworn personnel are civil service employees of the fire department who have taken an oath to perform their duties. Fire departments that assign firefighters to the fire prevention bureau do so in a variety of ways. Some fire departments assign them to the fire prevention bureau; others ask for volunteers to transfer into the fire prevention bureau or require them to work in the fire prevention bureau a predetermined amount of time as part of the promotional process. Still others have fought hard to keep firefighters in the bureau but due to a significant lack of interest have started offering incentives by creating promoted positions. Typically though, these are short-lived because the increased cost of personnel forces departments to pursue alternative, less expensive staffing, such as civilian or nonsworn personnel.

Remember that most firefighters hire on to do shift work, fight fires, and be on the trucks. Generally, if people are forced to do something they do not like or want to do, motivating them can be difficult. Forcing an individual into a position is never a good idea unless it is absolutely necessary. Certain skills for fire prevention are far different than those for suppression. On the other hand, there are those rare sworn personnel who eagerly volunteer for the opportunity to work in fire prevention. Putting one of these individuals in fire prevention can be an asset to the community as well as the department.

Fire departments in areas of the country where firefighters carry peace officer powers may prefer to use sworn personnel to conduct fire investigations. Historically, however, many firefighters placed into fire prevention generally have not had the necessary qualifications to perform the assigned duties. Most of their training was done on the job (OJT), and just when they got good at what they were doing (after two years or so) they would be transferred back to the line. Promotions are another killer. Good personnel do not sit still. These individuals are movers and shakers and generally are always trying to better themselves. In the fire service, how can employees better demonstrate their skills, determination, and leadership than by taking promotional exams and being successfully promoted? While this stands well for these people, the bureau loses high-quality performers. Of course, in many cases successful leaders in the fire service typically held many staff positions, which helped them round ou.t their careers.

Staffing with Civilian Personnel

Civilian personnel are individuals who are not sworn into their position through an oath of office. In some fire departments, civilian personnel may wear a fire department uniform and also hold a rank. Civilian personnel do not fall under a board of fire and police commission or other governing body such as civil service. Most civilian positions do not require an employee entrance exam and subsequently are not protected under civil service laws. These individuals are typically hired on an open-competitive basis, which means they must interview and show their best qualifications for the job while competing among a field of many candidates.

Occasionally you may find departments that debate the issues of civilian vs. sworn and of who can take direction from or report to whom. In some cases, sworn ranks may develop an elitist attitude over civilian rank or status, thinking they should never work under or for a "civilian." If you suffer these difficulties as a manager, we offer the following discussion. Most chiefs are not within the civil service rank and file, and although they likely swore an oath, they are considered civilian. The city manager, mayor, or other public official who is the chief's boss is likely a civilian. Most certainly the public we all serve are civilian, and they are not sworn but are undoubtedly our bosses. The fact is, all sworn personnel are employed and directed by civilians. So, for individuals who have problems and conflicts about civilian and sworn staffs, we offer the following: Keep your eye on your job and your responsibilities, and don't worry about issues that have absolutely no impact on what we need to do in protecting our community.

Some advantages of staffing with civilian fire prevention personnel are:

- Cost savings

- Consistency

- Quality

- Decreased turnover

- Specialized technical education

Our discussion of sworn personnel emphasized logistical problems, such as having a sharp individual become well trained just in time to rotate back to the field. Civilian staffs typically allow fire prevention bureaus to hire someone for a specific job who can provide productive and consistent longevity. Individuals with specialized training may be more productive in the long run and have lower turnover rates than sworn personnel. An example of an employee with specialized skills and training whom the fire prevention bureau can recruit would be an individual with a degree in fire protection engineering. Most fire departments have personnel with degrees, but few have sworn firefighters with degrees in fire protection engineering who are willing to work in the fire prevention bureau. As discussed earlier, the escalating responsibilities and duties of positions in the fire prevention bureau have created a need for highly skilled technically qualified individuals.

Disadvantages of using civilians for fire prevention work can include:

- Lack of fire service experience

- Limited promotional opportunities

- Occasionally high turnover due to salary issues

The issue of fire service experience can be overcome by posting minimum requirements for the job that require some degree of experience or fire service training. The City of Colorado Springs has employed this type of requirement for some time and has been very successful at recruiting highly trained personnel who came from other departments or were retired from within their own organization.

Limited promotional opportunities can be frustrating to young, ambitious employees. In some cases there is very little room for advancement unless the size of the community warrants a larger fire prevention bureau. This can become more of a policy issue within the department, which might be modified to retain these individuals. Refer to the various organizational charts we have looked at previously to see how different departments address this issue. Individuals may realize the only way to advance in their careers is to move to a larger department, particularly if the management-level positions in its fire prevention bureau are civilian or it has different job classifications and levels of inspectors, life safety educators, or investigators.

The turnover rate is more often than not attributed to a lower pay scale for the civilians. Many departments have strong labor/management relations tied to civil service. These departments typically fight for and receive higher pay for sworn ranks. Civilians within the same department may tend to feel that management or the city administration views their jobs as less important than that of the firefighter.

In some organizations civilians may not have the equipment, skills, or expertise to take an active role at emergency incidents. In others they may have a significant role in such tasks as evacuation implementation, emergency operation or coordination center (EOC or ECC) functions, or Incident Management System (IMS) functions such as planning, logistics or finance, damage assessments, and flood monitoring. Does this mean that civilians cannot contribute to the organization if they do not have any fire service background? The answer is absolutely not! Each staffing option has advantages and disadvantages. The key to successfully choosing the one for your organization is to identify the strengths and weaknesses of each option in relation to your needs. Determining the best staffing option will also entail selecting solutions that address the weaknesses of the individual. What is necessary is the establishment of good policy, proper procedures, and sufficient training to accomplish the required functions and tasks regardless of whom you employ.

> The key to choosing the best staffing option for your organization is to identify the strengths and weaknesses of each in relation to your needs.

Outsourcing Fire Prevention Services

When budgets are tight and the demands increase for quality services at lower prices, outsourcing of services can become an option to consider. This may be used for purposes as specific as system plan reviews or as general as inspection section functions. In instances of high workload and service demands, it may be beneficial for a bureau to contract a third-party plan review or inspection service. This can reduce some of the bureau's work while still holding contractors and designers accountable.

A common method of using contractors is to have clients submit plans directly to the third-party reviewer, who will in turn do the review and bill the client directly. Plan review comments will then be forwarded to the AHJ, after which permits can be issued. This eliminates invoicing issues for the department and allows the client to deal directly with the third-party contractor. One example is Fire Safety Consultants, Inc., of Schaumburg, Illinois. This group offers a full range of fire protection activities services including fire and life safety and building code consultation encompassing plan review services, inspections, and on-site investigation and reports.

In the scheme of bureau outsourcing, the contracting of services is a form of privatization. **Privatization** is the transfer of functions or duties previously performed by a government entity to a private organization. This strategy is sometimes used to address either personnel issues or funding in a fiscally challenged organization. Many municipal administrators throughout the country have used outsourcing to solve their budget woes. Most administrators initially examine outsourcing as a means to save costs or address concerns regarding the quality of service. One reason that outsourcing might reduce costs is that private organizations have incentives to keep costs low. They need to operate effectively and efficiently in a competitive environment. Most government entities do not have the same incentives as private business to keep a rein on the cost of their service. Business goes bankrupt when it has no customers. Government goes bankrupt when it has no taxpayers. Businesses can choose to change their business and evolve. Government can only provide the services it has been given authority to offer.[3] Many view competition as a means to improve performance and enhance customer satisfaction. Government bodies are not always portrayed in a positive light when it comes to customer satisfaction. Generally this is because of a burdensome bureaucratic process. Also, the regulated are generally never happy with the regulators. Many fire departments have now become cognizant of how important customer service is in the fire service.

Customer service is not restricted just to providing quality fire and emergency medical services but also includes offering quality fire prevention services. One of the superior benefits of privatizing services is the competition. Often, government agencies, since they are the sole source of their services, become complacent and unmotivated to change. Businesses on the other hand, must change in order to remain competitive with one another. One method that private companies use to stay competitive is to reduce costs and still provide quality service. Management in private industry can achieve this by establishing incentives that encourage cost savings. The difficulty for government is that it typically enforces its existence by demanding compliance under threat of penalty rather than trying to do the "right" thing.[4]

Rural Metro Fire Department is an example of a successful privately owned company that has been specializing in providing both fire and emergency medical services in Maricopa County, Arizona, since 1948. This department serves several metropolitan areas such as Scottsdale, Arizona, and its operation relies heavily on prevention and mitigation, such as mandatory fire sprinkler installations throughout all new construction.

Elk Grove Rural Fire Protection District, an unincorporated area of Cook County, Illinois, is another of the many areas of the United States protected by a privately owned fire department (**Figure 5.6**). American Emergency Services provides fire, EMS, and fire prevention services under a contract with the fire district. The fire district is surrounded by municipalities that operate traditional municipal fire departments. Gary Jensen, the company's owner,

✔ **privatization**
the transfer of functions or duties previously performed by a government entity to a private organization

has served as fire chief for the department since the company began providing fire protection for the fire district. This privately owned fire department functions in the same manner as the neighboring municipal fire departments. It is a full participant in the suburban mutual aid program and has automatic aid with neighboring communities.

Figure 5.6 Elk Grove Township (Illinois) Fire Department. *Courtesy of Gary Jensen*

Another solution, known as **enterprising**, may actually become more prevalent for the fire prevention bureau than for any other division of the fire department. An enterprised organization is run like a business, and the services it provides are avenues for the entire organization or a division of the organization to operate fully on a cost-recovery basis. These departments generate revenue and in turn use it to cover their expenses. As we already stated, the demand for qualified, technically competent individuals with specialized skills has been identified within fire prevention divisions. The foreseeable increase in performance-based designs, complex hydraulic sprinkler calculations, and computerized fire alarm systems are just some of the issues facing the person responsible for construction document reviews. This can become overwhelming for an ill-prepared review and inspection staff. It is highly likely the skills needed to address these technical demands may not be available from the pool of fire department members.

Like other businesses and divisions within fire departments, fire prevention bureau personnel may periodically see an increase in the demand for their services. However, the fire prevention bureau is not always allocated the resources to adjust to fluctuating workloads. In some cases the demand for services may increase seasonally or temporarily, as during construction seasons or development booms. It can be difficult to justify hiring a person to assist with these short-term work demands. Budget processes to hire new employees can take two to three years in many locations. Seeking a private contractor for fire prevention services is a means to address these issues.

Many people in the fire service are concerned when the discussion of privatization comes up. Their concern stems mainly from a perception, real or imagined, that privatized services will lack the intuitive skills and knowledge of the "real" fire service. Some fear that decisions or variances may be granted

✔ **enterprising**
running a service organization or a division of the organization so that it operates fully on a cost-recovery basis

that ignore tactical needs or concerns. In either case, if careful management and thoughtful processes are used to match the right people and resources to the right job, success will reign.

Staffing a Fire Prevention Bureau in Volunteer Departments

Often, fire prevention bureaus in volunteer departments are staffed by part-time paid staff, by paid staff, or sometimes by the volunteers themselves. Obviously there are different requirements and expectations for each of these. Some volunteers have more zeal and dedication than "professional" staff in other departments. In all cases, if people are properly trained and adequate numbers of staff are provided, the results should be the same. The aspect of paid versus volunteer should only matter in the realm of remuneration and corresponding laws, policies, and procedures, not in the way we treat our clients or perform our tasks.

Tasks Within the Bureau

Fire Protection Engineering or Plans Examination Section

We tend to think of fire protection engineers as the "thoroughbreds" of the fire service. This is not always an endearing term, but one that typically does not offend either. Engineers as a group take great pride in their work. The term *thoroughbred* gives an indication that you probably do not want them pulling the plows, because they likely would refuse. Instead they would try to figure out a better and faster way to have the plow move on its own. However, you certainly would want the engineers running your fastest race and standing by your side when you were trying to figure out the best way to extinguish an unusual fire in a petrochemical plant.

Fire protection engineers are typically responsible for conducting high-level plan reviews and design work on a multitude of design and construction aspects such as development plans, plats, zone changes, new building design and construction, fire detection/suppression systems, process design or methods, and the like. Basically any design the fire service may have an interest in looking at or dealing with is fair game for review by this section or, in some smaller fire departments, this person. This position provides the first opportunity to critique and tweak a design before it is permitted for construction or actually installed. It has increased in popularity over the past decade or so because of the realization that early input and review by the fire service provides long-term benefits to managing risk. Identifying problems or verifying code compliance issues early in a design process helps assure not only increased protection for occupants or businesses but protection of fire crews when they are responding to an incident.

Fire protection engineering is a relatively new field. Only over the last twenty years or so have fire protection engineering professionals begun graduating in large numbers from accredited engineering or engineering technology schools. For a number of years, chemists, engineers, and others who were formally schooled in technical scientific fields began practicing the art of fire protection engineering. Fire is basically a chemical reaction that emits heat and light. The study of this process stretches across many disciplines using chemical and engineering sciences such as military research, architecture, manufacturing, fire protection, and others. Even manufacturing boilers requires an understanding of fire behavior, dynamics, and control. It is these technically trained professionals who devise the safest and most efficient ways to use and control fire.

Fire protection engineers are becoming more commonplace in the design industry and consequently more prevalent in the fire service. Since most fire departments of any significant size review construction plans for new buildings, processes or systems, they need a competent staff to perform that function. In years past, those departments that hired engineers or architects rather than taking sworn firefighters off the line to handle this task were generally large municipalities or large departments, and they were the exception by far, not the rule. Because of the changes occurring in the model codes and other standards, departments need degreed individuals with engineering or science backgrounds to act as liaisons and resident experts on these matters.

Not all departments can afford qualified engineering staff. However, if a smaller community or organization desires plan reviews, it is not precluded from having them; it only means that their level of competency will be less than that of a qualified engineer. The expectation of the fire service should always be to do the best we can with what we have. Therefore, any individual who receives training and certification in such activities can review plans. The National Fire Protection Association and other model code groups still offer certifications for plans examiners based on NFPA 1031, *Professional Qualifications for Fire Inspector and Plan Examiner*. This certification is very important if the plans examiner cannot or has not obtained degreed credentials. It also provides credible documentation for the already experienced and certified engineer.

The only drawback of certification as opposed to degreed or licensed personnel is the limited theoretical and academic knowledge and experience one will have when dealing with design professionals, who generally are degreed, highly trained, and experienced.

Those departments that choose to contract out will lose some degree of ownership as they will not have direct control over all the aspects they otherwise could. In many cases, there will be a lack of quality control regarding a true vested interest in the overall fire department's mission. More importantly suppression personnel within the fire department are among the customers supported. Fire protection engineers seek not only to protect the building occupants but the firefighters as well. It is imperative that all fire prevention bureau personnel have the interests of fire suppression personnel in mind when they are performing their fire prevention duties.

An example of reduced ownership would be a limited perspective on fire department operations and tactics, which could result in decisions or alternative approaches that may not be in the best interest of the fire department. Communication can also become more problematic as issues have to be discussed and transferred among more individuals, lending opportunity for missed steps, decisions, or expectations. Still, this option provides a good alternative for those departments not yet large enough to perform this activity on their own.

An important point to remember is that like doctors having a license to practice medicine, engineers have a license to practice the science of engineering. This means that they are allowed by law to invent things based on good engineering judgment. There is not always a code or standard that specifies how something is to be designed and built. If that were the case, we never would have put man on the moon, developed plastic milk jugs, or invented personal computers. When an engineer decides to try something new and different that may not be codified in some standard or ordinance, how can a person with lower training and qualifications prevent it? Model fire codes give the chief authority to prevent such activities if they are unsafe or risk the public's well being. However, this begins to tread on thin ice when professional and technical arguments come up against statements like, "Because I said so." For that reason, the best professional and technical expertise should be enlisted to appropriately handle all our clients, the public as well as design professionals.

A larger engineering section might be divided as follows:

- *Life Safety Group.* The life safety group reviews new or remodel construction plans and hazardous-materials related operations or processes. The bigger the jurisdiction, the larger the volume of construction plans there will be. Hazardous materials processes or systems are generally not that large in volume, but frequent enough to require dedicated positions. By combining both of these functions, the work group can verify that the construction methods and requirements are commensurate with the needs of both the building code and the fire code. New construction projects that involve hazardous materials require extensive communication. Combining both in the same group of assigned responsibility should achieve the best of both worlds.

- *Development Review Group.* The development review group should be responsible for all conceptual and proposed projects including annexation, development plans, plats, zone changes, and wildland/urban interface issues if appropriate. This group is also attractive to your local economic development organizations, as it is a potent resource for clarifying hard to answer questions for businesses being recruited into the community. This group needs to communicate carefully and diligently with the life safety group because commitments or decisions will likely be made here as the first of many steps in the construction phase of a project. The client will want the process to flow well, and if these two groups misstep, they can cause major problems and delays.

- *Systems Group.* The systems group should be geared for handling water plans; fire detection, alarm, and suppression plans; special hazard sys-

It is imperative that all fire prevention bureau personnel have the interests of fire suppression personnel in mind when they are performing their fire prevention duties.

tems; and anything else that falls in this category. They too will have to interface with the life safety group as theirs will be the last set of plans reviewed in the long line of plan reviews to come through the office.

There will undoubtedly be debate about how or why to break these groups up. Why not keep from specializing and make everyone generalists? Depending upon the size of your department and the workload you process, that may be feasible. In some fire departments, the size of the municipality may not dictate the need for separate groups, but the functions will be the same. However, the larger the demands, the higher the workload, the harder it is to maintain the expertise, quality, and control over all these areas. For that reason, it is best to segregate them when possible.

We recommend cross-training groups so that a baseline of support can be expected in the event of a required absence such as schooling, illness, or vacations. This is also beneficial to staff so they do not get stuck in one area too long and stagnate. The reality, though, is that no one person should be expected to be completely knowledgeable in every area. The person who did would be worth a lot of money, indeed. As we have said, small departments may have only one person doing these reviews. While one person can do them all, the quality tends to suffer.

Be sure to document all plan review activities as they not only become a permanent record of your work on given projects but also provide a technical reference for the designers, architects, and inspectors who will be following up on the project. The methods of data collection can vary. We recommend a computerized format since the amount of information can be substantial; however, whatever format your jurisdiction's attorney agrees with would be our choice (**Figure 5.7**). Document meetings, phone conversations, and file all correspondence. It is astounding how much communication can take place, particularly on large projects. If you do not keep track of decisions, changes, and modifications as you go, you will be in a sad way.

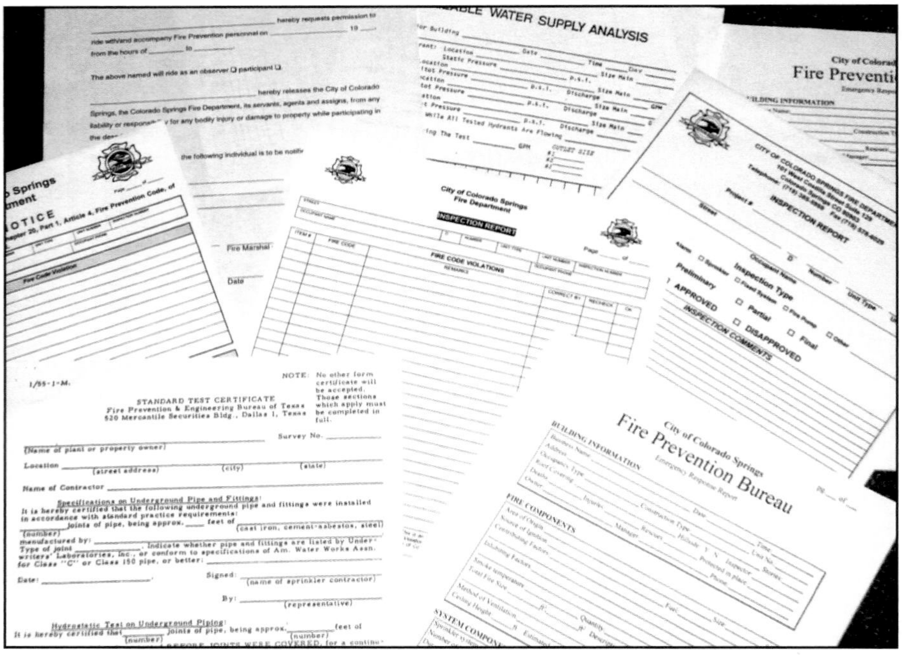

Figure 5.7 Data collection forms come in a wide variety.

If you do not keep track of decisions, changes, and modifications throughout the design and construction process, you will be in a sad way.

The importance of having a good solid engineering group is reflected in a CIGNA study that was distributed by the Resource Center for the Alliance for Fire and Emergency Management out of Ashland, Massachusetts. CIGNA surveyed over 40 percent of their insured accounts. Of those surveyed, 25 percent had design deficiencies in their fire protection systems. Water supply deficiencies were discovered in 14 percent. If a good, thorough engineering design review had been conducted with corrections made prior to construction, 100 percent of those surveyed would have had no problems. It is far better and easier to identify and correct a problem on paper than it is to find it after the fact and have to rebuild or never fix it at all.

Fire and Life Safety Education

Fire and life safety education is an increasingly valuable area of public fire protection. In most common practices, the fire service utilizes education for two purposes:

- Fire prevention education

- Fire reaction behavior modification

We propose a much wider usage. Assuming a fire department provides varied services such as emergency medical response, upwards of 70 percent of their call volume may be for medical emergencies. The National Fire Protection Association shows the distribution of fire department calls in 1988 included 53.9 percent as medical aid, 18.3 percent as fires, and 10.6 percent as false alarms.[5] In many departments in the United States, structural fires may account for as little as 3 percent of overall call volume. This being the case, why would we limit public education venues only to fire topics?

As in the engineering section, any number and type of individuals may staff the public education or fire and life safety education section of a department. More and more departments are utilizing professional educators for performing the directed tasks. These individuals are very highly skilled at utilizing the best educational methods to transmit our message to their selected audience. The standard referenced and used for training and maintaining qualified staff in this section is NFPA 1035, *Professional Qualifications for Public Fire and Life Safety Educator*.

In Chapter 8 we discuss in detail fire and life safety education and whom we should target as an audience. We typically have targeted the very young and the very old. While this makes sense, as those two age groups are most at risk, we need to think about the middle of the road folks, those individuals who are responsible for and care for the young and the elderly. It is this group that makes most of the decisions, takes most of the risks, and shapes much of what we do and think as a society.

Think about the ramifications of educating businesses in the proper use and maintenance of fire alarm systems. In Colorado Springs, Colorado, if educating this group on the topic reduced the incidence of false alarms and alarm malfunctions by just 10 percent, it would directly reduce overall annual workload responses by over 300 calls. In this particular community, that is nearly the same number of calls that determines the need for the construction of a new fire station at a cost of nearly $1.5 million a year. What an impact we could have nationwide!

The point is to think outside the box. Think about all the incidents that impact your organization and think how to best educate your public. It may be important, too, to distinguish education from awareness. Most of the adults in the middle target group we spoke of do not want to be educated, but they will accept being "made aware" of various issues. It's a simple semantics issue but sometimes can be critical in dealing with the masses. Topics need to be presented in a "teaching not preaching" approach. Even though these people may perceive themselves as simply becoming aware of issues, they are actually learning. Trained education professionals will help keep this issue in perspective.

For those departments that may not have the resources to hire specific staff for this purpose or that cannot afford to dedicate sworn positions, we strongly recommend forming collaborative relationships with local educators. Many groups and associations can provide input, volunteer support, guidance, and other tools to help you get the job done (see Chapter 8). Remember to pay special attention to cultural groups. Demographics, although a touchy subject, do play a part in our overall fire problem. Be sensitive to issues that may alleviate or aggravate a situation. Enlist help from those groups to make sure your message is right and will be heard.

The National Fire Protection Association uses two principal programs (**Figure 5.8**). The older and more traditional is Learn Not to Burn. The newer and more proactive program is Risk Watch. Both programs target specific elements of fire safety with Risk Watch being a more global approach to overall injury prevention. The Public Education Office of the United States Fire Administration has helped many departments and communities by developing comprehensive public fire education programs through technical support, workshops, networking, and funding.[6] Two other excellent resources are the NFPA Fire Protection Handbook, 19th Ed., Vol.1, Section 7.2 and International Fire Service Training Association's (IFSTA) *Fire and Life Safety Educator*.

Public education should be viewed globally. The fire service has done an exceptional job of marketing "Big Red" the fire truck and firefighters. Another widely recognized icon is Sparky, who is associated with "Stop, Drop, and Roll." However, we have failed miserably at many of our other tasks, particularly in fire prevention. We should take a more active marketing approach to all the services we provide, keeping our important safety messages and efforts intertwined so as to keep our entire community up-to-speed with our mission and therefore our efforts (Chapter 8 provides more detail on this). If Pepsi can keep encouraging people to buy their product, why can't we encourage our communities to "buy" our message? The answer is we can. We just have to do it differently than we have in the past. Think outside the box, and remember that mistakes and failures are part of learning and doing things differently. Don't get discouraged. Just don't make the same mistake twice.

Fire Inspection and Code Enforcement

Fire inspections historically have been and still are primary functions of a fire prevention bureau (see Chapter 11). Fire inspections are based on local or state laws that may require or recommend specific types of inspections for various operations or occupancies. Examples could include state licensing of daycare facilities, special-hazard occupancies, high-rises, or the like. Many fire departments perform different types of inspections not relegated to li-

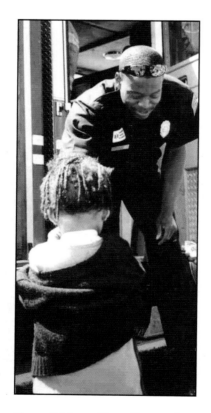

Figure 5.8 Learn Not to Burn and Risk Watch messages come from a firefighter.

censing, such as new construction, existing buildings, fire protection systems, or hazardous materials. Various voluntary inspection programs may also be established, such as home and business inspections. All inspectors should be trained to meet the appropriate level of inspector based on NFPA 1031, *Professional Qualifications for Fire Inspector and Plan Examiner.*

The details of these inspections vary depending upon the types of inspections to be conducted. Many departments perform voluntary inspections through line companies assigned to specific fire stations, while the more technically complex inspections are handled through the fire prevention bureau or division. The quality and complexity of an inspection must be considered. As the fire code and its related standards become increasingly complex and detailed, properly training line officers and firefighters in these duties is becoming harder and harder. Smaller departments may have a better ability to train their responders due to their smaller call volume, proximity to centralized training facilities, and overall cost efficiencies. Larger departments may find this more difficult because of numerous factors.

> *Example:* Say you have 18 stations, 7 of which are double-company stations (more than one principle piece of staffed apparatus). Your department runs three platoons or shifts. You want to put on a two-hour course for all officers, which means a total of 25 people each shift. You have a minimum staffing policy, which means you may have only three over hires per shift. To accomplish your goals for only a two-hour class you may be able to pull only five people per shift for a bare minimum of 16 days, assuming only one makeup day for a 24/48 schedule. Other departments may be able to accommodate more training if they have audio/visual support, but this example shows that providing detailed, technical training is difficult at best. For this reason, most technical inspections are assigned at the fire prevention level, where personnel are in a better position to handle and schedule them.

Fire inspections are conducted to help ensure a reasonable degree of fire safety based on fire code compliance. Inspections within a prevention bureau or division can be divided into three basic types:

- Existing buildings (annual inspections)

- New installations or new construction

- Other (for example, complaints, inspections for fire prevention permits, or business licenses)

This discussion will focus on existing buildings and new installations, the two most commonly encountered.

Inspections of existing buildings cover any and all elements, behaviors, or conditions that increase the hazard of a given building or process. These inspections are intended to prevent hostile fires when possible, mitigate the effects of a fire should one occur, and minimize hazards and thereby the risk. Housekeeping issues are common problems for correction in these inspections. The unsafe storage of combustible materials, debris, and access to attractive nuisances are just a few of the conditions an inspector should watch for (**Figure 5.9**). Existing buildings typically have many mechanical and other features that should be checked periodically. These include mechanical and elevator equipment rooms, smoke control systems, fire doors, detection, and alarm and suppression systems, all of which should be checked and/or tested periodically to make sure they are in proper order. This may be as simple as verifying a private contractor has completed the required regular maintenance and systems check, or it may be as complicated as requiring that the test be done and witnessed by the inspector.

The importance of fire inspections cannot be overemphasized. Additional results from the CIGNA survey revealed how critical good inspections are to maintaining a fire-safe environment. In that survey 18 percent of those surveyed had fire pump problems, 11 percent had nonfunctional alarms, 8 percent had shut water supply valves, 6 percent had fire door failure or obstructions, and 6 percent had fire detection system problems (**Figure 5.10**). Sprinkler protection deficiencies alone accounted for 65 percent of the total deficiencies (this includes the data discussed earlier in this chapter's fire protection engineering section as well as the data discussed

Figure 5.9 Unsafe storage practices pose a threat not only to occupants or tenants but to firefighters as well.

here). For these reasons, a competent and technically educated staff must work diligently to address the multitude of hazards that increase the risk not only to our clients, the public, but also to our firefighters.

Occasionally light-duty personnel may be assigned to the fire prevention bureau. These are the firefighters who have been injured and can do some work but have not been medically cleared to return to their regular fire fighting duties. These individuals can be very helpful in handling lower level or basic inspections; however, we strongly recommend putting them through some basic fire-inspection-training program prior to sending them out. Keep in mind our previous discussion of the "old way" of doing business and how all it did was frustrate people, get others in trouble, and make enemies of our clients and customers.

Figure 5.10 Often, critical equipment such as fire pumps and fire alarm systems are not operable but are discovered to be out of order only by routine fire inspections.

Public Information

The public information function has been dubbed many things, such as community relations, public relations, media relations, and so forth. It also has been given many varied levels of importance based on resource availability and community response. However, public information should be a year-round effort given high priority and substantial support. This function is more important now than ever before (Chapter 8 discusses this function in greater detail). The department's effectiveness in providing public information directly impacts other efforts such as fire and life safety education.

We are in the media age. CNN news is in everyone's home. Instant reports from around the globe keep us apprised of regional and international events. Because we are an "information starved" society, we desperately need to feed the machine by keeping people informed about what we are doing, what we can do and what we plan to do. The media inevitably will portray an image of the fire department. It is up to the fire department to use the media to its advantage.

The fire service typically is a public governmental agency. We are supported and funded by public dollars, and therefore we need public support. In today's tough political environment the chief needs all the ammunition he or she can get to keep important issues in front of the department and in the open for everyone to see. The media can be either a godsend or a curse. The only way to maintain your media as a godsend is to be proactive and form partnerships with them (**Figure 5.11**). They can help you in ways you could never imagine. But if you have formed no relationship or alliance, they can barbecue you on the spit if push comes to shove.

Figure 5.11 A fire chief meets with media representatives.

What better way to assist your fire prevention mission than by using the media? Why wait for a catastrophe to hit before talking to them? Let them carry your public education messages. Let them carry your message of engineering services. Let them support your inspection program. Think of the contacts you can generate. A good resource on the topic is Mark Mathis's book *Feeding the Media Beast*. It provides excellent rules for using the media to your best advantage.

Annually, the Colorado Springs Public Education and Information staff provide detailed reports on the number of contacts they made with public safety education messages. If they get a fireworks safety message out to the public via corporate e-mail and public safety announcements say, three times, through an initial audience of 100,000 people, that is 300,000 contacts. This could not happen without established relationships and aggressive public information officer policies, practices, and support.

The public information functions are critical to a department of any size. Smaller departments may defer the job to the chief. Larger departments may delegate these duties to officers or other individuals filling different full-time positions. Still others may dedicate staff and resources to the job. In any case, it is important to spend time on this function. This position not only can keep your clients informed of periods of fire danger, help communicate when evacuations are necessary, or warn of restricted areas due to fire or a hazardous materials release, but can also help your department maintain a positive image year-round.

Remember, the heroes of the job are the emergency responders. They are the ones who show up at your clients' door when they need help on the worst day of their life. Prevention personnel are the ones who show up when someone least expects or needs them, finds nothing but problems, and forces the client to spend hundreds or possibly thousands of dollars to fix them, just to have us come back again next year and find something else in need of fixing. Who needs the image help here, firefighters or fire prevention?

When the incidence of candle fires becomes epidemic, we do not have the staff or the resources to go door-to-door telling people to be careful. However, utilizing a good public information program, we can immediately bring television, radio, and the press together to help us communicate with the masses. How much money does Budweiser spend on three or four Super Bowl ads? Thousands, hundreds of thousands, maybe even millions of dollars? How much would it cost you to deliver half that airtime for a critical life safety message without the help of the media? Be smart, think outside of the box.

As with any program, established policies and procedures or guidelines are critical. These need not spell out exact steps and elements, but they should define responsibility, accountability, and expectations. This way, everyone can be on the same page, know what to expect, and how to perform.

Preincident Planning

Preincident planning is very important to fire crews who respond to emergency incidents. Unfortunately, many departments do not spend nearly enough time doing it. We'll start by explaining what preincident planning is, or at least what we think it should be. Our view may be contentious, as it differs some from other people's. Again, the amount of detail in preincident planning depends on the size of your department; however, we propose keeping it simple, understandable, and easy to use.

✔ **preincident planning**
the process of identifying specific occupancies, buildings, or locations that will likely require special treatment or operations during an emergency

Preincident planning is the process of identifying specific occupancies, buildings, or locations that will likely require special treatment or operations should an emergency occur. We recommend first identifying target hazards. These **target hazards** are locations or buildings that are different than those that are "typical" throughout your jurisdiction.

What does this mean? We define typical as those locations that are bread-and-butter from an operational standpoint. There will always be times when the bread-and-butter operations go south, and there may be no such thing as typical. For our purposes, however, typical is that incident that your first-alarm assignment can respond to and reasonably handle without additional resources or unreasonable concern. In our example, a typical, or bread-and-butter, location would be a detached single-family dwelling. Anything "different" that may require an automatic second or greater alarm, such as a high life hazard (hotel, nursing home), might require hazardous materials response, or may have biohazards, is a target hazard (**Figure 5.12**).

✔ target hazard
location or building that is different than those that are "typical" throughout a jurisdiction

Once you have a list of target hazards, you should develop a form, or emergency "incident cheat sheet," that provides critical information at a quick glance, to assist the incident commander or company officer in making quick tactical decisions. Develop a customized form to assist you with policy or guidance decisions based on your department's operational tactics. Another way to look at preplanning is through comparing it to a simple risk analysis. Evaluating the following items can assist you in this task:

- Life risks

- Contents

- Construction

- Built-in protection

- Time

- Suppression resources

Limit the information on each location to no more than one sheet of paper. It is hard to fit three-drawer file cabinets in the cabs of most apparatus. Driving to a fire at 0300 hrs in blinding snow, talking on the radio, and trying to open a three-inch three-ring binder while people are yelling at you is not conducive to low blood pressure. You need good information immediately available in small bites. Keep it simple. Some fire departments have elected to keep it simple by putting the information in an electronic format. Mobile data terminals and good geographical information system (GIS) support are invaluable (see Chapter 14).

Figure 5.12 Target hazards such as hospitals become priorities for fire prevention personnel.

The line companies themselves are the best people to conduct preincident planning. Although fire prevention staff can do it, the line is far better served if they look at the premises, touch them, experience them, and then record those things they view as important. Firefighters in Colorado Springs, Colorado, perform this duty regularly and are encouraged to complete an inspection form if they see violations while doing the survey. The principle interest is for the crews to complete the survey with a secondary emphasis on the inspection. Generally the business owners like the firefighters who visit them, and indirectly this motivates them to "clean their shop."

In some fire departments, such as Mount Prospect, Illinois, the fire prevention bureau works hand-in-hand with shift personnel in maintaining the preincident planning data. The information obtained by the fire prevention staff during fire inspections is used to update the preplan, which was most likely developed or drawn by line personnel. This works well in some communities that do not have enough line personnel to visit the occupancies frequently and need another means to keep the preincident plan current.

Fire Investigations

Fire departments throughout the country deal with fire investigations in extremely varied ways. Some do nothing because fire investigations are the responsibility of the local law enforcement agency. Others will perform origin and cause determination and leave the investigation of arson to the law enforcement agencies. Still others perform all of these functions, having staff members who are certified peace officers with the authority to investigate and arrest.

Many jurisdictions delegate the responsibility of fire investigation to the fire chief. In these cases, it is common for the fire department to have dedicated members perform the investigative duties (**Figure 5.13**). Fire investigations are a critical and integral part of the overall fire prevention mission. The information gleaned from fire investigation and postincident analysis is important to feed back into code development and public education or public information. It is critical for prioritizing fire safety actions. Without this link, a department can run on the same or similar incidents time after time without ever eliminating their cause. Specific information from a good fire investigation program is key to determining the specifics of the local fire problem. Fire cause trends can be established, fire prevention issues identified, and then measurement of changes evaluated.

Deliberate communication with local or state law enforcement agencies is also a must (**Figure 5.14**). Collaborative and cooperative relationships must be nurtured for different agencies to communicate developing commonalities or criminal trends. Often, arson is not these individuals' only crime. They commit other crimes, which if unnoticed cannot be connected, thereby allowing them to get away. The fire investigation unit's organization within a department is just like the other groups we have discussed previously. The standard of good practice to follow is NFPA 1033, *Professional Qualifications for Fire Investigator*. The success of your program will depend on resources and commitment. However, we offer the following guidelines:

Figure 5.13 Fire department personnel investigate an office fire.

Figure 5.14 Cooperating with other agencies is a key to managing major incidents successfully.

- Develop a good process or system for fire origin and cause determination. This is the most critical part of any investigation. You cannot prosecute criminals if you cannot determine they caused the fire. You also cannot correct a fire safety issue if you are never certain how or why a fire occurred.

- Develop good policies and/or guidelines for conducting the operations. Typically you will find that the individuals who gravitate to this job are lone wolves and independent thinkers who will need a solid structure to keep them on track.

- Establish very detailed yet flexible data recording systems. This will be invaluable to keeping track of all the data you may want to review later.

- Establish formal relationships with your jurisdiction's legal authority (district attorney, etc.), your law enforcement agencies, BATF, FBI, state fire marshal's office, and all other local, state, and federal agencies with whom you may come in contact. Due to the events of 9-11, there are more mandates for communication and cooperation among the various agencies than ever before. Take advantage of these channels and you may find opportunities and resources you never knew existed.

Occupant Service Section

The occupant service section is probably the least familiar and least supported function in any department. This group functions much like customer service representatives. Its members are responsible for taking care of the public, holding their hand if you will, through all of the fire department's processes. This may include working through the plan review process, obtaining permits, or recovering after a fire or other disaster.

As a fire department, we are great at responding to a crisis and taking care of the emergent issues, only to pick up our stuff and go home. What do occupants who just had the worst day of their life do after we leave? Generally they do not get much help but are left to fend for themselves. The occupant services section can help greatly tying up all the loose ends or serving as the go-to person when things are not going well. This group needs to have a well-balanced knowledge of the department and of the fire service in general. Its members might also coordinate a town-hall type meeting with the entire neighborhood after an event. This is a good forum to explain what occurred.

The occupant services section can be an enormous asset to the department, as people generally enjoy being treated well. This section also can be used as your department's quality control division and may even include the person(s) who do your public information officer's (PIO) functions. Their feedback on the issues they deal with and hear about can go a long way to enhance the quality and type of service your department provides. Keep in mind, the general public does not grasp the devastation caused by fire or the actions taken by firefighters during a fire incident. The intent of the occupant service sector is to provide a designated person to help tend to the needs of occupants where fires occur. The resources needed to do this can be simple and inexpensive:

- Boxes for gathering belongings
- Plastic bags for gathering belongings
- Writing paper
- Pencils or pens
- Information packets such as "After the Fire" (available from FEMA)
- Local information packets about the rebuilding or permitting process and city contacts
- Disposable camera

Occupant service packets containing some of these items can be stored in a vehicle and distributed after the incident. Some departments assign this task to a staff person or a member of the fire prevention bureau. Very large departments will assign it to a crew of people, and the services they provide may even include methods to temporarily relocate businesses. This is a great service and can be among those performed after the fire by another division, such as fire prevention.

Wildland Risk Management

Wildland risk management is a relatively new commitment for most fire departments. Although it affects only those departments that have a wildland/urban interface, it is very involved and complex, requiring real commitment (see Chapter 13).

Relationships are hugely important to wildland risk management. All through this chapter we have emphasized the importance of maintaining relationships, but wildland risk management is more interdependent than any other task. Wildlands in proximity to a city or location within a county or state present many challenges. Not only are there private lands to consider but public, local, state, federal, and maybe even tribal. Each landowner must meet specific responsibilities and expectations and abide by specific restrictions and rules, let alone potentially having to enforce them. Managing wildlands is a political love-fest like no other. There are environmentalists to deal with, users, clients, adjoining property owners, people who you never even knew existed, all having a concern and care for land that may burn.

The job of managing the wildland/urban interface is tough. The first thing you must determine is whether you are the right authority to deal with the problem. Generally the fire department is the first agency called to fight a fire, but if the fire is in a national forest next to your jurisdiction, how much authority do you have? These are the types of questions that must be addressed.

Once the areas of authority have been established, you must determine your real risk. Again, Colorado Springs, Colorado, is an excellent example of a progressive, interactive wildland risk management program. Their Web site not only illustrates how involved and complex the issues are but also explains how they determined their risk. The most basic issue is determining a boundary between your forested areas and your urban core. Draw this line on a map and you have defined your wildland/urban interface (**Figure 5.15**).

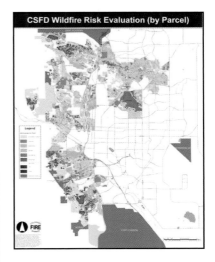

Figure 5.15 Map of the wildland and urban interface in Colorado Springs, Colorado.

Once the risk has been identified and valued, you can begin to manage it. This will be a long and ongoing process as it is dependent upon the will of your policy makers to deal with the risk. You should include the following considerations in the course of framing your program:

- Is this a new and upcoming problem or an existing one?

- Will an ordinance or regulation settle the issue completely?

- Can we use public education to influence behavior?

- What resources will we need?

- Prioritize the available mitigation methods from the most effective to the least as they relate to your community. Your choices are:

  — Fuels management

  — Construction methods

  — Public awareness

Planners have to realize that structures play a more significant role in the wildland/urban interface than previously thought. A review of the Los Alamos, New Mexico, fire revealed that the most important role in the destruction of the community's structures was played by the structures themselves, not the forest. That does not mean the forest had nothing to do with the firestorm; however, it does mean that if we begin treating structures as part of the problem rather than just the vegetation, we will go much further in mitigating wildfire threats.

Careful consideration needs to be given to this task. More and more American communities are facing drought conditions. This shortage of water increases the threat of fire to dry vegetation. Major fires in forested watersheds cause tremendous pollution that costs millions of dollars to correct. Damage to watersheds in an already drought-stricken region only reduces the available water that much more. People are moving away from urban cores to more rural settings. Insurance companies have to cover the cost of unprotected homes destroyed by wildfires, and ultimately we all pay for insurance losses. This is a community wide problem that must be addressed differently than in the past. Remember Albert Einstein's words that we quoted at the end of Chapter 4: "Thinking as we are has brought us to where we have already been. In order to go somewhere else, we must think in a different way."

With all these functions and potential responsibilities, the number and types of staffing required for wildland risk management can be significant.

Training

Given the importance of maintaining a technically strong, competent, and professional staff, how do we recruit them? How do we maintain them? Training is a critical part of this objective and it requires money and commitment.

Many training courses are available: short courses, seminars, college courses, on-line classes, even guest lecturers. The more qualified your staff the more expensive it is to keep them schooled. For example, if you have engineers on staff, they typically have annual or two-year reregistration or recertification requirements. Meeting them requires time in courses that generally are not given locally. Other staff members who are certified also must receive contact hours on coursework related to their certification.

Unfortunately, the fire service is ill prepared to support the prevention staff. We do a good job of training our recruits and of keeping our line personnel up to speed on evolutions and tactical operations, but we do a poor job of training our engineers, inspectors, educators, and others. Chiefs must be encouraged to address this need. Typically it is the prevention staff who provide classes for the line personnel on systems, water supply, investigations, and the like (**Figure 5.16**). Without a doubt, it is in the best interest of the fire service to begin addressing more specifically the required training for the experts in the fire prevention divisions upon whom the rest of the department so heavily relies.

Summary

Fire departments deal with hostile fires in two ways, prevention and suppression. The structure of the division responsible for fire prevention will vary depending on the size of the fire department was well as the organizational structure of the municipality or fire district.

Typically fire prevention bureaus perform three core functions: education, engineering, and enforcement. Other duties commonly performed by fire prevention bureau personnel include fire investigations, public information, and assistance to the incident commander during emergency operations.

The staffing of a fire prevention bureau can utilize sworn fire personnel, civilians, or outsourcing or a combination of all three. Each staffing option has advantages and disadvantages. It is up to the fire department to develop a staffing plan that will enable its fire prevention bureau to provide the level of service needed by the organization. Today's fire prevention bureau staffs

Figure 5.16 Fire prevention personnel can be a resource for providing training to suppression personnel.

require a diverse technical background. The level of professionalism in the fire prevention bureaus will continue to increase in the 21st century. The days of only the sick, lame, and lazy being assigned to the fire prevention bureau are becoming a cliché of the past.

Chapter 5 Review Exercises

5.1   Identify the different methods to staff fire prevention. _____

_____

_____

_____

5.2   Compare and contrast the use of civilian personnel and sworn personnel to staff a fire prevention bureau. _____

_____

_____

_____

_____

_____

_____

5.3   What is outsourcing? _____

_____

5.4   What are the advantages of outsourcing a service? _____

_____

_____

_____

5.5   Identify and explain three functions performed by fire prevention bureaus. _____

_____

_____

_____

_____

_____

5.6   What rank is typical for a fire marshal? _____

_____

5.7   What are the two ways the fire department deals with hostile fires?

_____   _____

5.8   List at least five things you should consider when starting a new fire prevention bureau. _____

_____

_____

_____

_____

5.9   Define span of control. _____

_____

5.10 Name the types of reviews a plans examiner is expected to perform.

_____

_____

_____

_____

5.11 What was the historical problem from which staffing of fire prevention suffered? _____

_____

_____

_____

5.12 What are performance-based designs? _____

_____

_____

5.13 Discuss how turnover impacts both firefighter- and civilian-staffed fire prevention bureaus. _____

_____

_____

_____

5.14 Discuss some options for outsourcing fire prevention services.

_____

_____

5.15 Contrast both private and public fire prevention bureaus.

_____

_____

_____

_____

_____

_____

_____

5.16 Briefly explain what the following sections do: engineering, fire and life safety education, inspections, investigations, public information.

_____

_____

_____

_____

_____

5.17 What is NFPA 1031? _____

_____

5.18 What general types of inspections can the inspection section can do?

_____

_____

5.19 What is preincident planning? _____

_____

_____

_____

5.20 What is NFPA 1033? _____

_____

5.21 List four key concerns a good investigation section should address.

_____

_____

_____

_____

5.22 Explain what the occupant service sectors should do._____

_____

_____

5.23 What is wildland risk management? _____

_____

_____

5.24 How should fire prevention bureaus address training issues?

_____

_____

_____

_____

NOTES

1. Oren Harari, "A Leadership Primer from Colin Powell," *Management Review* (December 1996).

2. Arthur E. Cote and Jim L. Linville, *Fire Protection Handbook,* 17th ed., Quincy, Mass.: National Fire Protection Association, 1991.

3. Ronny J. Coleman, "It's the Fire Service, Not the Fire Business," Chief's Clipboard, *Fire Chief Magazine* (April 1997).

4. Ibid.

5. Cote and Linville, *Fire Protection Handbook,* 17th ed., Quincy, Mass.: National Fire Protection Association, 1991.

6. Ibid.

Fire Prevention Applications
Chapter 6: Risk Assessment

FESHE COURSE OBJECTIVES

1. Understand risk.
2. Identify the benefits of a risk assessment.
3. Understand mitigation.
4. Understand prevention.

Chapter 6

Risk Assessment

Defining Risk

Many available publications discuss and describe risk. Some explain in great detail the specific science involved in a good risk assessment process. However, Webster's simple definition of **risk** is the exposure to possible loss or injury. While this is pretty clear, let's see how it applies to fire service applications. We can group all of our fire service activities into two separate umbrella categories:

- Preventing, mitigating, or controlling hazards to minimize risk

- Dealing with emergency incidents to minimize injury, suffering, and loss

It is also important to note that throughout this chapter, the term **injury** will include monetary impact, job loss, and aesthetic impact as well as personal injury. It basically refers to overall community injury.

Since we are trying to become skilled and motivated fire protection and suppression experts, we need to discuss a paradox. While we traditionally call our work fire prevention, people in the business can easily debate the reality of what we actually prevent. Some argue that we do little in the way of actually preventing incidents and at the very least have a difficult time proving or articulating what we actually prevent. Because of this, we see a trend in departments marketing our functions differently using terms like *fire and life safety services* or *hazard mitigation division*. We do prevent fires and incidents, but more frequently we mitigate them. We define **mitigation** as the prevention or reduction of severity of an undesired event. In the quest to mitigate community injury, our objective is to reduce, or limit as much as possible, truly serious loss of life and property incidents.

Think for a moment about how we address risk and the hazards we are charged to deal with. First, you must recognize the assets at your community's disposal. What emergency response equipment or methods are you able to respond with? Answering this question provides much information about the type of emergency your community can handle. Doing so requires extensive interaction with those fire department personnel responsible for emergency response, and seeking their input in the process is a must.

✔ **risk**
the exposure to possible loss or injury

✔ **injury**
personal injury, monetary impact, job loss, or aesthetic impact

✔ **mitigation**
the prevention or reduction of severity of an undesired event

For example, let's say you run a smaller department with two stations. Let's further assume you have two engines and one ladder truck. We'll then assume your response tactics are to respond with the first-due engine and begin a "quick attack" with that crew. The second-due engine responds and secures a water supply and backup lines for the first-due company. Now let's assume the ladder truck responds to provide forcible entry and ventilation. We'll also say that one of these companies will also be responsible for primary and secondary searches and any other functions your policies and procedures call for.

In this example then, we could deduce that for a typical single-family dwelling fire, the response likely would be adequate for containing and extinguishing a fire in the area or room of origin. This adequate response then could be determined sufficient to handle your community's typical fire.

Now let's consider a two-story office building that is roughly 20,000 square feet. Depending upon the situation, could your typical response handle a fire in one of the floors of this building? If the entire floor is open office cubicles, the total area or room of origin may be as much as 10,000 square feet. Maybe the office is a mix of closed offices and open cubicles. If the fire starts in one of the enclosed offices, it likely would be no different than a room-and-contents in the single-family dwelling. In either case, only you, based on your department's operational capabilities, can make the appropriate determination. Let's say we decide the fire in an open cube arrangement would likely be beyond our typical response capabilities. This being the case, we could further assume that the fire will progress, likely consuming the entire structure, or at least creating damage sufficient to render the entire structure unusable.

Our summary then would validate our example that a single-family dwelling should be considered our typical response. Larger buildings that are not subdivided into similar compartments and are of a similar light-weight wood frame construction are not typical but should be considered a higher hazard risk. This allows us to simplify our model: a low-hazard risk on its own would not burn much, so it likely would not damage adjoining properties or exposures or our fire crews. Moderate-risk occupancies pose a moderate threat to adjoining structures and without your department's intervention could cause a conflagration and minor injuries to our crews. A high-hazard risk, then, would be an unusual event, likely extending beyond your current control, assuming desired expectations or outcomes to be the same as those of a low or moderate hazard risk.

The point here is that the overall risk analysis effort need not give much consideration to typical hazards or risks, at least not yet. The hazards you should be most concerned with are those that will be unusual (not typical) and likely will need to be treated differently. So, if the office building in our example is mostly divided offices, it likely will present a typical scenario because fire can be physically confined to smaller areas. However, if one or both floors are open cubes, you may need to treat it as unusual or a higher risk occupancy (**Figure 6.1**)

The risk analysis should be most concerned with those hazards that will be unusual and likely will need to be treated differently.

What we are talking about is the definition or delineation of risk. Any risk that is moderate or lower does not require much more than our usual thought process; we can handle the risk because it is what we are trained, supported, and expected to do. Any risk greater than that (a high risk) needs to be identified and targeted for more consideration and thought, particularly by your policy makers or your governing body. This high risk may need to be treated differently or consciously debated as being acceptable as long as everyone has all the factual information and shares realistic expectations. Let's dig a little deeper.

What is a Risk Assessment?

Risk assessment can be very complex and studied and subdivided into many parts. A basic **risk assessment** consists of analyzing the risk impact and the risk perception and then combining the results.

Risk Impact

Risk impact is simply a measure of the probability that something will occur and the severity of its results. This can be done any number of ways. How many buildings will we lose? How many lives could be lost? How many serious injuries could occur? How much money will this event cost? (Do not forget to include both the direct and indirect costs.) Statistical information is collected for nearly all of the events we respond to in the fire service. Some departments obviously do a better job of collecting information than others. Those that do well with risk assessments typically do an excellent job of information gathering before and after an event. For good risk impact evaluations, start by tracking the amount and type of loss incurred based on what is valuable to your community (Chapter 9 covers tracking data in more detail; understanding and defining community value is explained later in this chapter). This concept of risk impact can be difficult to grasp. Some may measure the severity in square footage and dollar amounts, others in tenant spaces and dollar amounts. Still others may measure it in dollar amounts and injuries or deaths. To perform a credible risk impact analysis you need to look at your response history and loss experience and determine how many of those events or incidents you should expect on your target hazard. If your community is small, look to larger cities or towns similar in demographics and economics and use their figures.

Risk Perception

A **risk perception** determines the actual "value" of the risk. Basically, this is what we will discuss as public opinion. The risk perception study for a municipal department must involve the public it serves and the political body or policy makers for whom it works. This is basically a business decision for the community.

Figure 6.1 Office spaces such as large cubicles can pose a certain risk. In its early stages the risk analysis should focus on unusual risks.

✔ **risk assessment**
process of analyzing the risk impact and the risk perception and then combining the results

✔ **risk impact**
a measure of the probability that something will occur and the severity of its results

A credible risk impact analysis requires looking at response history and loss experience and determining how many similar events or incidents to expect at the target hazard.

✔ **risk perception**
the actual "value" of a risk

If you are a private fire department for a petrochemical plant, your defined risk perception would be much easier as it is basically left to the plant manager. Let's say that as the plant fire chief you have convinced plant management to follow a policy that requires all buildings on the site to be protected by automatic fire sprinklers. An outbuilding storing piping and flanges is currently unprotected by automatic fire sprinklers. If the pipe and flanges are worth $500.00 and the building is an old metal garage that is worth more torn down than it is standing, why would the plant manager consider installing a $4,000 sprinkler system just because your policy says to (**Figure 6.2**)? His or her determination whether to install automatic sprinklers will be a business decision. After thinking about it for about 15 seconds, the plant manager will have conducted a risk perception evaluation and determined nothing in or around that building was worth $4,000.00, so the best decision is to "let it burn!" This is one example of a good risk perception decision-making process.

What is the bang for the buck? What are citizens or your community willing to pay for certain levels of fire protection? Is it more economical to lose a 20,000-square-foot office building that is insured and owned by someone outside the state than to pay a million and a half dollars more in taxes each year for an additional fire station? These are the business decisions that your public and your policy makers must make. As a fire protection professional, your role should be only to inform and advise your customers of the facts. As a fire protection professional you will generally be working for someone else; it will be very rare, indeed, for you to have autonomous authority and discretion to issue mandates and affect whatever "rules" you choose.

> As a fire protection professional, your role in decision making should be only to inform and advise your customers of the facts.

Figure 6.2 Risk analysis weighs the cost of protecting a structure against its value in both dollars and public opinion.

Why Do a Risk Assessment?

A risk assessment is critical for long-range strategic planning in the fire prevention bureau, let alone the entire department. A risk assessment basically clarifies what your problems are now and likely will be in the future, and it provides a basis for determining how best to address these problems.

This planning is crucial not only for people within the department to make appropriate decisions but also for those outside the department such as the city council or village board. A municipal city council must be kept regularly informed on the status of the community's fire problem. By identifying the risks, the council will be able to communicate better with the department administration to set priorities for dealing with the right issues in the best time frame. Nothing would be worse than a fire department trying to fix a huge problem that the city council does not believe exists. Not only will fire department members become frustrated and feel abandoned, but also the city council may develop serious doubts about administration's grasp of reality in addressing community concerns.

The important thing to remember here is that a good risk assessment is necessary to properly identify the target. You must know where you need to go, how you need to get there, and what you need to support the venture. Without a map, how would you ever find your way around an unfamiliar city or state? Yes, you can use the Columbus Method (search and discover), but in today's competitive economy, you likely will not have that luxury, nor will your customers appreciate slow arriving results. We live in a society of instant gratification. Everyone wants his or her pain and problems fixed today, not tomorrow, let alone five weeks down the road.

Remember that a good risk assessment is necessary to properly identify the target.

Issues to Address in the Risk Assessment

A good risk assessment provides many benefits. Not only will it describe your problems but it also will allow you to forecast future demands and prioritize solutions. Perhaps the largest single benefit is the ability to communicate critical concerns and needs to your policy makers. This assessment will provide an honest picture of where you are now and where you are heading.

Any number of tools are available for communicating this analysis, some of which will be detailed later in this book; however, the key is gathering the appropriate data for dissemination among those who control the resources to accomplish your objectives. Important considerations include the following:

- Your public's view of their level of acceptable risk
- Paradigm shifts
- The truth hurts
- Engaging the public on risk
- The nuts and bolts

The remainder of the chapter will discuss these concerns.

What Does Your Public View as Their Level of Acceptable Risk?

Ask us for the single hardest question to answer in the fire service, and this is probably the one. What does the public view as their established comfort level with their acceptable risk? (Keep in mind that your public includes your elected officials.) The truth is, they probably do not even know what this means. If they do, their perceptions likely will be all over the board because we in the fire service have failed to make adults aware of what this really means to them.

Based on our nation's fire history, we have emphasized fire and life safety education for the two principle target groups with the greatest risk of being injured or dying in a fire: the very young (stop, drop, and roll; call 911, etc.) and the very old (take a pot holder with you when cooking, no smoking in bed, etc.). However, we have failed miserably at addressing the most critical age group that is responsible for taking care of both these age groups, working class young adults in their twenties to late thirties. This is the same vote-wielding group that determines our destiny with regard to municipal bonding, tax increases or rollbacks, and other key financial issues. We must target them and inform them better to help us map our planning.

For example, consider the following analogy. A thirty-year-old father of three decides to go for a ride on his bicycle with his oldest child. The father cares very much for his child's safety and therefore makes sure he/she wears a helmet during their ride. However, without consciously thinking about it, he makes a decision about his acceptable risk by choosing not to wear a helmet himself.

Riding along, they round a corner and hit a layer of sand deposited by a recent rainstorm. They both lose traction and crash their bikes. The child ends up with some abrasions to the arms, hands, and legs while the father strikes his head against the curb. The father's injury results in a depressed skull fracture causing permanent brain injury, leaving him debilitated and nursing-home-bound for the rest of his life.

This injury has results in loss of principle earnings for the family, long-term health care bills that are the wife's responsibility, at least a short-term loss of a father-figure role model, and unknown future problems compounded by the loss of half the family nucleus.

Did the father think about all this before the incident? Likely not. As an average American, he probably thought he and the child were only going out for a few minutes, didn't want to mess up his hair, or maybe didn't want to wear a helmet in the heat. Thus, his level of acceptable risk was to gamble on a very infrequent event of very great consequences.

How can we engage the public on issues of fire and life safety, getting them to consciously make educated decisions on how to best protect themselves and finally when to rely on a public or private service to step in and provide that extra level of protection? The answer lies in public process.

What is public process? Our definition of **public process** is the act of engaging the public with factual information concerning issues that are important to them and learning from them "what they want and can't live without" (**Figure 6.3**). These include:

- Services the fire department provides today (fire protection, EMS, hazmat response, etc.)

- Factual benefits and outcomes of that level of service (response times, basic life support outcomes, advanced life support outcomes, efficiencies or benefits of those services, availability, etc.)

- Cost of current services (personnel, stations, capital, ongoing; generally shown in a cost per capita)

- Public desires and expectations (finding out what services they approve of and expect and those they want but are not currently receiving)

✔ **public process**
the act of engaging the public with factual information concerning issues that are important to them and learning from them "what they want and can't live without"

- What additional costs are they willing to pay for (again, typically given in a cost per capita figure)

- What services you are providing that they do not think are necessary

You also should offer the public your factual explanation of what you view as risks. In response you should obtain from them:

- Their agreement or disagreement on what they view as risks

- Consensus on what community risks are and are not

Public process is complex, time consuming, and labor intensive. However, it is the only reasonable method to engage and understand the public will and your mission.

Determining your public's acceptable risk is crucial. Otherwise, the fire service will continue to be in the position of "telling everyone what is good for them" based on our opinions and biases, rather than performing our job, which is to do what the public wants and in fact pays us to do.

Paradigm Shifts

What is a **paradigm shift**? Stephen R. Covey refers to a paradigm as a way of understanding and explaining certain aspects of reality.[1] Shifting your paradigm means you get rid of the old ways of thinking and open the door for new insight, new methods, and different views. Basically, you start looking at things through different goggles.

For many years, the public has relied upon the fire chief to tell them how best to protect themselves and the community from fire and, sometimes, other disasters. As a single administrative position or department head in most communities, the chief has had tremendous leeway, respect, and autonomy. It was the chief, however, who was left holding the bag when disaster struck, and it was the chief who most easily walked in front of a governmental body to tell them what needed to happen to fix a dangerous issue. For years, the chief would be the one to give his/her professional opinion on what needed to be done, and the public would often blindly agree because "the chief said so." This led to power and authority's potentially being misplaced or misused, particularly if the chief really did not know the true issues or if inappropriate political will was being exercised. That is not to say such things happened a lot, but the possibility was always there. The evolution of our country's political system has led to mistrust of government and constant questioning of nearly

Figure 6.3 Often, fire department officials are required to take part in the public law-making process as shown in this community public input meeting.

Although public process is complex, time consuming, and labor intensive, it is the only reasonable method to engage and understand the public will and your mission.

✔ **paradigm shift**
a change from old ways of thinking that opens the door for new insight, new methods, and different views

everything that government does. The net result in many communities is a public that questions every cent spent and offers opinions of what is right or wrong regardless of their knowledge, just because they do not trust the government or the people who run it.

The difficulty is that the community, time after time, has a very hard time seeing what disasters or problems lurk until they actually happen. Then of course, they are quick to blame someone for not telling them or taking action sooner to prevent such an occurrence. We Americans are very apathetic. Thus, our current communities tend not to listen as well as they used to because they think "it can never happen to them"—until it does. This was especially evident in our view of a possible terrorism attacks on U.S. soil prior to 9-11.

This said, the fire service more than ever before must rethink our way of communicating, looking at problems, and proposing solutions. Our service needs to shift paradigms. Rather than telling the public what is good for them, we must begin crafting our facts, our anecdotal stories, to educate our middle-aged voting populous on what "real" risk means and what the "real" hazards are. When we cannot define those real risks and hazards, we must let the voting public define them for us. We have the professional expertise available to propose good solutions. However, unless the public understands the risk, the expectations, and the outcomes, how can we expect them to help us solve the problems? Remember, these problems are not ours (the fire service's). They are the community's. We all suffer or we all benefit. It is a community-based decision process that must involve everyone. No longer can we tell the public what to do or what is good for them. As a society, we have become far too educated for that. We must change our way of approaching our communities and help them to help us find the right answers.

The risk of doing this is that we may hear answers that we do not agree with. Remember our example at the beginning of this chapter? As fire service members we have been trying to win the zero loss game. No deaths, no property damage. This objective is hardly attainable. People will die and property will be lost. Our job is to provide reasonable protection from reasonable incidents. Good risk management will not address every single event unless someone provides the money to support that objective. NASA is a good example. They spend billions of dollars to prevent fires in the space station because they cannot call the Houston Fire Department if someone up there smells smoke. Therefore, they do support financially the elimination of fire potential through engineering, education, and enforcement through policy and procedural methods. In a large community here on Earth that has from hundreds to millions of people in various jurisdictions, this solution is not reasonably attainable. So, we use a cadre of methods, means, and schemes. We need to do these differently than we typically have done them in the past. Proof is evident in some of the more progressive departments throughout the country. They have had to learn how to look at problems and think them through differently, if for no other reason than sheer survival.

Risk assessment is a community-based decision process that must involve everyone.

The Truth Hurts

Granted, the solutions and answers we get from our public may be contrary to our opinions. The reality is, if our boss understands the facts of an issue and tells us to do something, we most likely should do it. This is not to say that in all cases the public's view is the answer of choice; however, the reality is that if they know the facts, they will defer the decision to us and therefore we can act upon our will. We propose that the public should be viewed as reasonable and prudent in their choices, decisions, and opinions. After all, our nation was founded through a government whose decisions were intended to represent the will of the populace.

If the public knows the facts, it will be reasonable and prudent in its choices, decisions, and opinions.

Consider this example. As a fire protection professional, you know that the more fire safety inspections are conducted, the lower will be the fire incident rate and the magnitude of fires that do occur. So, you propose to hire 10 more inspectors for your fire prevention division; however, to do this will require an increase in taxes, which requires a vote of the people. The vote is cast and your public says not only no but *heck no!* Are you still going to hire the ten inspectors? Not likely. Is the public's decision wrong or bad? No. That is, not if you have provided them with all of the relevant information necessary to make an informed decision. Through the vote, they made a decision of their acceptable risk. They believe that the potential increase in fires does not offset the cost of adding ten additional employees to prevent them.

Our point is that the public's decision is legitimate. You as a fire protection professional need to accept it. Do not confuse the aspects of informed decision making. Your job as a professional is to inform your citizens and public officials—your stakeholders—of the relevant issues surrounding the decision. What is relevant information? Therein lies the true test of your ability and professionalism, not to mention leadership. As long as the public understands the issues, their decision defining their acceptable risk will be reasonable.

How to Engage the Public On Risk

Our young adult voting populace—those in their twenties to late thirties—is very busy during this time of their lives. They have children in school, parents needing care, soccer practice, little league, and religious activities. They also have jobs, sometimes two, and many other distractions just trying to live a "normal" life. How can you possibly tell them everything you know about the fire service in order for them to make the "right" decision? You can't. That's why they hired you. They expect you to know. However, they do want to know what the real issues are, what the potential outcomes are, what you can do currently to mitigate or solve the problems, and how much it will cost to achieve a different outcome. Remember the acronym KISS (Keep it simple, stupid)? The public is not stupid, but they are likely ill informed. The following steps will help you to work toward a solution:

1. Succinctly identify the real problem(s)—not the perceived problem(s) but the real one(s).

2. Prioritize the issues from most hazardous to least.

3. Recruit a good cross section of stakeholders from the community (businesses, citizens of diverse incomes and locations, regulatory agencies, anyone and everyone you can think of who has a vested interest in the outcome, and do not forget the people from economic development).

4. Break these people into focus groups if the number is too large. Remember, the more you involve, the more accurate your outcome.

5. Discuss with these people the problems' understandable (simple) outcomes or threats. Anecdotal references will go a long way here.

6. Accurately (no Hollywood) define for them your capabilities for solving or mitigating the problems and what they should expect. If you find they expect more than you can deliver as an organization, make sure they realize the additional costs.

7. Engage these people or groups to provide at least two (and no more than five) possible solutions with their resultant outcomes. Consider this the menu of choices, no different than if you went to a restaurant to choose a dinner.

8. Sort these options in descending order from most costly to least.

9. Present this final list to the same group(s) for confirmation or readjustment.

10. Publish the document of findings and use them as the key component of your risk analysis as you have just defined the risk perception.

The Colorado Springs (Colorado) Fire Department has used this process successfully several times to accomplish different objectives, all tied to defining the acceptable risk and achieving community goals, objectives, and appropriate expectations. The major community impacts were:

- A resolution establishing single company response times of 8 minutes 90 percent of the time and effective force response times of 12 minutes 90 percent of the time. This facilitates future station planning, expenses and program development with little explanatory effort.

- Adoption of a comprehensive wildfire mitigation plan community wide. (This has been a resounding community success impacting 51,000 addresses.)

- Passage of a Class A roof ordinance prohibiting any solid wood product, citywide. The ordinance was a landmark achievement for a city of 375,000 people.

Although this process is extremely time consuming and labor intensive, it is the only way to gauge the public's degree of acceptable risk. The answers you find may not be the ones you would choose. However, the community will support and defend you on them all the way to the bank. Let us be clear. We are not saying the entire public will completely agree with you, but at the very least they will grudgingly go along with you. This is the greatest victory you can reasonably expect to achieve.

The Nuts and Bolts

Now that we have laid all the ground-work on risk analysis, we will close this chapter with a nuts and bolts of discussion of how to do one. This process is relatively generic and can be used for many types of specific applications.

As we have discussed, start by defining the relevant and credible threats and outcomes. Remember, you cannot protect everyone from everything. Make sure the threats you include are among those that your mission statement addresses (**Figure 6.4**).

Figure 6.4 High-risk areas are frequently visited by fire departments.

Once you have defined the threats, what are the possible outcomes? Explore both the direct and indirect effects. What are the monetary impacts to individuals, the community, and other areas of concern? What is the duration of these affects? Identify the costs of recovery and reclamation, not just the actual damage. What are the life threats (**Figure 6.5**)? Despite death's tragedy, our experience has been that people tend quickly to become apathetic after a fire death occurs. For reasons that only credible psychologists can dare explain, people acknowledge the horror and tragedy of a fire death but soon afterward take the approach, "Sad it happened to them. Good thing it will never happen to me." You will find that the one common issue is money. Money speaks. It ripples through a community like ripples in a pond. Even in considering

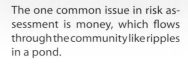

The one common issue in risk assessment is money, which flows through the community like ripples in a pond.

Figure 6.5 Some schools pose a significant risk due to the type and age of occupants.

wildfire risk, timber has a price (logging) and aesthetic value (someone will always pay for pretty land, including the Bureau of Land Management or the United States Forest Service). Historical structures have a value (how much to restore and maintain). Manufacturing plants have a value (number of employees and lost income, structure, business interruption costs, lost customer base, etc.) (**Figure 6.6**).

Conduct a comprehensive analysis of your local incidents by area of study. Global information system support will be an invaluable tool in accomplishing this. Other computer-generated data will also be beneficial in this process. These data not only provide you with the number and types of incidents but give you a graphical representation of their location and magnitude. The adage that "a picture is worth a thousand words" is never truer than in this type of analysis.

Determine the risk impact next. Study the frequency and history of events by parcel, occupancy type, or whatever other data field best suits your objective. At the same time, look at the impact of your losses as a result of specific consequences for these specific data fields. For example, how many apartment fires are you having per year and in what parts of town? Next ask what are the life and monetary losses for each of these fires in each of these areas. Overlay and compare the data to get a perspective on which locations are in the worst shape.

Rank your risk impact results. Again, the order of priority will depend on what you are trying to accomplish. We recommend classifying risks by occupancy types to start with. Next, determine your department's level of perceived awareness; explore your management capabilities to deal with the identified areas and your currently available resources to address the risk. These data will be critical for the risk perception phase.

Conduct your risk perception following the steps outlined previously in this chapter. This is a critical but slow process. Do not try to shortcut or dilute the process. It will anchor everything that follows. At the same time, develop a good understanding of national standards of good practice. What are other people doing about this problem? What other codes, standards, or ordinances address it? What other various ways (think out of the box) can we use to mitigate or solve this problem? Once you have completed this step and can readily evaluate and communicate your risk impact in combination

Figure 6.6 Monetary cost is a significant factor in evaluating risk, whether it involves the value of timber (**a**) or the cost of restoring a historical structure (**b**).

with your risk perception, you have completed your analysis. Remember, your analysis only provides a tool to communicate your risk issues. It does not solve the problem(s).

Once your risk analysis is complete, combine those results with your standards of practice information. Plug this combined information into your previously determined risk classifications and forecast through modeling the possible effects of these solutions on your overall identified risk. Assuming the proposed solutions will change the outcomes for the better, then determine what resources you will need to accomplish your objective. These should include all three elements of fire prevention work: engineering, education, and enforcement.

The next step is to try to implement your recommendations (**Figure 6.7**). Obviously, this will require support from many sources. Once you have implemented your recommendations, regularly evaluate your results. Determine what effects both mitigation and response have had on the outcomes, and plug these results back into your risk perception process and incident analysis by area of study. Continue to make changes as necessary for the program's overall success and effectiveness.

Summary

Risk assessment should be a main staple of fire prevention functions. To deal properly with community injury problems, the finite target and actual risk must be understood. Risk is often misunderstood or attempts to deal with it are misdirected. Risk is commonly defined as the chance of injury, damage or loss. However, in a broader sense, we in the fire service may define it a little more practically based on whether or not we can deal with an issue. If we have enough resources and equipment to handle an unwanted event such as a particularly hostile fire we may consider it a low risk. If we have insufficient resources or equipment to handle a potential event, that may be considered a high risk.

To identify methods of handling risk, we must conduct a risk assessment. From a fire service perspective, we should keep our focus fairly basic and keep things a little more simple; in this light, a risk assessment involves identifying the risk impact and the risk perception and then combining those results in order to properly identify our target.

Figure 6.7 Good risk management will move risks such as this wildland/ urban area (**a**) from a high-hazard condition to a lower-hazard and more controlled condition (**b**).

Risk impact is a measure of the probability and severity of a particular event, series of events, or calamities. A risk perception is the actual community weighted value of a risk. It is what the tax-paying public believes is the actual value of protection. This assessment is essential for effective long-range strategic planning and provides a clear road map for future endeavors.

By identifying your public's acceptable risk, you will in turn identify what you need to do to satisfy their desires. Maybe we as fire safety professionals worry more about things than our "bosses" (the public) think we should. It is better to know risks up front than to spend a ton of time and resources trying to achieve a goal that will not be politically viable or, worse, will not be funded and supported. We as a fire service must also look at shifting some of our own paradigms. This is essential if we plan on hitting the right target and going after the right problem. We must also help our public understand their risk and our capabilities. We must then use these findings, decisions, and outcomes to mitigate those risks that can be dealt with. Remember, prevention deals with actually stopping unwanted events from occurring. Mitigation is simply the modification of an unwanted outcome to a level that is sustainable, survivable, or nearly nonexistent due to active protection measures.

Chapter 6 Review Exercises

6.1 What is risk? _____
_____

6.2 What are the purposes of a risk assessment? _____
_____
_____
_____
_____

6.3 What are the benefits from a risk assessment? _____
_____
_____
_____

6.4 Contact the local fire department and discuss if they have conducted a
risk assessment and what they have determined to be the most significant
risk in the community they protect. _____
_____
_____

6.5 What is mitigation? _____
_____
_____

6.6 Explain the difference between mitigation and prevention. _____
_____
_____

6.7 Provide an explanation of what "typical" risk could be and give some
examples. _____
_____
_____

6.8 Define risk impact. _____
_____

6.9 Define risk perception. _____
_____

6.10 What is public process? _____
_____
_____
_____

NOTES

1. Stephen R. Covey, *Principle Centered Leadership*: Summit Books, 1991), pg. 173.

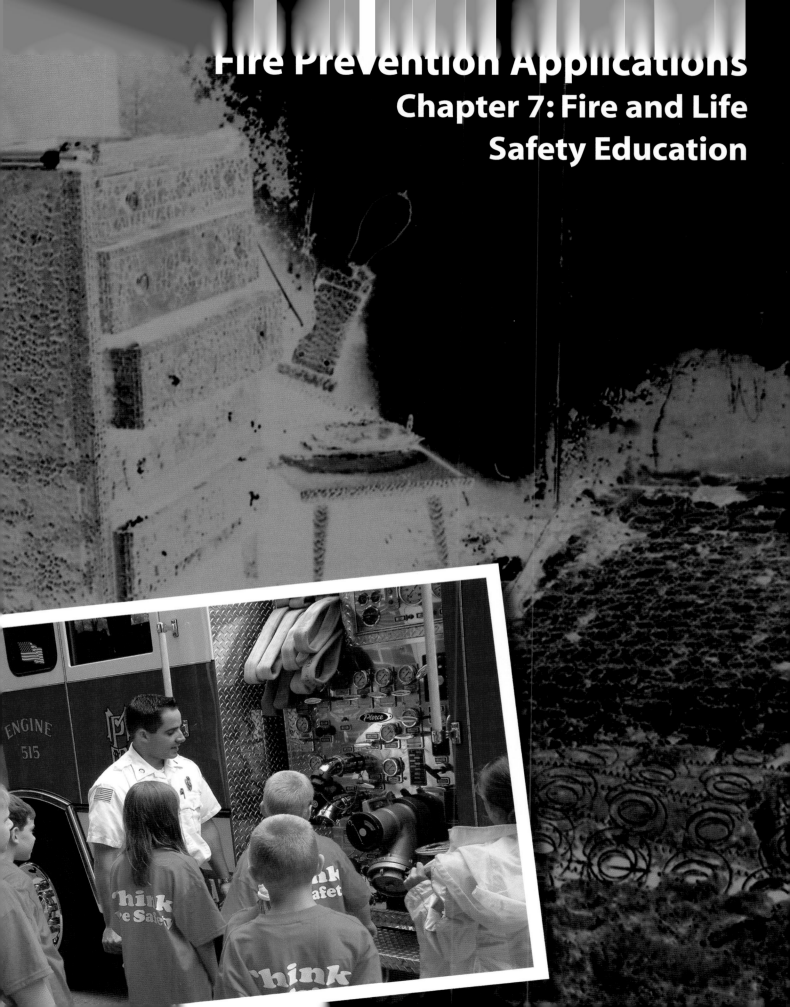

Fire Prevention Applications
Chapter 7: Fire and Life Safety Education

FESHE COURSE OBJECTIVES

1. Understand how to design media programs.*

2. Discuss the major programs for public education.*

3. Identify programs for fire safety education.

4. Identify the different types of media that can be used in fire safety education.

5. Identify various presentation methods.

6. Identify sources of potential funding of fire safety education.

*U.S. Fire Administration Objective

Chapter 7
Fire and Life Safety Education

What Is Fire and Life Safety Education?

Fire and life safety education is by far one of the most effective methods to prevent injuries from fire or other types of emergencies. To occur, a fire needs heat, fuel, oxygen, and something to bring them together. The something that brings them together is usually a person, or what is sometimes referred to as the human factor. In fire prevention we can address the prevention and mitigation of fires by eliminating one of the three elements listed above. The elimination of the heat and fuel is accomplished in a number of ways, most commonly through fire engineering and enforcement. We can effectively address the human factor by focusing on behavior modification through fire and life safety education. Fire and life safety education's main objective is to motivate the public to act in a fire-safe manner. This may require modifying some of their ideas or perceptions about fire. To change people's beliefs or attitudes toward a fire problem, we must first educate them about the threat of fire and how or where that threat exists in their environment. Fire and life safety education can accomplish this. Later in this chapter, we will discuss how the role of the life safety educator has expanded beyond just the reduction of injuries from fire.

Preventing fires is an essential element of fire safety education; however, fires do occur and people do need to be prepared to react correctly should one happen in their home, school, office, or elsewhere. For instance, we teach children how to stop, drop, and roll when their clothes are on fire and teach adults in high-rise buildings how to safely evacuate during a fire. Fire safety education is a proven method to teach people how to react when fires occur. The documented cases of families being alerted by their smoke detectors and following their escape plans to meet safely at their meeting place are found in all parts of the country. In just a few years, the same scenario will occur with the difference that the homes will have had little fire damage and the occupants will have been able to evacuate easily because of their residential sprinkler system.

> Fire and life safety education's main objective is to motivate the public to act in a fire-safe manner.

Why is Fire Safety Education Important?

Fire safety education is very important for several reasons:

- The fire department cannot be instantaneously everywhere a fire may occur.

- People are a main cause of fire, and if they maintain good fire safe behavior, fewer fires will occur.

- People's basic instincts are often very different from person to person (i.e., some may try to run for help if their clothes catch fire rather than dropping to the ground to smother the flames).

- American's are apathetic and spoiled to a degree, not having any intrinsic training or familiarization with how to use fire or heat properly; we depend on others or on devices to protect us.

- As a community, we should be able to rely on one another in times of crisis.

- More and more families are two-income with latchkey children home alone.

- The number of retirees and seniors will soon increase.

> The real role of fire safety education is to modify behaviors and/or instill basic appropriate behaviors at an early age.

The real role of fire safety education is to modify behaviors and/or instill basic appropriate behaviors at an early age (**Figure 7.1**). As a country, we are just now seeing adults appearing from the generation of children to whom Sparky the Fire Dog and Dick Van Dyke urged a lot of fire safe messages like Stop, Drop, and Roll. Only now will we be able to better measure the benefit

Figure 7.1 Fire departments need to promote fire and life safety education beginning at an early age.

of our efforts to reach a larger population. Our goal as fire service professionals has been to instill these proper behaviors into the entire population. Unfortunately, many immigrants and others who come to this country have not received this type of education. We still reap rewards, however, because their children are compensating and acting on these behaviors in the absence of their parent's knowledge. Frequently we see children who are recognized as the heroes in emergencies either because their parents were not home or did not speak English and did not know what to do. Some people ask, "Are these stories just public relations?" The answer is unequivocally no!

History of Fire and Life Safety Education

What we know in the 21st century as fire and life safety education has had several names. It was and still is in many parts of the United States referred to as fire prevention education and public fire education or pub ed. The need for fire safety education began in the late 1800s but was well documented in 1909 when the National Fire Protection Association's (NFPA) Franklin Wentworth began to send fire prevention bulletins to local newspapers in hopes of getting them published. As shown in **Figure 7.2** on the next page, fire and life safety education has made significant progress since 1909.

Some of the more notable early impacts were the Junior Fire Marshal Program, the birth of NFPA's Sparky the Fire Dog, and the establishment of NFPA standards for professional qualifications for fire inspector, fire investigator, and fire prevention education officer.

The *America Burning* report published by the National Commission on Prevention and Control brought the nation's fire problem to the forefront (see Chapter 2). Not only did this document depict the significance of the fire problem in the United States, it identified educating people about fire as one of the best ways to reduce fires and fire related deaths and injuries. This document's impact on recognizing the need for fire prevention efforts was again recognized in the summer of 1999 when the Federal Emergency Management Agency director formally recommissioned *America Burning*. The 2000 United States Fire Administration (USFA) report *America Burning Re-Commmissioned* states, "There is wide acknowledgement and acceptance that public education programs on fire prevention are effective . . . no prevention effort can succeed without a public education component."[1] The commission considered that fire departments now respond to more than "just fire" and are the first line of response to an array of disasters that communities face throughout the United States. The commission determined *America at Risk* to be the correct title and orientation of its report.

In the past, fire departments focused their educational efforts only on fire prevention and fire survival topics such as stop, drop, and roll and practicing a home escape plan. Today, they have expanded their role in educating the public to preventing injuries in a number of areas. With the inclusion of these additional prevention topics the name of the fire department's education activities evolved to fire and life safety education.

Time Line of Events Affecting Public Fire and Life Safety Education

1909 NFPA's Franklin Wentworth begins sending fire prevention bulletins to correspondents in 70 cities, with the hope that local newspapers will publish the bulletins as news articles.

1911 Fire Marshals Association of North America proposes the October 9 anniversary of the Great Chicago Fire as a day to observe fire prevention.

1912 *Syllabus for Public Instruction in Fire Prevention*—a collection of fire safety topics for teachers to use in the classroom—published by NFPA.

1916 NFPA and the National Safety Council establish a Committee on Fire and Accident Prevention. Communities nationwide organize Fire Prevention Day activities.

1920 President Woodrow Wilson signs first presidential proclamation for Fire Prevention Day.

1922 President Warren G. Harding signs first Fire Prevention Week proclamation.

1923 Twenty-three states have legislation requiring fire safety education in schools.

1927 NFPA begins sponsoring national Fire Prevention Contest.

1942 New York University publishes *Fire Prevention Education*.

1946 U.S. government publishes *Curriculum Guide to Fire Safety*.

1947 Hartford Insurance Group begins the Junior Fire Marshal Program, perhaps the first nationally distributed fire safety program for children.

1948 American Mutual Insurance Alliance publishes first edition of *Tested Activities for Fire Prevention Committees*, based on Fire Prevention Contest entries.

1950 In October, 7,000 newspapers receive the ad, "Don't Gamble with Fire—The Odds are Against You," developed by the Advertising Council and NFPA.

1954 Sparky® the Fire Dog is created.

1965 *Fire Journal* begins a regular column on "Reaching the Public."

1966 "Wingspread Conference" highlights the need for public education.

1967 Three Apollo astronauts die in a fire in their spacecraft, drawing national attention to the need to be prepared for fire emergencies. Later, attacks on firefighters during urban riots attract more public attention.

1970 President Richard Nixon appoints the National Commission on Fire Prevention and Control.

1973 The National Commission on Fire Prevention and Control publishes its report, *America Burning*.

The Fire Department Instructors Conference offers its first presentation on fire and life safety education, delivered by Cathy Lohr of North Carolina.

1974 NFPA and Public Service Council release the first television Learn Not to Burn® public service announcements starring Dick Van Dyke.

Fire Prevention and Control Act establishes the National Fire Prevention and Control Administration.

NFPA report by Richard Strother *A Study of Motivational Psychology Related to Fire Preventive Behavior in Children and Adults* explains the effectiveness of positive educational messages.

1975 The National Fire Prevention and Control Administration holds its first national fire safety education conference.

1977 NFPA 1031, *Standard for Professional Qualifications for Fire Inspector, Fire Investigator, and Fire Prevention Education Officer*, is published.

National Fire Prevention and Control Administration releases *Public Fire Education Planning: A Five Step Process*. National Fire Academy offers its first public education course on the same subject.

National Fire Prevention and Control Administration launches national smoke detector campaign.

1979 J. C. Robertson's *Introduction to Fire Prevention* published by Glencoe Press.

Project Burn Prevention, funded by the Consumer Product Safety Commission, develops educational strategies and materials for reducing burn injuries—a significant milestone in the shift from "fire education" to "all-risk education."

The *Learn Not to Burn® Curriculum* is published by NFPA.

International Fire Service Training Association releases IFSTA 606, *Public Fire Education*.

International Society of Fire Service Instructors establishes its Public Education Section.

1981 NFPA establishes its Education Section.

TriData Corporation releases *Reaching the Hard to Reach*.

1985 The National Education Association recommends the *Learn Not to Burn® Curriculum*.

NFPA publishes *Firesafety Educator's Handbook*.

1986 Learn Not to Burn® Foundation incorporated.

1987 The first edition of NFPA 1035, *Standard for Professional Qualifications for Public Fire Educator*, encourages civilians to become public fire educators in the fire department.

TriData Corporation publishes *Overcoming Barriers to Public Fire Education*.

1990 Oklahoma State University publishes the first issue of the *Public Fire Education Digest*.

TriData Corporation releases *Proving Public Fire Education Works*.

1995 NFPA and National SAFE KIDS Campaign begin developing all-risk school curriculum called *Safety Sense*.

This time line relies in part on information from Pam Powell's "Firesafety Education: It's Older Than You Think," *Fire Journal*, May 1986, pp.13+

Figure 7.2 Time line of events affecting public fire and life safety education.

The fire department took on these additional educational topics for a number of reasons. One of the most notable is that fire departments have expanded their role in emergency response from just fire fighting to include such incidents as emergency medical response, swift water rescue, ice rescue, hazardous materials, and in more recent years, terrorism response. With the increased emergency services, fire departments were seeing citizens injured from a variety of activities. These included drowning while swimming, fractures and head injuries from skateboarding and biking without helmets and pads, deaths and major injury from not wearing seatbelts or proper infant and child safety seats. These types of preventable injuries and the local cry to prevent them were driving forces for fire departments to include educational topics in addition to fire prevention. In 2003 a fire in a New Jersey nightclub resulted in multiple loss of life. This tragedy occurred within days of a nonfire incident in an overcrowded Chicago nightclub that resulted in a number of deaths because of inadequate exiting. Immediately after these incidents, a public outcry to prevent similar incidents led many local fire departments throughout the country to begin conducting nighttime inspections of assembly or nightclub-type occupancies. Another example is the increased threat of terrorism that spawned tremendous requests to assist in the development, training, and approval of emergency action or preparedness plans for businesses and other organizations in our communities. The *America Burning Recommissioned* report published in 2000 reached two major conclusions. First,

> We have a fire problem because our nation has failed to adequately apply and fund known loss reduction strategies. The primary responsibility for fire prevention and suppression and action with respect to other hazards dealt with by the fire services properly rests with the states and local governments.

And second,

> The responsibilities of today's fire departments extend well beyond the traditional fire hazard. Fire protection expertise can be shifted from reaction and response and used for prevention activities.

Today many fire departments are providing injury prevention or all-risk reduction programs to include a number of topics such as:

- Bicycle safety
- Natural disasters
- Water safety
- Ice safety
- Pedestrian safety
- Babysitter training
- Cardiopulmonary resuscitation (CPR)
- First aid
- Environmental hazards
- Seat belt and car seat training

Preventable injuries and the local cry to prevent them were driving forces for fire departments to include educational topics in addition to fire prevention.

The importance of fire and life safety education will only continue to escalate into the 21st century. National and international organizations that make up the North American Coalition for Fire and Life Safety Education determined the need for a combined approach to address the fire death and injury rates in targeted audiences, which included those within the high-risk populations. The first symposium took place in 1998, and follow-up meetings with fire prevention experts and advocacy organizations for target audiences took place in 1999. The report *Solutions 2000* published their joint recommendations for improved safety for young children, older adults, and people with disabilities.

In April 2001, the North American Coalition for Fire and Life Safety Education conducted a symposium to address solutions from the *Solutions 2000* symposium held in Washington, DC, in April 1999. The symposium offered an avenue for experts in the area of fire safety to meet with those who had specific concerns about older adults, people with disabilities, and children. The attendees report, *Beyond Solutions 2000,* suggests solutions for actions that will impact fire safety for high-risk groups. (The report may be accessed electronically at www.usfa.fema.gov.) The report built upon the recommendations in the first report with its primary focus on targeting the high-risk groups. The recommendations of the report focus on decreasing fire deaths and injuries in the targeted groups by improving fire safety in the areas of (1) egress capability, (2) early warning, and (3) fire sprinkler protection. It was clear that more aggressive education is needed to heighten the awareness of the fire problem in all of the target groups. People need to understand the threat of fire better before they will be motivated to change their behavior or their environment.[2] This only reemphasized the need for further fire safety education.

Fire and life safety education will play a significant role in fire department services in the 21st century. Not only will fire departments take on a community risk reduction approach; they will be taking it on with other agencies. In fact, they cannot effectively do it alone. The number of citizens we need to reach, combined with fiscal and resource constraints, are among the reasons fire departments must seek outside assistance in developing and implementing their fire and life safety education programs. A principle way of gathering this support is through coalition building. Community involvement through coalition building only helps to encourage good fire and life safety behaviors, as well as to heighten the community's awareness of the problems. Among many others, community coalition members may include:

- News affiliates
- Printed press members
- Schools
- Neighborhood associations
- Housing authorities
- Apartment associations

Fire departments must seek outside assistance in developing and implementing their fire and life safety education programs.

- Grant providing entities

- Fast food restaurants

- Grocery stores (particularly chains)

- Chambers of Commerce

- Economic development

- The library

- Civic groups, such as Kiwanis, Rotary, Lions Club, etc.

There are perhaps more private and sponsored funding options than ever before. In fact, you likely will experience more problems trying to keep up with writing grant applications because the possibilities are so numerous. There are likely local organizations in your community that provide endowments, grants, loans, and other assistance. Make sure that all donors get some sort of recognition for their generosity (**Figure 7.3**).

Figure 7.3 Always provide public recognition for your donors' support.

It may also be possible to establish trust accounts specifically set up for individual programs to which anonymous donors can contribute. You can also establish not-for-profit mechanisms such as 501c(3)s offering the department opportunities to earn and collect money that it could not through normal bureaucratic channels. Be careful to check with your department's attorney and fiscally adept advisors. Trust management and accounting involve some serious issues. While trusts offer more financial flexibility, you must exercise great care to keep yourself and your chief out of trouble.

Fire and life safety education programs will not just take place in the school and local fire stations. They will become a part of the workplace as well as more companies and businesses see the need to educate their workers on good fire and life safety behaviors.

Does Fire and Life Safety Education Really Work?

Fire and life safety education is a core element of all fire prevention programs. Essentially, in every aspect of fire prevention, members of the community are educated either about the fire problem or ways to reduce the impact of a fire if one should occur in their home or business. For example, the owners of a new industrial facility may learn about the benefits of automatic sprinklers once they are required to install them in their new facility. The owners may have been reluctant at first to spend the funds on something "they will never use." Through our educational efforts, we can hope that, after those owners discuss this issue with a member of the fire prevention bureau, they will understand how sprinklers operate and how effective they are. Routine fire inspections are an example of fire and life safety education constantly taking place but not always being identified. Far too often, owners or occupants are reluctant to address deficiencies identified by fire inspectors because of either the financial impact or their belief that the deficiency is not significant or important. The fire inspector's job is not only to obtain compliance but also to educate and sell the occupant or owner on the importance of addressing the issue (see Chapter 11 for further discussion). More importantly, if the fire department's leadership or governing elected body does not see that fire and life safety education works, it may become a target for reduction or elimination when difficult budgets arrive.

To evaluate a fire and life safety education program, it is paramount that those individuals conducting fire and life safety education programs know their audiences understand and can apply the behaviors taught. For the purpose of this discussion, keep in mind we are evaluating the effectiveness of the fire and life safety education program, not the instructor. According to the text *Fire and Life Safety Educator,* published by the International Fire Service Training Association, effective evaluation can provide the following information[3]:

- The level of knowledge or skills of the target audience before the presentation or program

- Whether the target audience learned the desired information from the presentation or program

- Whether the target audience can perform the behaviors presented

- Whether the members of the target audience have applied the information in their homes or workplaces

- The strength and weakness of the instructional methods used by the educator

The text *Fire and Life Safety Educator* further examines in detail many evaluation methods that include:

- Pretest/posttest
- Skills test
- Survey
- Inspection
- Observation
- Injury loss statistics

All fire and life safety educators need to learn and understand these evaluation methods. The *Fire and Life Safety Educator* manual is a must for any fire and life safety educator because it was written and validated by experienced life safety educators.

We have identified how to evaluate the program's effectiveness for individual participants, but how do you evaluate the fire and life safety education program's overall impact on the community's fire problem or other hazards? There are a number of methods to determine if the fire and life safety education programs work. In this text, we have previously compared the fire department's operation to the private sector's. Measuring the results of a fire department's program is subject to the same comparison. The effectiveness of a fire safety education program should be measured by its impact on the "bottom line." In this case, the bottom line would be the reduction or elimination of the community's fire incident, injury, and death rates.

The auto industry strives to keep defects (problems) to the lowest number possible. Our approach should be the same regarding incidents as defects. We do not want defects; therefore, we do not want incidents to occur. In the business world the bottom line may be profit. The fire safety education program's largest profit is zero fire deaths and injuries. However, like the business community, even if you do not reach your largest profit margin you may still show a net gain.

In fire and life safety education, we can compare our communities' fire-injury and death rates to those of similar communities throughout the country. If we have a successful fire and life safety education program, our profit will be shown in fewer fire injuries and deaths than the norm. Understand that fire and life safety education alone will not achieve this. We have discussed how every component of our fire prevention effort includes a part of fire and life safety education. A number of fire and life safety education programs have been implemented and evaluated. When establishing a fire and life safety education program, you may be wise to see how the program was effective in other communities.

TriData Corporation's text *Proving Public Fire Education Works* cites specific examples of the measured success of fire and safety education programs in an array of communities across the United States and Canada. It further examines methods for fire departments to examine the impact of their fire

An effective fire and life safety education program's bottom line is the reduction or elimination of the community's fire incident, injury, and death rates.

and life safety education program's impact on the community's fire problem. It discusses comparing one part of the community with another part of the community as well as comparing the community to similar communities in the United States.

Fire departments can compare their fire and loss records to three national fire databases: the annual surveys of fire departments by the National Fire Protection Association, the National Fire Incident Reporting System (NFIRS) of FEMA/USFA, and the Fire Incident Data Organization operated by NFPA. This works well if your community uses NFIRS. However, not all communities use this system, and some decision makers may want to see more local statistics than national. Making your case always requires you to have some local statistics.

What Do the National Statistics Show?

Fire prevention officers can compare local statistics to national norms for similar size communities to show the need for further fire and life safety education programs in their communities. The data can be used to compare how low the community's loss is compared to similar communities or how high its reoccurred losses are. Many individuals will shy away from statistics for fear of getting too complicated in their report or of being overwhelmed with facts and figures and then trying to put them into a readable format.

Sometimes technology can make homegrown databases so user friendly that reports become worthless data collection instruments. For example, if you are a computer user, you are familiar with the screen's drop-down menus. You click on the arrow to the side of the drop-down box and a menu of actions from which to choose appears. In homegrown databases, people often suggest adding another field if the program doesn't already have one that exactly fits a call. Soon they will grow a list of 100 call types, which then cannot be queried from. In this example, let's say we are targeting fires in schools. We tap into our trusty desktop computer and query for fires in schools. If you see only two or three, you might assume you are doing a good job. However, because you read this book, you know to look more. Voila! Upon opening other incident reports you find out the people at the station were taking the easy way out or were confused by the huge list and clicked on whatever type of call they thought came closest. In fact, the first category is automatic alarm, because it starts with an *A*. Upon reading the actual reports, which takes forever, you see that several fires were actually wastepaper baskets burned in the restrooms of the schools but that box wasn't checked. The real story is the fire set off the alarm by activating the smoke detector in the hall and it was an automatic alarm and it was a fire.

Our point is to be careful with tracking data. Be aware of how and who is doing it and from the outset develop a clear understanding of what you want. We strongly recommend obtaining a copy of *Fire and Data Analysis Handbook,* which is free, from FEMA/USFA. This text simplifies using data and interpreting and presenting the results. The ability to gain insight into the community's fire problem allows fire and life safety educators to address the root of the problem with a specific program designed to meet the needs of the citizens in the area concerned.

Planning a Fire and Life Safety Education Program

In 1977 the National Fire Prevention and Control Administration published a public educator's document that incorporated a planning model for fire safety educators that is still in use today. In 2001 FEMA and the USFA published *Public Fire Education Planning: A Five-Step Process*, an excellent free resource. This material is still mostly relevant, but you must always consider your audience. The basic steps will remain the same but the content and approach to your audience will change. This text provides great detail on the five-step planning process used by many fire and life safety educators. The five-step planning model for fire education planning is an excellent tool for starting a fire safety education program. Fire departments can use it to begin their first fire safety education program or to add a new components to an existing fire and life safety education program.

The five-step planning process consists of the following steps that can be used for a variety of fire and life safety education programs:

Step 1: Identification of major fire problems

Step 2: Selection of objectives for education program

Step 3: Design of the program plan

Step 4: Implementation of the program plan

Step 5: Evaluation of the program's impact

The five-step process contains a number of activities and decisions that will present program planners a clear direction. **Figure 7.4** (located on the next page) provides a brief overview of each of the planning steps.

The first step, identification, is typically accomplished by conducting a community analysis that will determine the major fire hazards, the high-risk locations, the high-risk times, the high-risk victims, and the high-risk behaviors. Even though it may identify the community's worst fire and life safety problems, it also serves as the foundation for developing the programs to address them (see Chapters 6 and 14 for guidance).

The second step, selection, assists in determining the targeted audiences and begins the process of finding sources for developing the community partnerships essential to a successful fire and life safety education program. The selection step of the planning process provides a framework for including these partners in the development of the fire and life safety education program.

The third step, design, determines what to say in the fire and life safety education program based on the intended message and the available resources. The program may be designed for a specific hazard. The message will be placed into the best format to match the audience. This step will also determine the best forum for communicating that message. Remember that your audience changes almost daily nowadays. The older audience is more comfortable with reading and listening, while the younger group is better reached by television, compact discs, computers, and video games.

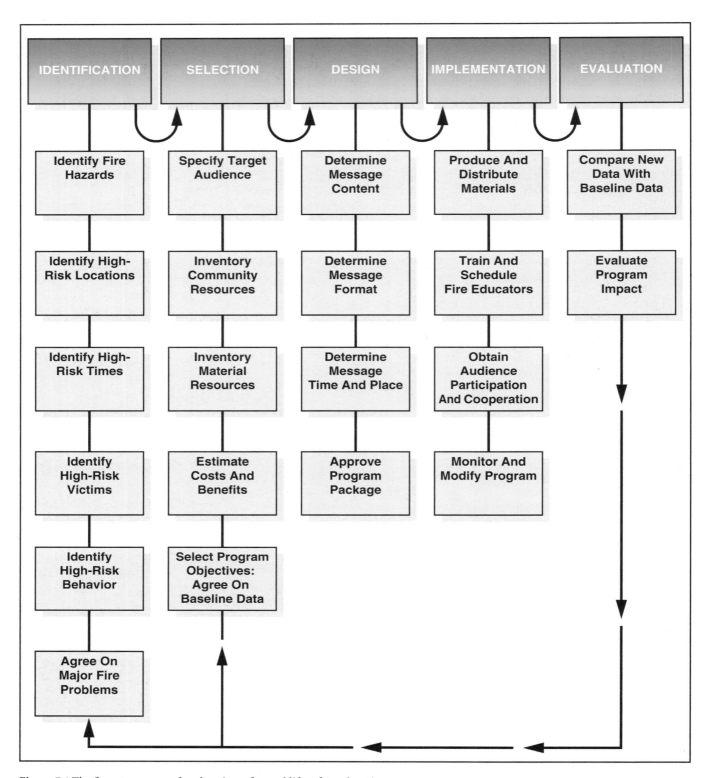

Figure 7.4 The five-step process for planning a fire and life safety education program.

The fourth step, implementation, is the nuts and bolts of the fire and life safety educator's work. This step consists of delivering effective programs to their target audiences. It may first be a pilot program so that modifications can be made to enhance its presentation and content. Pilot programs offer an excellent opportunity to make changes based on the target audience's response. During any implementation phase, whether a pilot or the full Monte, be sure you have a mechanism in place to measure where you were before you started and where you ended up. Nothing will frustrate a city manager, council member, or budget official more than requests for more money "just because."

The last step, evaluation, determines the bottom line of the program's effectiveness. As we discussed, the evaluation tools allow the fire and life safety educator to show that his or her efforts are reaching the target audience and that the target audience grasps what was presented. This also lays the groundwork for determining the program's overall reduction of losses and injuries in the targeted audience and the community as a whole.

The five-step planning process must be a continual program. Communities are not stagnant. They are constantly changing in size, culture, and demographics and in injuries sustained. Fire and life safety education programs must change to reflect the community's needs, and the best way to accomplish this is through the five-step process.

Designing Presentations

In the business world, you can have the greatest idea for a product or a service, but unless you have the ability to deliver and market that product or service, your idea is worthless. The same holds true for a successful fire and life safety education program. We just identified the importance of the program; now we will examine how to deliver the program for our targeted customer.

Targeting Your Audience

Before we can discuss types of fire and life safety education programs, we must consider who our target audience is and their level of learning. It is important to determine the learning characteristics of the audience to ensure the program design will be conducive to their learning. For example, the way a preschooler learns behavior is different than the way a teenager does. Even though the message to each group may be similar, how it is presented is very important to achieving the program's goals. For example, the way you present an educational message about lighters and matches will differ from one age group to the next. Preschoolers will learn that hot things hurt them and if they find a match or lighter they should tell an adult. Elementary students will learn that matches and lighters are tools, not toys. Finally, adults will learn to keep matches and lighters out of reach of children. The format will be different as well because of each group's level of learning. **Tables 7.1 and 7.2** indicate the cognitive development of each age group as well as its motor and personal development. **Table 7.3** (all tables on next page) identifies attitudes and implications for educating adolescents. The presentations will also include educational ideas conducive to the appropriate learning behavior of the age group.

Fire and life safety education programs must change to reflect the community's changing needs.

Before developing a fire and life safety education program, you must consider your target audience and their level of learning.

	TABLE 7.1 How Preschool Children Grow			
Age	**Cognitive Development**	**Motor Development**	**Social And Personal Development**	**Education Ideas**
3-4 years	Begins to understand sentences with simple "if/then" or "because" relationships			"If you get burned, it will hurt."
	Follows a two-step direction			"Don't touch matches or lighters. Tell a grown-up"
	Understands "Let's pretend"			Use storytelling and "let's pretend" to explain simple fire and burn safety concepts.
	Can listen to a story for 5 minutes			Limit stories or activities to 5-10 minutes.
	Asks "how" and "why" questions			Talk about why fire hurts (because it's hot).
	Repeats three numbers in order			Teach them to remember 9-1-1, even though they may not be able to remember their address
		Very interested in controlling whole body movements		Provide activities such as "Stop, drop, and roll" and "Crawl low under smoke"
	Has difficulty understanding cause and effect		Washes and dries hands	The scald hazard is significant.
			Lacks ability to sympathize	Will not respond to fire and burn safety approaches such as "Wouldn't you be sad/sorry if your friend got burned?"
	Has difficulty understanding another person's point of view			Is difficult for them to understand that their actions affect others.
			Begins dramatic play, acts out whole scenes	If given a pretend situation ("Your clothes are on fire" or "You find a lighter"), can act out what to do ("Stop, drop, and roll" or "Tell a grown-up")
			Learns by observing and imitating adults	Will copycat safe and unsafe behaviors

Table 7.1 How Elementary Children Grow,
Table 13.2 from Fire and Life Safety Educator

	TABLE 7.2a How Elementary Age Children Grow			
Age	**Cognitive Development**	**Motor Development**	**Social And Personal Development**	**Education Ideas**
5-6 years	Attention span increases, learns through adult instruction			Fire and burn safety activities can be longer and explain more.
	Can match pictures, colors, shapes, and words			Enjoys safety materials that involve matching pictures, etc.
	Can stay with one activity for about 20 minutes			Fire and burn safety activities can be longer and explain more.
	Likes to talk (and does!)			Expect children to talk about their real or pretend experiences with fire and burns.
		Colors within lines		Enjoys fire and burn safety coloring books
		Likes to climb, jump, throw, and march		Enjoys activities that use large muscles, such as "Stop, drop and roll," "Crawl low under smoke," and escape drills
			Likes to anticipate events, such as holidays and birthdays	Fire prevention week is an "event" for these children.
6-7 years	Begins to develop sense of time and space			Can begin to understand how fast fire is
		Very active, but clumsy		Expect children to run, shove, and push during escape drills.
			Loves and respects (and often quotes) parents and teachers	Can be very influenced by firefighters and other authority figures
			Wants to know what is good and what is bad	Responds well to fire and burn safety rules

Table 7.2a How Elementary Children Grow,
Table 13.3 from Fire and Life Safety Educator

		TABLE 7.2b (CONTINUED)		
		How Elementary Age Children Grow		
Age	**Cognitive Development**	**Motor Development**	**Social And Personal Development**	**Education Ideas**
7-8 years	Will stay with learning activities for long periods			Fire and burn safety activities can be longer and explain more.
	Understands time			Needs to know how much longer a fire and burn safety lesson will last
	Is ready for simple map work			Can draw a home escape plan
	Understands space and can find way around the community in proper order			Would enjoy walking with a parent to see the fire station
	Listens to long stories, but often misinterprets the facts		Begins to think teachers and parents are more unfair; often afraid of new situations	May still regard firefighters as heroes
	Talks about cause and effect by using "because" and "so"			
			Is impatient in large groups	
			Plays dress-up	
			Fears monsters or other fantasies	

Adapted from "Developmentally Appropriate Learning Activities," presented by Faye Ann Presnal, Early Childhood Specialist, at the Oklahoma Public Fire Education Conference, August 7, 1991.

Table 7.2b How Elementary Children Grow,
Table 13.3 from Fire and Life Safety Educator

	TABLE 7.3	
	Helping Adolescents Cope	
Attitude	**What It Means To Adolescents**	**Implications For Fire And Life Safety Education**
A sense of self-worth	Feeling respected and valued for yourself, not just for what you can do	"Because you are a valuable person, we want you to be safe."
A sense of competence	Knowing that you can do several things well—and can excel at something	"Because you know how to be fire safe, you can show others how to be fire safe."
A sense of acceptance	Knowing that groups you care about care about you	"Because you care about your friends, you care about their safety."
A sense of responsibility for others	A commitment to looking out for people you care about	"Because you care about your family, you care about their fire safety."
A future vision of self	Having ideas about what your future life will be like	"Because you want your home to be safe, you'll want a smoke detector."

Table 7.3 Helping Adolescents Cope,
Table 13.4 from Fire and Life Safety Educator

The message of your presentation should be applicable to the audience. One way to help do this is to choose data to which they will relate. For instance, you might use data on the frequency and severity of injuries in your audience's age group. You might base a fire and life safety presentation on national statistics, but you will need to tailor it to meet the needs of your community. The national statistics and types of injuries per age group will not necessarily be the same as in your community. Another important point to consider is the season of year. For example as we enter the winter months people begin to use their fireplaces. This is a good time to discuss fireplace safety.

Fire and Life Safety Education Topics

The topics for the fire department's fire and life safety education programs need to reflect the community's fire problems. The following topics tend to be relevant to most communities.

- Matches are tools, not toys
- Stop, drop, and roll
- Smoke detectors: where to put them, when to test them
- Addresses: a responder's friend
- Crawl low in smoke
- Adopt a hydrant: remove snow from your hydrant
- Home fire-escape plan
- Fireworks safety
- Hot liquids burn
- Fire extinguishers
- Call 911 for emergencies
- Make the right call (don't abuse 911, save it for emergencies)
- Fireplace safety
- Safe cooking
- Carry a pot holder with you
- Cooking outdoors
- Campfire safety
- Drown your campfire
- Remember, only you can prevent forest fires
- Don't play with fire
- NFPA risk watch (a comprehensive all-risks program)
- Bicycle safety
- Water safety
- Outdoor safety (camping, hiking, etc.)

Fire and Life Safety Education Programs

The fire department can conduct a number of programs on topics of the audience's choice (**Figures 7.5 and 7.6**). Essentially these are opportunities to have a "captive audience":

- School visits
- Use of fire safety trailer
- Fire station tour

- Citizen fire academy
- Children's safety academy
- Children's fire safety festival at a local mall
- Block party visit by the fire department
- In front of the grocery store while the fire department personnel are shopping
- Birthday party in the station
- Sleepover at the fire station
- Fire department open house
- Sprinkler demonstration

Figure 7.5 A visit to the school with a fire apparatus is a great opportunity for conducting fire safety education. *Courtesy of the Mount Prospect (Illinois) Fire Department*

Figure 7.6 Fire department open houses are great opportunities to educate the public about the services the fire department provides as well as to conduct informal fire and life safety education presentations such as where to place your smoke detector. *Courtesy of Mount Prospect (Illinois) Fire Department*

Figure 7.7 Puppets are a great way to attract a child's attention for a fire and life safety education program. Courtesy of "Fireman Frank," Mount Prospect (Illinois) Fire Department

Figure 7.8 The cast of "The Safety Hop," a fire and life safety education presentation.

Figure 7.9 Large sponsors can help provide money or talent for the production of songs that emphasize fire and life safety messages.

What Makes a Great Presentation?

There are as many ways to entertain and get across a message as there are audiences. The City of Colorado Springs, for example, uses a number of venues to capture target audiences. A preschool and kindergarten program utilizes an arm-puppet Sparky in combination with the department's smoke trailer. Although this age group is very scared of clowns and big Sparky characters, the arm puppet works especially well (**Figure 7.7**).

A clown and puppet troupe goes to elementary schools and older groups up to seniors. This group gives phenomenal performances, such as "The Safety Hop," done to a late 1950s and '60s sock hop theme (**Figure 7.8**). They also have done shows that are spin-offs of famous and current events, such as "Gigantica" (from the Titanic) or "Safe Trek" (based on *Star Trek*). Each of these programs utilizes musical themes or songs from its source with lyrics revised to encourage safe behavior. A month or so in advance, the troupe provides the music to school music teachers, who can integrate it into the curriculum. When the troupe arrives to do their skit, the whole school sings along.

The clown and puppet troupe's programs use small puppets, clowns, portable stages, and backdrops to give the whole effect. With the help of Intel Corporation, the Colorado Springs Fire Department produced 10,000 compact discs of the music (units) to provide to all the kids that saw the program—an excellent example of the coalition building that is vital to every fire prevention program (**Figure 7.9**). The Colorado Springs Fire Department is fortunate to have a cast of very creative employees who do a great job of singing, thus shaving the production costs of hiring additional professional talent. The response to the CDs was so overwhelming that requests for more and more copies of the disc flooded in from all over town. Once people heard the lyrics to the familiar music, the words stuck in their heads like gum on your shoe. We say this only because the only complaint that the department ever got was from parents whose children would not stop playing the music. What a success!

Figure 7.10 For over 25 years the Mount Prospect Fire Department, Mount Prospect, Illinois, has transformed a local shopping center to a children's fire safety festival. Surrounding fire departments participate in the weeklong event. Courtesy of the Mount Prospect (Illinois) Fire Department

Another successful idea for fire safety education is to combine the fire department's efforts with surrounding fire departments. Mount Prospect (Illinois) Fire Department for the last 24 years has been conducting a children's fire safety festival at a local shopping mall (**Figure 7.10**). Seventeen surrounding fire departments join in. Children are bused to the event and spend a few hours going to educational stations where they are entertained and educated by Fireman Frank the puppet, who discusses a variety of fire safety topics. They also get some hands-on stop, drop, and roll training after practicing evacuating from a bedroom while crawling low under artificial smoke.

Getting Your Message Out

The media are indispensable for getting out your fire and life safety education message. Every fire event contains a fire safety education message that you can incorporate into the press release. An apartment fire started by children playing with matches that ended in the children safely evacuating after the smoke detector activated would be a good example of how we can deliver our fire and life safety education message through the media. The press conference or press release will indicate the exact details of the incident pertaining to the response of the fire department, time of day, where the incident occurred, and so forth. The fire department spokesman also should discuss the cause of the fire. Tell the media that fire started from children playing with matches and explain that matches are tools, not toys, and adults should be aware of the dangers associated with matches and lighters. Now is also the time to go to the data. Give them the local and national statistics for fires caused by children playing with matches. Also use this opportunity to show how important a working smoke detector is and how having a planned escape route saved the family. A good way to do this would be to ask inspectors or whatever personnel might be available to check all the smoke detectors in all the units in the affected building. It is not uncommon to find only 3–6 percent of battery-operated detectors in working order. This is a powerful statistic to put on the news. The media are a great tool to reach a large number of people and if used appropriately can be the fire and life safety educator's greatest allies.

Is this fire and life safety education, public relations, or public information? The answer is simply yes to all! We can use the media for fire and life safety education, but they are also an avenue for building a positive image of the fire department within the community. Conversely the media can also portray a negative image. Using the media is usually called providing public information. Public information is simply the process of informing the public of our operations or actions. As you can see, fire and life safety education, public relations, and public information are all inseparable.

What about the nonemergency use of the media? Do we have to wait for an event to occur before we seek the media? Absolutely not! In fact using the media before the big event helps fire departments to become familiar with the various media representatives and to gain their trust. As shown in Chapter 8, this will help during the "big event."

Every fire event contains a fire safety education message.

Fire and life safety education, public relations, and public information are all inseparable.

Summary

America Burning demonstrated that fire prevention efforts cannot be successful without public education. Public education has since evolved into fire and life safety education. This term better describes the diverse topics presented by those fire prevention personnel performing the task of public education. The fire service continues to be called upon to perform a variety of emergency services. From those services, the fire service has seen the important need to provide a comprehensive safety program that encompasses more than just fire prevention. Topics presented by fire departments may range from ice safety to bicycle helmets.

The goal of fire and life safety education is to motivate individuals to behave in a safe manner by modifying their behavior. To succeed, fire and life safety educators must create programs utilizing the five-step process. The programs must be appropriate for the target audiences. Fire and life safety educators can improve the success of their fire and life safety education message by selecting a delivery method that is most appropriate to the age of the audience. Using the Internet, computers, and videos in the 21st century will be a more common method of presentation for children.

As budgets for fire and life safety education are scrutinized more and more, fire and life safety educators need to look for alternative funding for their programs and think outside the box for methods to deliver the fire and life safety education message.

Chapter 7 Review Exercises

7.1   Explain the five-step process.

Step 1: _____
       _____
Step 2: _____
       _____
Step 3: _____
       _____
Step 4: _____
       _____
Step 5: _____
       _____

7.2   What is the goal of fire and life safety education? _____
      _____

7.3   Why is fire and life safety important? _____
      _____
      _____

7.4   How did the term fire and life safety education evolve? _____
      _____
      _____
      _____
      _____
      _____

7.5   Why do fire departments conduct presentations on topics other than
      fire?_____
      _____

7.6   Identify six safety-related programs other than fire prevention that
      fire departments can present._____
      _____
      _____

7.7   Discuss the stages of elementary children's growth and how they apply
      to fire and life safety education topics._____
      _____
      _____
      _____
      _____
      _____

7.8 Discuss how to prove fire and life safety education works. _____

_____

_____

_____

_____

7.9 List 12 fire and life safety resources available for free. Indicate where they can be obtained. _____

_____

_____

_____

_____

_____

_____

_____

_____

_____

_____

_____

7.10 Identify six programs not mentioned in this chapter that can be used for fire and life safety education. _____

_____

_____

_____

_____

7.11 Discuss the different types of media that can be used in fire safety education and who would benefit from their use. _____

_____

_____

_____

7.12 Discuss the various presentation methods that fire and life safety educators can use and which audience you most likely would use them for. _____

_____

_____

_____

7.13 Identify six sources of potential funding for fire safety education in your community and explain how you would go about securing funds from them. _____

_____

_____

_____

_____

_____

_____

7.14 What did *America Burning* say about fire and life safety or public education? _____

_____

_____

_____

7.15 Read the report Beyond 2000 and write a one-page summary.

7.16 List at least 10 community businesses or organizations that can participate with you as a fire prevention and injury reduction coalition.

_____

_____

_____

_____

_____

_____

_____

_____

_____

_____

7.17 Write several brief paragraphs comparing how you would teach a kindergartner, a third-grader, and an elderly person what to do if their clothes caught fire._____

_____

_____

_____

_____

_____

_____

_____

_____

_____

_____

_____

_____

7.18 Make a 5–10-minute class presentation on a fire and life safety education topic of your choice.

7.19 How can the media help you present life safety messages? _____

_____

_____

_____

_____

_____

NOTES

1. U.S. Fire Administration. *America Burning: Re-Commissioned* (Washington DC: US Fire Administration, 2000).

2. Beyond Solutions 2000 Report, United States, January 2001.

3. *Fire and Life Safety Educator* (Stillwater, Okla.: IFSTA, 1997).

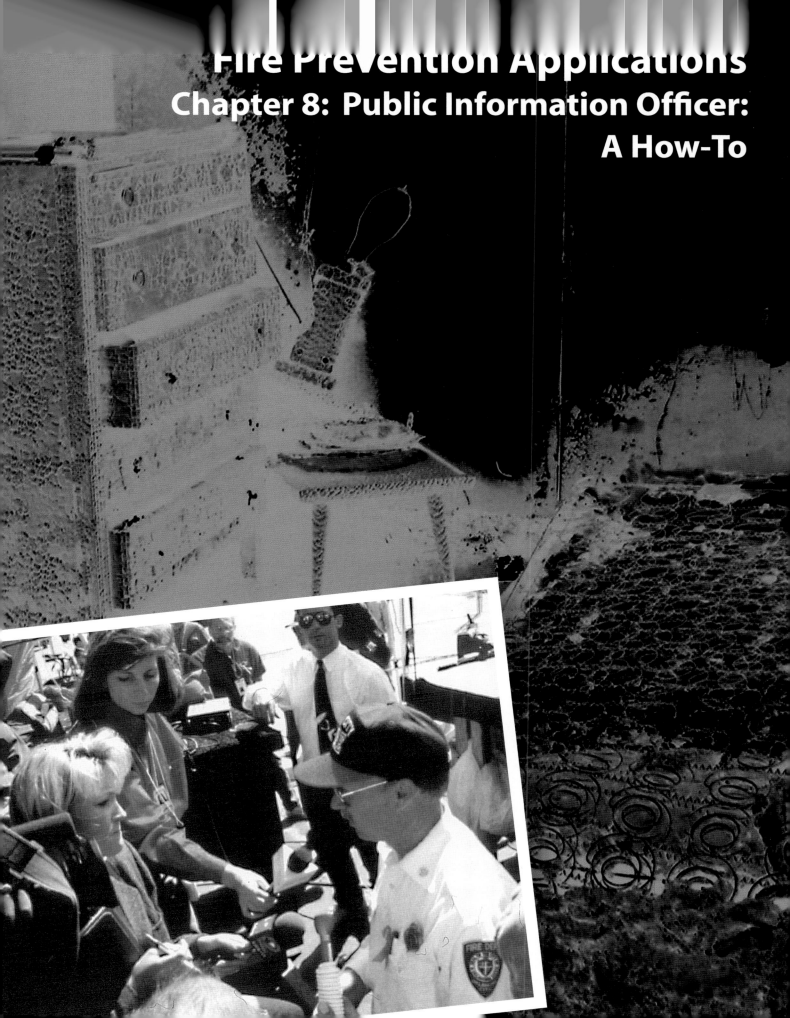

Fire Prevention Applications
Chapter 8: Public Information Officer:
A How-To

FESHE COURSE OBJECTIVES

1. Understand the importance of good community relations.

2. Understand the role of the public information officer.

3. Identify standards for the position of public information officer.

Chapter 8

Public Information Officer: A How-To

The Importance of Public Information

The role of the public education officer is critical to maintaining the image of the fire department and to the department's ability to disperse accurate information to the media. From the fire service perspective, public information is information that is provided to the general public so they remain informed about events, become better educated and/or prepared for various situations, and remain motivated in fire- and injury-prevention behaviors. People may use this information to make decisions, act on those decisions, and to help the fire service in mitigating situations or circumstances that may harm our overall community.

To properly perform the functions of fire and life safety education (public education) and public information, a dedicated position such as a public information officer (PIO) is beneficial. While many smaller fire departments do not have full-time staff to fulfill this function, they somehow should integrate these tasks into the organization's overall operational plan. Whenever possible, they should use a person or group with some training for performing the duties of the PIO. NFPA 1035, *Professional Qualifications for Public Fire and Life Safety Educator*, provides some guidance that can be applied to public information. Whether you are an experienced PIO or just learning, the IFSTA *Public Information Officer* manual is a great resource. We recommend placing this position or responsibility in the fire prevention division or bureau where the bulk of routine public interaction and education takes place.

✔ **public information**
information provided to the general public so they remain informed about events, become better educated and/or prepared for various situations, and remain motivated in fire-and injury-prevention behaviors

Figure 8.1 Discussing hazardous fire conditions with the media is one way in which a public information officer might try to modify the public's behavior.

Fire departments rely on citizens to receive information and modify their behavior accordingly to prevent fires or injuries (**Figure 8.1**). An underlying but no less important motive in disseminating this information is marketing the fire department and its services. Essentially this accomplishes the role of public relations, which is important because fire departments are engaged daily in some form of public relations.

At one time the release of information took hours or days if it happened at all. Now we live in an age where information can be disseminated almost simultaneously with actual events. No matter where you are in the United States, or the world for that matter, the news brings you real-time images of disasters, shootings, fires, and elections, not to mention the creation of local, state, and world policy. People routinely make judgments based on what they see and hear from the media. Messages flood the airwaves, print, and other media, reaching more people than ever before. The problem is that with limited control over what the media can and will communicate, particularly among different countries, countless mixed messages proliferated throughout the world generate endless controversy.

> We live in an age when information can be disseminated almost simultaneously with actual events and in which people routinely make judgments based on what they see and hear from the media.

An example of how important it can be to have the message portrayed and interpreted favorably is that of a fire marshal presenting a sprinkler ordinance for approval by the elected officials (**Figure 8.2**). If local developers and builders oppose the ordinance, the media could portray it

Figure 8.2 Whether the public perceives sprinkler systems as an expensive burden or life-saving benefit will depend largely on how the facts are presented.

as costly, burdensome, unwarranted, and of no benefit to the general public. Remember, the facts of the situation remain constant, but consider the same ordinance being portrayed as a means to reduce property loss and save lives. Perhaps the community could offer incentives or tax breaks for installing these appliances. Public opinion may become more positive. Now, what if the ordinance specifically addressed multifamily occupancies and was being presented in a community that just experienced a multiple life loss from fire in a nonsprinklered multifamily occupancy? The public's view of the ordinance may be totally different from the initial picture of its being overly restrictive, burdensome, and too costly. How can this be when all sides are discussing the exact same issue and have the exact same facts? It's because of the way the media receive the information and present it.

This is never more evident than if you compare an issue of global proportions as portrayed in the media. For example, when two countries have opposing viewpoints over a military action, the media in one country may portray the action as evil and having terrible consequence while the media in the other country portray it as good for global security and preventing potential harm to others.

As a part of good government practice we should always assume everyone's approach and judgment are reasonable and prudent given appropriate information. That does not mean everyone will agree all the time, but most reasonable people look to solve problems and understand things in similar ways. When the media present consistent and factual information, public opinion and insight should be fairly similar. However, that being said, the media frequently put "spins" on stories or messages to get attention and sell their product. This does not mean they are purposely trying to mislead, but it does show that the media are human organizations run by human beings.

> As a part of good government practice we should always assume everyone's approach and judgment are reasonable and prudent given appropriate information.

Returning to our sprinkler ordinance, the media would spin the ordinance differently after a significant fire death than under other circumstances. They will form different opinions in the interest of balanced journalism based upon what they are told or what they see and believe. Unfortunately, the media not uncommonly portrays an opinion or view that may be contrary to what the "sender" is trying to say.

In *Feeding the Media Beast* Mark Mathis explains, "Journalists are not the enemy. In spite of what you have been led to believe, news people are not dangerous vipers. To the contrary, the vast majority of folks who work in the business are passionate professionals who want to make the world a better place. They tend to be idealists, but that's a good thing."[1] Why is that a good thing? Because if we pay attention to Mathis's statement, we know the angle from which journalists typically will approach the fire department PIO. The reality is that fire protection professionals are generally idealists, too (**Figure 8.3**). Without even trying we are already in a better position to communicate with the so-called "Beast" because we understand its idealism. Not only must we try to understand the media, we must become students of the media and continually focus on improving our public information skills.

Figure 8.3 Fire protection professionals' and journalists' shared idealism can be the basis for successful public relations.

PIO Skills

The PIO must develop a basic set of communication skills. Seven areas that good PIOs routinely practice and that require some level of proficiency are:

- Community relations
- Media relations
- Writing

- Public speaking
- Audio/visual presentation
- Fire department operations and functions

Community Relations

It is important for people who perform the PIO functions to have a good understanding of the community along with a good grasp on their target audience. By this we mean knowing who works, invests, and maintains a high profile within your community—individuals, businesses, corporations, philanthropic organizations, and others. The PIO should also have a keen awareness of organizational relationships and partnerships. A good understanding of these networking issues can provide not only a wealth of information but also a good preface for complimenting and thanking folks when good things happen.

It is also important to understand the community's views and concerns regarding emergency preparedness, their political opinions, and volunteer involvement. Do not forget to understand the different cultures and value systems throughout the community. Although the community as a whole may have a common set of values and beliefs, it may also have subgroups, each with its own set of values and beliefs. Such background information is critical if you are going to propose a new program that the community may not consider important. This would be particularly true if the program required money at a time when the community may have just voted down any new tax increases. It may not make your job easier, but your chief may appreciate not being led into a pond full of alligators.

Having a well-rounded view of your community (your target audience) provides tremendous insight into how you can motivate your community. The right approach can move them to support your department's requests and endorse the department's attempts to accomplish its mission.

Media Relations

Media relations are likely the most challenging and frustrating part of a PIO's job. As the PIO you must be willing to work very hard at establishing credibility with all members of your local media. An old adage says, "The media will always have the last word!" This is mantra and you need to buy into it, because they do have the last word. If you do not help them get a story, they will modify, mold, or in the worst cases fabricate any information to create the story. It is imperative that you become the media's friend. With the variety of media available you cannot focus just on building a relationship with a single medium, such as the local newspaper. You must establish good relations with all the key participants in the business. The better your relationships, the better your flexibility and the better the support and participation you will get from them.

Treat them ethically and reasonably and they will do the same for you . . . as long as it fits their desires and deadlines. Does this sound one-sided? It is. Their job is to get a story. Everything is on the record. Never, ever, ever think

> People who perform PIO functions must clearly understand their community and grasp their target audience.

> The PIO must work very hard at establishing credibility with all members of the local media.

for one second that anything is "off the record." Reporters do not understand those words. But do not think they are disingenuous, either. Think about what their job is and what your job is. If you have information that should not be released or is off the record, keep it to yourself. We cannot tell you how many times we have seen individuals come unglued with regret after sharing something with a reporter by prefacing it as off the record. That is like dropping by a fire station and telling the on-duty crew "I just saw somebody get hit by a car down the street, but don't tell anybody or do anything because we shouldn't get involved." Why would we expect the media to be any different than us?

It is also important that PIOs become familiar with how their various media work. Visit their businesses and see how they create their productions, make their newspapers, or produce their broadcasts. This insight will provide you valuable information about their need to meet deadlines and their preferences for product. In return it will give them ownership in a joint relationship. We like to show off our fire stations; why would we think they don't like to show off their work sites? Getting to know them before a "big event" makes talking to them during even the biggest event easier because you already have a level of trust and a foundation for your professional relationship.

Develop a perspective on the journalistic community. Mark Mathis explains that "They are manufactured in America's universities in a liberal arts curriculum. Journalism schools teach students that they are 'the voice of the people.' Reporters are to stick up for the poor, the downtrodden, and the disadvantaged, in our sometimes-oppressive capitalist system. It is their job—so they are taught—to 'comfort the afflicted and to afflict the comfortable.'[2] As the PIO, do you think you will be considered afflicted or comfortable? Many fire service personnel have spoken harshly of reporters because "they don't even respect what we do" or "they don't even know the history of why things are the way they are." But most reporters are not from your community and are merely on one of many steppingstones to another promotion in another market. The process of networking and getting to know them must never stop because their movement never stops. The news is a dynamic business and must be respected as such. Remember, too, that these same media folks are snooping for that "big scoop," the portfolio and résumé builder. This is all the more reason never to reveal anything "off the record." If they do not understand why and what you do, then you should take the time to inform them. Educate them about who, what, when, where, why, and how you do things before they show up at your door step!

To succeed in getting your message across to the media, you should follow some basic guidelines. Below are some of the more common, as adapted from Mark Mathis's *Feeding the Media Beast*:

- Remember that to the media, things that are important are not necessarily important unless they are different. This means you should consider your message and emphasize what is "different" from other similar issues and stress that difference.

- Reporters always prefer emotional messages to the factual messages.

> Never, ever, ever think for one second that anything is "Off the record."

- Reporters and newscasters like information in small bites. Be concise but powerful with the message using key points.

- Have a group of "canned" messages or information you want to release. You never know when a similar story may break, giving you an opportunity to interject yours, which is slightly "different."

- Make sure the information is easy to give and easy for media to get. Help them as much as possible to entice them to play.

- Treat the media with respect by answering all of their questions but make sure you direct and redirect your answers to what you want to communicate.

- Repeat your message just like in teaching. Tell them what you are going to tell, tell them, and then tell them what you told them.

- Important event information or messages should be modified slightly for each different delivery. You can still pass along the same general message but remember number one above. . . . make it different each time to grab more attention. Remember, each member of different media would like his or her own scoop.

- Never, ever make stuff up. If you don't know, admit it and research the answer and get it back to them.

- Never, ever speak for another agency or official that has not given you permission and verified what you are going to present.

- Never, ever say "No Comment." That tells them you are hiding something. Be truthful and explain why you don't have information or why you can't release it.

- Don't give your personal opinion. Any opinion you give will be assumed to be that of the organization regardless of how you preface it.

- Assume you are always on camera and/or on tape.

- If you don't want information or comments on the nightly national news, don't say it.[3]

The media generally want typical, similar information about any event or disaster. They generally focus on who, what, where, when, why, and how, and so should you. Worksheets are a good way to keep your information on track (**Figure 8.4**). Below is a list of common items that you could use to create simple, customized worksheets of your own:

- The cause if known and the situation encountered

- Eyewitness accounts or reports by responders

- Extent of response to incident (who was there and where they were from)

- Statistics that communicate the scope (dollar loss, lives lost or injured, firefighters and or equipment on scene, etc.)

- Types of injuries

- Survivors and their stories

PUBLIC INFORMATION WORKSHEET — Page 1

PUBLIC INFORMATION WORKSHEET

DATE: ______________________________ Fire ____ EPS ____ Hzmt ____

TIMES: Dispatched: ___________ On Scene: ___________ Controlled: ___________
Tapped: ___________ Cleared Scene: ___________
Alarms: 2nd ___________ 3rd ___________ 4th ___________
Zone: 1 ___________ 2 ___________ 3 ___________ 4 ___________

DISPATCH: Reason Dispatched: ______________________________
Address: ______________________________
Occupancy: ______________________________
Owner: ______________________________

OCCUPANCY: Residential Structure: ______________________________
Multi-family: ______________________________
Commercial: ______________________________
Business/Function: ______________________________

APPARATUS:

Engines	____	Aid	____	Cmd Cars	____
Ladders	____	Hzmt	____	Medic	____
Amb	____	PD	____	WNG	____
DOE	____	EPA	____	PUD	____
RC	____	Support	____		

MUTUAL AID DEPARTMENTS/RESOURCES: ______________________________

SITUATION ENCOUNTERED/ACTION TAKEN: ______________________________

Figure 8.4 Examples of PIO worksheets for varying incidents.

PUBLIC INFORMATION WORKSHEET — Page 2

SPECIAL HAZARDS/ACCOMPLISHMENTS/RECOMMENDATIONS: ______________________

INJURIES/FATALITIES: Civilian (C) ____ Firefighter (FF) ____

Name	Sex	Age	Injury	Where Taken

DAMAGE: ______________________

$ ESTIMATE: ______________________

CAUSE: ______________________

PUBLIC EDUCATION MESSAGE: ______________________

SMOKE DETECTORS: Installed ____ Operating ____

Figure 8.4 Examples of PIO worksheets for varying incidents. (*Continued*)

HAZARDOUS MATERIALS INCIDENT WORKSHEET — Page 1

HAZARDOUS MATERIALS INCIDENT WORKSHEET

DATE: ______________________________ Fire _____ EPS _____ Hzmt _____

TIMES: Dispatched: ____________ On Scene: ____________ Controlled: ____________
Tapped: ____________ Cleared Scene: ____________
Alarms: 2nd ____________ 3rd ____________ 4th ____________
Zone: 1 ____________ 2 ____________ 3 ____________ 4 ____________

DISPATCH: Reason Dispatched: ______________________________
Address: ______________________________
Occupancy: ______________________________
Owner: ______________________________

OCCUPANCY: Residential Structure: ______________________________
Multi-family: ______________________________
Commercial: ______________________________
Business/Function: ______________________________

APPARATUS:

Engines	_____	Aid	_____	Cmd Cars	_____
Ladders	_____	Hzmt	_____	Medic	_____
Amb	_____	PD	_____	WNG	_____
DOE	_____	EPA	_____	PUD	_____
RC	_____	Support	_____		

MUTUAL AID DEPARTMENTS/RESOURCES: ______________________________

SITUATION ENCOUNTERED/ACTION TAKEN: ______________________________

Quantity & State: ______________________________
Product Use: ______________________________

INJURIES: ______________________________

Figure 8.4 Examples of PIO worksheets for varying incidents. (*Continued*)

HAZARDOUS MATERIALS INCIDENT WORKSHEET — Page 2

COMPANY/INDIVIDUAL NAME (ADDRESS IF DIFFERENT THAN LOCATION): _____
_____
_____
_____
_____

PRODUCT NAME: _____

SPECIAL CONSIDERATIONS - FIRE/WATER/AIR/HEALTH: _____
_____
_____
_____
_____

ROAD CLOSURES/EVACUATIONS: _____
_____

CONTAINMENT/CONTROL: _____
_____

ENVIRONMENTAL HAZARDS: _____
_____

DECONTAMINATION: _____
_____

CLEAN-UP: _____
_____

FOLLOW-UP: _____
_____

Figure 8.4 Examples of PIO worksheets for varying incidents. (*Continued*)

PIO WORKSHEET — Page 1

PIO WORKSHEET

Address ______________________ TOA ________ Arrival ________
Owner/Resident ______________________ Age ________
Alarm # ________ Type of Structure ______________________ Units ________

Unit _____ Arrival _____ Command ______________________
Unit _____ Arrival _____ Safety ______________________
Unit _____ Arrival _____ Liaison ______________________
Unit _____ Arrival _____ Operations ______________________
Unit _____ Arrival _____ City Safety ______________________
Unit _____ Arrival _____ City Public Relations ______________________
Unit _____ Arrival _____ Medical ______________________
Unit _____ Arrival _____ Investigations ______________________

MEDIA WORKSHEET

Unit ________ Name ______________________
Unit ________ Name ______________________
Unit ________ Name ______________________
Unit ________ Name ______________________
Unit ________ Name ______________________
Unit ________ Name ______________________
Unit ________ Name ______________________
Unit ________ Name ______________________

CAUSE OF FIRE

Location of Ignition ______________________
Cause of Ignition ______________________
Contributing Factors ______________________
Smoke Detector Present: Yes _____ No _____
Operate: Yes _____ No _____
Awoke Residents: Yes _____ No _____
Comments of Investigator ______________________

Figure 8.4 Examples of PIO worksheets for varying incidents. (*Continued*)

PIO WORKSHEET — Page 2

INJURIES

Name ______________________________ Age _____ To/By ______________

Injury ____

Name ______________________________ Age _____ To/By ______________

Injury ____

Other Information ____

____

____

____

AGENCY SUPPORT

Agency ______________________________________ POC ______________

Type of Support ____

Agency ______________________________________ POC ______________

Type of Support ____

Comments by PIO ____

____

____

____

____

____

____

____

____

____

____

____

____

____

____

____

____

____

____

____

____

____

____

____

____

Figure 8.4 Examples of PIO worksheets for varying incidents. (*Continued*)

- Past history of similar events

- Community (civilian) actions

- Time or duration of interruption or repair

- Action taken

- Fire and life safety education message related to the event

Things to consider for the media if you are on the scene when they show up:

- Staging location for portable "live or remote" broadcasts

- Schedule of briefings

- Identifying their contact and giving regular briefings

- Information on phones, lodging, food, and other logistics

Written Communication

Proficiency in all forms of written communication is essential to public information functions. Press releases, letters, faxes, e-mail, for instance, all have become mainstaysofcommunication. Be sure you can organize your thoughts and messages on paper in a fashion that will get your points across. Be able to adjust your style to accommodate a wide variety of audiences. In the fire service we deal with a wide range of people from highly skilled engineers to political appointees to folks from other countries. Be cognizant of your audience and deliver your messages appropriately. Be as grammatically correct as possible because good grammar shows professionalism. Know how your local media like to receive various types of information (**Figures 8.5 and 8.6**). You can learn this through the meetings you should have while getting acquainted. These formats include:

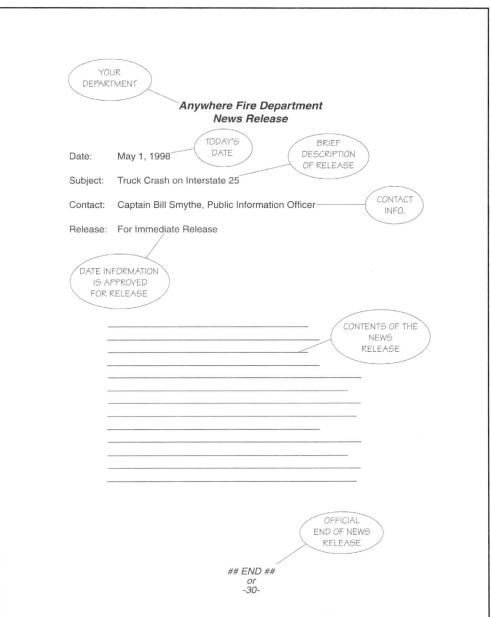

Figure 8.5 News releases are among the public information officer's most valuable tools.

150 S. 12th Street
Phoenix, AZ 85034-2301
(602) 534-0953

Phoenix Fire Department

PHOENIX FIRE DEPARTMENT HONORS "PET PROTECTORS"

MEDIA ADVISORY

Contact: Bob Khan   (phone number)
             pager   (phone number)

WHAT: The Phoenix Fire Department is proud to bestow *Official Commendations to two special heroes...a dog who saved a family of humans and a little girl who worked hard to save two dogs and a cat. "Chance", a rottweiler, awoke his owners with an unusual bark* alerting them to a *house fire across the street.* Had he and his owners not notified its sleeping occupants, *they would have perished. Mary Beth Fisher, 11,* was riding as an observer with her father, Captain Dan Fisher, when they responded to a house fire. Mary Beth *quickly assisted in the resuscitation of dogs "Carmel" and "Taz" and cat "Spaz",* although only "Taz" survived. The Phoenix Fire Department is proud of the quick actions of both "Chance" and Mary Beth. People can *learn more* about saving all members of their family by attending *"Survival Saturday for Pets and People"* this Saturday.

WHEN: Friday, August 28, 1998
             3:00 p.m.

WHERE: Phoenix Fire Station 9
              330 E. Fairmont

Contact on Site: Captain Chris Ketterer
                   pager: (phone number)

Figure 8.6 Media advisories alert journalists to important information about the department.

- Reports of various kinds (annual, monthly, statistical, etc.)
- Public service announcements (PSAs)
- Fact sheets
- Media advisories
- Pamphlets, newsletters, brochures, and so forth

Use current publishing software in order to make attractive, quality documents that reflect your department's professionalism and dedication to good communication.

Public Speaking

People in our communities love to talk to fire department personnel, so PIOs should be groomed for this job. The types of public speaking engagements you may be called upon to participate in are numerous (**Figure 8.7**). These may include:

- On-scene emergencies
- Camera interviews
- Live radio broadcasts
- Panel discussions
- Seminars
- Presentations to business organizations, government agencies or policymaking groups, and neighborhood associations

The public generally asks many questions, some of which can be very challenging. If you have not done a lot of public speaking, offer yourself to as many civic organizations as possible for simple question and answer sessions. That way, you do not have to make a specific presentation but can become comfortable standing in front of large groups passing on information. Toastmasters is an excellent organization that can greatly enhance your speaking abilities.

To speak well in public, you must be able to construct good written outlines that are easy to use for you or someone else in your organization. If you have accomplished this goal, and anyone in your field can use the same outline to communicate sufficiently, then you will know you are preparing your presentation well. If you also have mastered the PIO's writing tasks, public speaking should be fairly easy.

Figure 8.7 Public information officers often use news conferences to provide information to the media at incident scenes. *Courtesy of Oklahoma City (Oklahoma) Fire Department*

Below is a list of "what not to do" when speaking in public:

- Pacing from side to side. This can be very distracting and makes everyone in the audience look like they are watching a tennis match.

- Reading to your audience. For heaven's sake, if you are going to read a speech to your audience, save everyone including yourself a lot of embarrassment and time and make copies of your speech and just hand them out.

- Holding onto the podium for dear life. Sometimes people uncomfortable with public speaking grab onto the podium like they are in the middle of a tornado. This makes your audience tense and will make you tired.

- Using hypnotic fillers, words, or phrases like "uh," "okay," "ya know?" or "all right." We all have sat through presentations where people repeat these phrases or words so often that five minutes into the talk we are more interested in counting the repetitions than in listening to the speech. "Ya know" is our favorite because if the audience already knows, then why are you telling them?

- Looking sloppy. People look at the fire service as a professional organization. This does not mean in terms of paid versus volunteer but in terms of demeanor, appearance, knowledge, and application. Think of Shakespeare's phrase, "The clothes make the man"—or in this case, the person.

Try to take advantage of the media or someone else to videotape your presentations. If local television stations tape any of your presentations for their news coverage, ask if they will share dubs so you can critique yourself. Many reporters will help guide you on how to give the best sound bites. Don't ever be ashamed or afraid to ask them to do another take. They are likely more than willing to help you out if you do the same for them. When your presentation is over, review the tape for constructive criticism of yourself. Learn by your mistakes and those of others. Likewise, when you see or hear a good presentation ask yourself, "What made this speaker so effective and how can I do the same?"

Audio/Visual Presentations

We recommend going to any number of the one- or two-day workshops on this topic that are frequently held in different parts of the country. Skills in photography, computer operations such as PowerPoint, desktop publishing software, and word processing applications can be used daily in this job position. Remember, your job is to communicate with any number of people. Using a variety of these media to deliver the same message to different audiences can have a profound impact on your success.

Understanding how newsletters can be constructed can be a huge asset to a number of organizations. For example, a local apartment or renters organization may be happy to use preprinted or already laid out material. Various business organizations use newsletter formats (**Figure 8.8**). Nursing homes are another location where newsletters are popular.

When visiting local televised media, spend some time learning from them about video production. They would love to show off, and the experience would work wonders for your understanding of how to get the most from digital or taped formats.

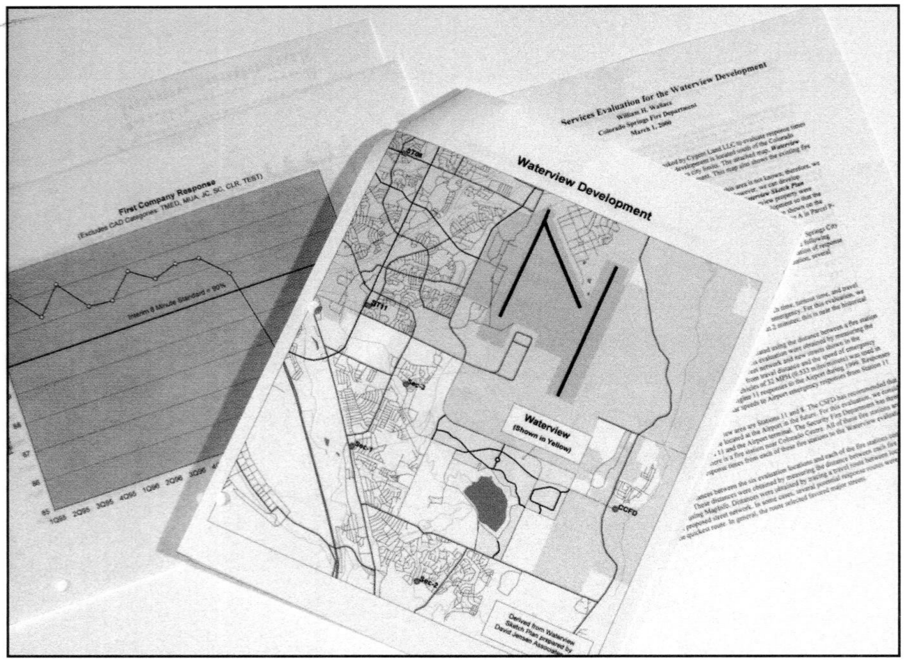

> Using a variety of media to deliver the same message to different audiences can profoundly impact the public information officer's success.

Figure 8.8 Sample fire-service related story prepared for a newsletter.

Fire Department Operations and Functions

To do the best job possible of communicating fire protection or prevention messages or communicating on-scene media issues, familiarity with your department's operations is crucial. Become intimately familiar with policies and procedures. If you are new to the fire service, read through the National Fire Protection Association's *Fire Protection Handbook* and become a diligent student of the fire service. To communicate the emotional and factual sides of your messages, you have to become familiar with your business. The public looks to the fire service to provide comfort and confidence when things are going badly. It is not in our interest or theirs to provide critical information from an uninformed or ignorant perspective. Nothing could be worse than presenting critical information to a concerned public about an emergency incident and then falling on your face when you do not know the answer to a simple procedural question. The public and the media want authority and credibility. These are easy to establish if you are careful and diligent. True finesse comes through on-the-job training and years of experience or to very dedicated individuals who have spent countless hours learning their trade.

> To communicate fire protection or prevention messages or handle on-scene media issues, familiarity with your department's operations is crucial.

Legal Issues and Responsibilities

Be sure to develop good guidelines or policies that specifically itemize the information you can and cannot give out. Personnel matters are a good example. Typically, personnel or disciplinary issues are private and confidential and therefore cannot be disclosed in any detail. Make certain that you and your chief and your legal counsel share a good understanding of your role. This may mean getting signoffs on press releases or anything else intended for publication before it goes to the media. Do not release the names of minors if they are involved in criminal activity such as arson. Breaches of legal protocol, not to mention policy issues, can generate far more mistrust and discontent concerning the fire department than refusing to answer questions at all.

Summary of Strategy and Tactics for the PIO

Be proactive. Establish relationships with your local media and be prepared for national attention. Remember, CNN can be anywhere within minutes. Know what your community expects of your department and be able to deliver it. Be familiar with the hazards and risks your department faces. Be able to articulate and explain them, as well as how your department mitigates and responds to them. Plan ahead. If you live in a region of the country prone to wildfire, have prepared burn restriction or ban release information and material so you do not have to react spontaneously. Have information on evacuation preparedness and vegetation management ready to go. Holiday hazards are generally similar and typical, like Christmas trees and candles. Do not wait till the last minute to prepare for these information releases. Another important aspect is to be timely in disseminating information. Be aware of your media's deadlines and help reporters to meet them.

> Know what your community expects of your department and be able to deliver it.

Remember, everyone including the police department looks to the fire service for answers on many community emergency issues. The job of a PIO is easy except when things are most demanding, most important, and most challenging. People expect quick solutions to problems and factual information with which to react. They need professional reassurance and confidence to help them deal with tragedy and loss. Regular contact and information are critical to generate and secure public trust and calm. Recognize the difference between emergencies and nonemergencies. When commercial aircraft crashed into the World Trade Center on 9-11-2001, fear and anguish struck the hearts of Americans everywhere. In these types of incidents the good PIO is immediately available and talking to the media.

Develop your delivery of product based on your public's needs. People make value judgments about your department during major emergencies or challenges, even those that do not occur locally. Be prepared to handle the stress, the questions, and the information professionally and meaningfully. You become the icon for your department. Dress the part, act the part, and garnish the confidence necessary to protect and inform the public you serve. We usually have a great story to tell about our services. Let your passion for the fire service be reflected in a professional and positive fashion.

Summary

The role of the public information officer is important in maintaining the image of the fire department. This position also is critical in presenting factual information to the public and others about public events, disasters, emergencies or other vital information.

Years ago transmitting or conveying information could take months. Today, CNN News can be at your doorstep in less than 15 minutes broadcasting to the world. Technology has made instant communication possible; however, many fire departments have yet to realize the significance of this to departmental functions.

To provide the highest level of protection possible, reliance on our communities (our citizens) is vital, particularly when we are supposed to be providing more services for less. The best way to disseminate large amounts of good information is through our media. This includes print media such as newspapers, as well as broadcast media such as television and radio. To perform this task effectively, proper training, resources, and personnel should be provided. The role of the public information officer (PIO) is to disseminate information regularly and consistently. This involves community relations, media relations, and extensive written communication. Public speaking also is a critical function.

In the new age of video phones, computer presentations, and simulations, it is wise to have skills in creating quality audio/visual presentations. Children especially are used to high-quality graphics and fast-moving computer and video games. To properly communicate our messages, we must constantly seek ways to make our presentations more engaging. Use of computer Web sites and the like also provides good opportunities. However, be sure to consult with your legal advisor, as you do not want to violate any unknown copyrights or infringe on sharing or use agreements.

Finally, remember that many people will see you, and first impressions are very important. Dress the part, speak the part, and be professional at all times.

Chapter 8 Review Questions

8.1   What is NFPA 1035? _____

_____

8.2   What is the role of the public information officer? _____

_____

_____

_____

8.3   What are five skills that PIO should have? _____

_____

_____

_____

_____

_____

8.4   List four key aspects of community relations that a good PIO should
know. _____

_____

_____

_____

8.5   Create a job description for a news media person._____

_____

_____

_____

_____

_____

8.6   Create a job description for a PIO. _____

_____

_____

_____

_____

8.7   Contrast your answers to questions 8.5 and 8.6.

_____

_____

_____

_____

_____

8.8 List ten common guidelines to use when dealing with the media.

_____

_____

_____

_____

_____

_____

_____

_____

_____

_____

8.9 On a separate sheet of paper, create a sample PIO worksheet (cheat sheet) for collecting data on scenes.

8.10 Create a press release on some incident that is published in a newspaper or fire trade magazine. _____

_____

_____

_____

_____

_____

_____

_____

_____

_____

8.11 List four "bad habits," or actions to avoid, when doing work as a PIO.

_____

_____

_____

_____

8.12 Create a media blitz campaign (press release, fax notification to newspaper, media interview information, injury prevention materials) for the July Fourth holiday.

NOTES

1. Mark Mathis, *Feeding the Media Beast* (West Lafayette, Indiana: Purdue University Press, 2002).

2. Ibid.

3. Ibid.

FESHE COURSE OBJECTIVES

1. Identify the purpose of conducting fire investigations.
2. Understand the importance of fire investigations in fire prevention program.
3. Identify the standards associated with fire investigations.
4. Understand the impact of arson on a community.
5. Understand the importance of gathering data during fire investigations.
6. Understand the importance for fire investigators to work with law enforcement agencies.

Fire Investigation

Why Investigate Fires?

We investigate fires for numerous reasons. We already have covered the importance of knowing the history of fires and how past fires have started. In this chapter we will explain in more detail the significance, purposes, and desired outcomes of good fire investigation.

Significance

Data gathered from fires are very useful in fire prevention. Not only do we need to complete fire incident reports, but failure analysis and reconstruction of events can play an important role as well. Most fire departments conduct critiques after incidents to identify the strengths and weaknesses of their suppression efforts. This is an excellent method to determine areas where training is needed or to find ways to improve performance. The same type of approach should be taken after a fire to determine what steps could have been taken prior to the incident either to prevent the event from occurring or to reduce the loss it caused. These could include code modifications, behavior modifications, suppression modifications, or other relevant measures. Consider the outcome of the tragic events of 9-11-2001. Detailed fire modeling and analyses of how the World Trade Center buildings and the occupants reacted to the events are taking place. Reluctance or failure to conduct an evaluation or poor data collection would severely hinder a good analysis of this event. We should learn all that we can from such incidents and incorporate our discoveries in reasonable modifications or solutions to prevent similar events in the future. By examining an incident after it has occurred we can gain critical insight into future design and needed fire protection features. The examination of an incident should not focus just on failures or poor performance but also on the things done right. This type of analysis has resulted in improved designs and performance of fire protection systems and superior fireground operations.

> We should learn all that we can from every incident and use that information to help prevent similar events in the future.

Fire Investigation as Fire Prevention

Fire investigation commonly is assigned to the fire prevention division, predominantly because this group usually is designated to track the type of information collected during fire investigation, inspections, and the like. Basically, fire prevention collects data on all or most buildings within the community. Most model codes also grant the fire chief the authority to investigate fires. For example, the 1997 Uniform Fire Code, Section 2.203, states, "The fire department is authorized to investigate promptly the cause, origin and circumstances of each and every fire occurring in the jurisdiction involving loss of life or injury to person or destruction or damage to property and, if it appears to the bureau of investigation that such fire is of suspicious origin, they are authorized to take immediate charge of all physical evidence relating to the cause of the fire and are authorized to pursue the investigation to its conclusion." That same section further states, "The police department is authorized to assist the fire department in its investigations when requested to do so" (**Figure 9.1**).

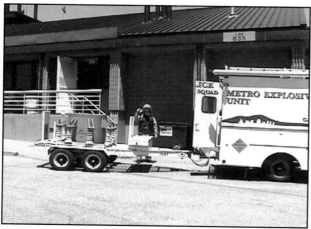

Figure 9.1 Collaboration and cooperation between the fire department and the police will become more important especially with homeland defense issues.

Like almost all fire department tasks, fire investigations can be handled differently among various jurisdictions. Some locations have modified state or local laws or have modified the adopted model codes allowing the state police or state fire marshal's office to handle some or all fire investigations. Others prefer to handle fire investigations at the county or city level. This is done by the police and/or fire department. No one way is necessarily better than another, as long as everyone receives the proper training and support and the data are shared appropriately to accommodate the needs of the community. The goal should not be to protect turf or territorial issues but to have a good investigative resource available to serve the public and achieve our mission. In some situations, state and federal assistance can provide depth of resources that are not available at the local level. Typically these resources will be in the form of equipment, staff, or laboratory services. Crime labs are a perfect example. Large metropolitan or state agencies can afford this type of facility, whereas a small town likely cannot.

Benefits of Fire Investigation

Fires are investigated to determine how they started and/or why they behaved as they did. Fire prevention bureau personnel can use this information to try to prevent similar events. One excellent method in using this information is through fire and life safety education. The information gained from a fire investigation can and should be used to educate and inform the public of potential fire causes. For example, an unattended candle might start a fire in a home and cause significant damage to the home without injury to the occupants. The investigation might then reveal that the occupants were awakened by their smoke detector and followed their escape plan to safely exit the house. The cause of the fire could be used to inform residents about candle usage and safety. The positive results of having a working smoke detector and an escape plan also could be used as educational messages.

If on a grander scale the fire received media attention, citizens might remember it during a fire safety education presentation. The cause of a significant fire can easily be connected to the presentation. Tracking the causes of fires will facilitate a fire prevention program that specifically addresses the community's fire problem allowing them to:

- Improve public awareness and education

- Implement more aggressive fire inspection practices

- Provide input into fire fighting tactics and operations

- Modify regulatory requirements to provide safer buildings or products

- Prevent or mitigate the impact of a similar occurrence

The value of good fire investigation is noteworthy. It provides benefits in many specific areas:

- Education

- Liability protection

- Code or legislative modification

- Research

- Consumer product improvement

- Identification and prosecution of the crime of arson

Incorporating the causes of fires into fire recruit training and required continuing education provides firefighters with knowledge to be better prepared during future events. The data on specific causes of fires by occupancy can prepare recruits for the type of incidents they may encounter. Understanding how and why arsonists do what they do can protect firefighters' lives by making them aware of potential hazards and enabling them to do a better job of scene recognition on their arrival. This in turn can help investigators do a better job of incident reconstruction and determination.

> Good investigative techniques secure the facts, thereby preventing or at least mitigating the degree of liability that a city or fire department may incur.

On fires where the fire department's performance may become a liability issue, good investigative techniques secure the facts, thereby preventing or at least mitigating the degree of liability that a city or fire department may incur. For example, determining that an accelerant was placed in multiple locations of a building and ignited will explain why fire suppression crews were overwhelmed and could not prevent the building from being destroyed (**Figure 9.2**). It may also protect business owners by factually determining an accidental cause of a fire, thereby removing them from liability for a careless or negligent act.

Figure 9.2 Physical evidence revealing a significant pour pattern.

The Coconut Grove fire discussed earlier in this book is a good example of how codes were modified and legislation was enacted to protect people who frequented assembly occupancies.

Fire investigation research of the Apollo space program tragedy of 1967 revealed how an oxygen enriched atmosphere in a command capsule led to a tragic fire killing all three of the astronauts. This led to a major change in design, policy, and practice that prevented any future mishaps of this type.

Many product safety recalls result from fire related problems. Without proper fire origin and cause determination, these faulty products would not be repaired or replaced, which could lead to millions of dollars in damage and countless life loss.

Arson crimes are unfortunately all too common. Proper investigations can lead to the apprehension and prosecution of the perpetrators, hopefully preventing these individuals from repeating their crimes. An example is the 1986 New Year's Eve Fire at the Dupont Plaza Hotel in San Juan, Puerto Rico, which killed 97 people in 12 short minutes. The individual who started the fire was apprehended and convicted but only as a result of good fire investigation work. This fire investigation also led to fire safety improvements in hotel design and protection and to the Hotel and Motel Fire Safety Act of 1990. Again, a good investigation program can spawn many benefits that greatly improve our overall fire prevention and fire protection efforts.

Identifying Trends

The fire service is busier than it has ever been. The need for accurate data and proper analysis of these data is becoming more and more important. As Tom McEwen points out in the *Fire Data Analysis Handbook,* "Balancing limited resources and justifying daily operations and finances in the face of tough economic times is a scenario that every department can relate to."[1] To identify our target and perform our work as efficiently as possible, not to mention to prevent future injury and harm, we must properly identify problems. Identifying trends is one way to do this.

The data to be collected on scenes are numerous. A typical National Fire Incident Report gives an idea of the amount of detail solicited just involving a victim (**Figure 9.3**).

- Date
- Day of week
- Time
- Victim's age or gender
- Type of casualty
- Severity
- Affiliation (civilian or fire fighter)
- Familiarity of structure
- Location at ignition
- Physical condition before injury
- Cause of injury

A — NFIRS-1 Basic

| FDID ☆ | State ☆ | Incident Date (MM DD YYYY) ☆ | Station | Incident Number ☆ | Exposure ☆ |

☐ Delete ☐ Change ☐ No Activity

NFIRS-1 Basic

B — Location Type ☆

☐ Check this box to indicate that the address for this incident is provided on the Wildland Fire Module in Section B, "Alternative Location Specification." Use only for wildland fires.

Census Tract ☐☐☐☐-☐☐

☐ Street address
☐ Intersection
☐ In front of
☐ Rear of
☐ Adjacent to
☐ Directions

Number/Milepost | Prefix | Street or Highway | Street Type | Suffix

Apt./Suite/Room | City | State | ZIP Code

Cross Street or Directions, as applicable

C — Incident Type ☆

Incident Type

D — Aid Given or Received ☆   ☐ None

1 ☐ Mutual aid received
2 ☐ Auto. aid received
3 ☐ Mutual aid given
4 ☐ Auto. aid given
5 ☐ Other aid given

Their FDID | Their State

Their Incident Number

E1 — Dates and Times

Midnight is 0000

Check boxes if dates are the same as Alarm Date.

	Month	Day	Year	Hour	Min
Alarm ☆						ALARM always required
☐ **Arrival** ☆						ARRIVAL required, unless canceled or did not arrive
☐ **Controlled**						CONTROLLED optional, except for wildland fires
☐ **Last Unit Cleared**						LAST UNIT CLEARED, required except for wildland fires

E2 — Shifts and Alarms

Local Option

Shift or Platoon | Alarms | District

E3 — Special Studies

Local Option

Special Study ID# | Special Study Value

F — Actions Taken ☆

Primary Action Taken (1)

Additional Action Taken (2)

Additional Action Taken (3)

G1 — Resources ☆

☐ Check this box and skip this block if an Apparatus or Personnel Module is used.

	Apparatus	Personnel
Suppression		
EMS		
Other		

☐ Check box if resource counts include aid received resources.

G2 — Estimated Dollar Losses and Values

LOSSES: Required for all fires if known. Optional for non-fires.   **None**

Property $ ☐☐☐,☐☐☐,☐☐☐ ☐

Contents $ ☐☐☐,☐☐☐,☐☐☐ ☐

PRE-INCIDENT VALUE: Optional

Property $ ☐☐☐,☐☐☐,☐☐☐ ☐

Contents $ ☐☐☐,☐☐☐,☐☐☐ ☐

Completed Modules

☐ Fire–2
☐ Structure Fire–3
☐ Civilian Fire Cas.–4
☐ Fire Service Cas.–5
☐ EMS–6
☐ HazMat–7
☐ Wildland Fire–8
☐ Apparatus–9
☐ Personnel–10
☐ Arson–11

H1 — Casualties ☆   ☐ None

	Deaths	Injuries
Fire Service		
Civilian		

H2 — Detector

Required for confined fires.

1 ☐ Detector alerted occupants
2 ☐ Detector did not alert them
U ☐ Unknown

H3 — Hazardous Materials Release   ☐ None

1 ☐ **Natural gas:** slow leak, no evacuation or HazMat actions
2 ☐ **Propane gas:** <21-lb tank (as in home BBQ grill)
3 ☐ **Gasoline:** vehicle fuel tank or portable container
4 ☐ **Kerosene:** fuel burning equipment or portable storage
5 ☐ **Diesel fuel/fuel oil:** vehicle fuel tank or portable storage
6 ☐ **Household solvents:** home/office spill, cleanup only
7 ☐ **Motor oil:** from engine or portable container
8 ☐ **Paint:** from paint cans totaling <55 gallons
0 ☐ **Other:** special HazMat actions required or spill > 55 gal (Please complete the HazMat form.)

I — Mixed Use Property   ☐ Not mixed

10 ☐ Assembly use
20 ☐ Education use
33 ☐ Medical use
40 ☐ Residential use
51 ☐ Row of stores
53 ☐ Enclosed mall
58 ☐ Business & residential
59 ☐ Office use
60 ☐ Industrial use
63 ☐ Military use
65 ☐ Farm use
00 ☐ Other mixed use

J — Property Use ☆   ☐ None

Structures

131 ☐ Church, place of worship
161 ☐ Restaurant or cafeteria
162 ☐ Bar/tavern or nightclub
213 ☐ Elementary school, kindergarten
215 ☐ High school, junior high
241 ☐ College, adult education
311 ☐ Nursing home
331 ☐ Hospital

341 ☐ Clinic, clinic-type infirmary
342 ☐ Doctor/dentist office
361 ☐ Prison or jail, not juvenile
419 ☐ 1- or 2-family dwelling
429 ☐ Multifamily dwelling
439 ☐ Rooming/boarding house
449 ☐ Commercial hotel or motel
459 ☐ Residential, board and care
464 ☐ Dormitory/barracks
519 ☐ Food and beverage sales

539 ☐ Household goods, sales, repairs
571 ☐ Gas or service station
579 ☐ Motor vehicle/boat sales/repairs
599 ☐ Business office
615 ☐ Electric-generating plant
629 ☐ Laboratory/science laboratory
700 ☐ Manufacturing plant
819 ☐ Livestock/poultry storage (barn)
882 ☐ Non-residential parking garage
891 ☐ Warehouse

Outside

124 ☐ Playground or park
655 ☐ Crops or orchard
669 ☐ Forest (timberland)
807 ☐ Outdoor storage area
919 ☐ Dump or sanitary landfill
931 ☐ Open land or field

936 ☐ Vacant lot
938 ☐ Graded/cared for plot of land
946 ☐ Lake, river, stream
951 ☐ Railroad right-of-way
960 ☐ Other street
961 ☐ Highway/divided highway
962 ☐ Residential street/driveway

981 ☐ Construction site
984 ☐ Industrial plant yard

Look up and enter a Property Use code and description only if you have NOT checked a Property Use box.

Property Use Code ☐☐☐

Property Use Description

NFIRS-1 Revision 01/01/04

The ☆ denotes a required field.

NFIRS 5.0 COMPLETE REFERENCE GUIDE

Figure 9.3 A National Fire Incident Report typically contains a wealth of important data. *(Continued on next page.)*

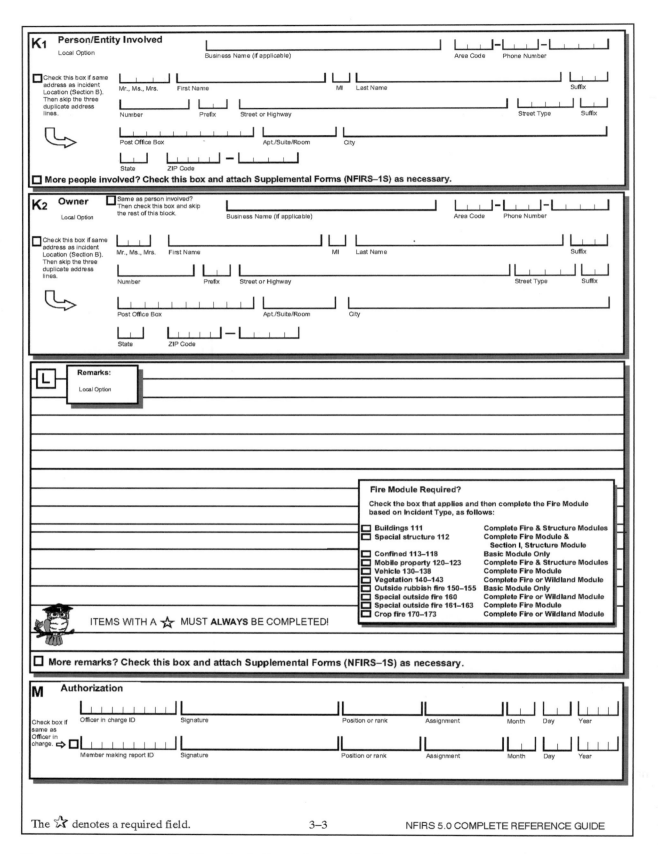

Figure 9.3 A National Fire Incident Report typically contains a wealth of important data.

- Activity at time of injury

- Body part injured

- Nature of injury

- What prevented escape

Another whole set of questions regards:

- Type of situation

- Property type

- Location

- Method of alarm

- Still district location (the geographical area of the first due responding apparatus)

- Shift fire occurred on

- Number of personnel

- Number and type of equipment

- Number of injuries and deaths

- Origin

- Cause

- Form of heat of ignition

- Material ignited

- Form of material ignited

- How extinguished

- Level or location of area of origin

- Dollar loss

- Extent of flame damage

- Extent of smoke damage

- Detector/alarm performance

- Suppression system performance

- Smoke characteristics (movement, largest single producer)

While company officers answer many of these questions, all are part of the fire investigation. The fire investigator is generally required to provide additional levels of detail to each answer. This information then provides a good analytical picture of what went wrong, how, and why. The resulting information can reveal trends, which can be considered for future workload prioritization and problem correction. For example, a fire investigator might develop a graph that shows how much impact juvenile arson has in relation to other juvenile crime. This is good information for a fire chief if he or she plans on addressing the problem.

National and state findings are a good source of data, but the local fire data determine the specific elements of the fire department's fire prevention efforts. One of the greatest benefits of conducting fire investigations is the opportunity to gain insight into your community's fire problem. The frequency of local incidents also will play a significant role in prioritizing fire prevention activities.

Data trends can provide a wealth of information:

- Day of the week fires most often occur
- Time of day fires most often occur
- Most common type of fires
- Most common ignition sources causing fires
- Most common locations where fire occurs

Trend identification is also important for justifying requests for more resources.

Remember not to lose the small data among the big data. Large headline events make it easier to procure resources and time for investigating, but many times it is the lower profile, less noticed fires that provide the real clues about what is going on. Statistically speaking, the big events often are thrown out as aberrations that do not factor into the real picture. Insurance claims, product liability, and subrogation claims (in which a third party assumes another's legal right to collect damages) are gathering more and more attention. Although not necessarily significant for data collection, this does increase the workload.

Responsibility

As previously mentioned, the fire department is typically responsible for the investigation of fires. Fire departments conduct fire investigations at different levels. Some fire departments will investigate to determine where the fire started and what is believed to have ignited it. This is referred to as origin and cause determination. The depth or detail of the investigation will also vary. Some fire departments may be satisfied with determining the fire's room of origin, while others may choose to determine the exact location within the room where the fire started.

Public investigators or investigations sections are not always responsible for going into as much detail as private investigators for other interested parties, such as insurance companies, may seek. Therefore, it is important that the public investigators' duties are clearly understood and codified in jurisdictional law, code, policies, or procedures.

Basic Investigation Training, Equipment, and Procedures

To do their jobs well, investigators must be properly trained in their tasks and duties. The nationally recognized standard of good practice for achieving this is NFPA 1033, *Professional Qualifications for Fire Investigator.* The IFSTA *Fire Investigator* manual is a good resource for fire investigators, as it follows the training requirements established in the NFPA standard. Remember, education and training is of the first order of importance. Determining the cause and origin of fires will most likely have legal implications. Insurance companies as well as attorneys may subpoena the investigation report. Those involved in the fire investigation must be trained to the level of confidence needed for testifying to their findings in a court of law (**Figure 9.4**).

> Those involved in the fire investigation must be trained to the level of confidence needed for testifying to their findings in a court of law.

Another important standard to become familiar with, although it is somewhat contentious, is NFPA 921, *Standard for Fire and Explosion Investigations.* More defense attorneys probably use this standard than fire departments or other public investigation agencies. The requirements are fairly rigid, and much of its content is very technical. Defense attorneys have been known to reference it in detail in an attempt to discredit the investigators. You should be aware of this standard and should become particularly familiar with it, regardless of whether or not your jurisdiction adopts it, because you likely will see it brought up while you are on the witness stand.

Figure 9.4 Fire investigators often are called on to testify in court.

If a fire is determined to be deliberately set, it is called incendiary. An **incendiary fire** may not be arson. For example, a person who burns his/her shed simply to dispose of it will have created an incendiary fire. The fire is intentionally set, but there was no desire to defraud or cause harm. If the fire was deliberately and maliciously set with the intent to defraud or cause damage or injury, it is referred to as **arson**. The exact legal definition of arson may vary from jurisdiction to jurisdiction.

✔ **incendiary fire**
any fire that is set intentionally

To begin a fire investigation, two questions need to be addressed:

- Is the focus of the fire investigation going to be strictly origin and cause?

- Is the focus of the fire investigation also going to include determining the crime of arson and subsequent arrest and prosecution?

In either case, if you are investigating fires to any degree you will need to meet some basic requirements.

✔ **arson**
the act of willfully and maliciously setting fire to a house, building, or other property

Training

Before you start investigating fires, you must have a proper education. Any individual or group of individuals who are going to perform origin and cause fire investigation should be prepared and adequately trained in:

- Basic fire science with emphasis on fire behavior
- An overview of insurance practices
- Report writing
  - Content of a good report
  - Sketches
- Interviewing
  - Verbal communications
  - Nonverbal communication
- Scene preservation and control
- Basic photography
- Origin determination
- Fire debris removal and evidence collection
- Cause determination
- Basic electricity
- Scene reconstruction
  - Burn patterns (low and high burns)
  - Depth of char
  - Spalling of concrete
  - Protected areas
- Working knowledge of resource materials (NFPA standards, etc.)
- Basic building construction
- Basic understanding of incendiary fire indicators
  - Multiple fire sets
  - "Trailers" of flammable liquids
  - Absence of accidental causes
  - Crime scene
  - Murders
  - Theft
  - Fraud
  - Delayed ignition devices

- — Flammable liquid pours
- — Motives present
- Basic fireground tactics used in suppression
  - — Ventilation
  - — Interior attack
  - — Exterior attack
  - — Overhaul

Equipment

Along with this basic training, you will also need the following tools and equipment to do a basic origin and cause investigation. Obviously, as you gain experience and determine your personal preferences, other tools and devices may help, particularly for more thorough investigations such as may be required for arson investigation.

- Personal protective equipment
  - — Helmet
  - — Coat
  - — Gloves (heavy and light)
  - — Boots
  - — Respirator or self-contained breathing apparatus (SCBA)
  - — Coveralls
- Flashlight
- Cell phone or portable radio
- Pump can (for hotspot touchups and cleaning the floor after debris removal for better examination)
- Portable electrical lights
- Hydrocarbon sampling device
- "Get after it and dig for it" equipment
  - — Trowel
  - — Scraper
  - — Shovel
  - — Small saw
  - — Chisel/hammer
  - — Wire cutters
  - — Multipurpose scissors
  - — Needle-nose pliers

- — Vise grips
- — Goose-neck pliers
- — Pry bar
- — Garden tools
- — Battery powered reciprocating saw
- Measuring tape
- Ruler
- Camera and film (digitals work well)
- Barrier tape
- Paper
- Pen or pencil (pencils always work in a variety of climates!)

While we cannot go into detailed instructions for using this equipment, these items usually will provide you the tools to investigate the fireground thoroughly.

Determining Origin and Cause

Investigators determine the origin and cause of most fires by analyzing the area of origin, the heat of ignition, the combustible or flammable materials involved, and the actions of the occupants at the time of the fire (**Figure 9.5**). Fire protection professionals must make every attempt to study all possible causes of fires to arrive at a more complete understanding of what took place and to help determine fire prevention solutions that address the community's overall fire problem. Investigation is also important because of the lessons learned that you can share with your fire protection colleagues.

Figure 9.5 Fire investigator directs firefighters at the scene of a blast in a dairy compressor room.

Investigators should be capable of evaluating a scene to determine the point of origin, source of ignition, the material ignited, and the act or activity that brought the ignition source and materials together.[2] They also should be able to secure the scene properly and protect potential evidence until it is no longer necessary. They should provide a good scene survey both inside and outside the building or area involved. Investigators should be able to recognize burn patterns and understand how the fire affected structural components. Proper examination of fireground debris requires the use of various tools and equipment. Using the tools and equipment provided, the investigator should be able to remove insignificant debris and preserve those elements of the scene that correlate to the origin and cause. Make certain that no evidence destruction takes place, should the determination be suspicious.

Reconstructing the area of origin is important. This can be done any number of ways, such as witness information, verified debris, and statements from fire crews. The inspector should be able to verify building mechanical equipment and any other special equipment to rule in or out accidental causes. Verification by experts in various fields, such as mechanical or electrical engineers, is also helpful. Determining explosive effects may also become important. The investigator should know how explosions can be caused and what impact they will have on a structure, vessel, or other area of origin.

Documenting the scene is critical. Photographs, diagrams, and measurements all are important parts of the investigation. Notes and documentation all will be fair game for evaluation and submission as evidence, so doing this thoroughly and accurately is very important.

Interviews with witnesses, residents, or workers provide invaluable information. Carefully document all relevant information and make sure you know where to find these people again after you leave. Information such as social security numbers, driver's license numbers, and dates of birth is important. Various available courses provide good advice and explain techniques for interviewing witnesses or suspects. We strongly recommend anyone doing investigations take these if at all possible.

Report writing, computer data entry, filing, and document preparation all are important follow-up duties. The better you are organized and prepared, the better you will be able to handle future inquiries on the events, particularly three years down the road when the case finally goes to court. That late date is not the time to try to remember what happened, what you saw, or what you did. Document as if you are preparing to testify in court the next day.

Arson Investigation

Arson, in the laws of the United States, is the act of willfully and maliciously setting fire to a house, building, or other property. Under common law, arson was the willful and malicious burning of the house of another person and was considered a felony punishable by death. The penalty for arson now consists of differing periods of penal servitude or simple imprisonment. If the act results directly or indirectly in the death of a person, it is treated according to the

> Investigators should be able to determine a fire's point of origin, its source of ignition, the material ignited, and the act or activity that brought the ignition source and materials together.

> Document every scene as if you are preparing to testify in court the next day.

modern definition of murder. Common law also considered the act of burning one's own house to defraud an insurer or destroy the property of another on the premises a crime, usually a misdemeanor. Under the penal statutes of some states, arson in the first degree is setting fire to any building in which a human being is present.

Training and Equipment

The basic techniques of arson investigations are not much different than those of simple origin and cause investigations. Investigators must follow the same procedures and practices for properly determining origin and cause, as that is still the key to prosecuting a crime. To properly capture and preserve evidence for use in criminal trials, however, they must perform other tasks that require a higher level of training and additional equipment.

Arson investigators typically need basic legal training in the following law enforcement concepts and procedures:

- Court decisions

- Burden of proof

- Warrants

- Arrest procedures and rights

- State statutes related to arson

- Federal statutes related to fire investigation

- Evidence collection and processing

Keep in mind that different jurisdictions may have different requirements depending upon their policies and procedures.

In addition to the basic equipment for origin and cause determination, arson investigations generally will require the following items (**Figure 9.6**):

Figure 9.6 Typical equipment used for collecting evidence. *Photos courtesy of Investigator Kirk Schmitt, Colorado Springs Fire Department, Colorado Springs, CO.*

- Unlined paint cans with secure fitting, airtight lids

- Paper and plastic (sealable) bags

- Tape

  — Duct

  — Masking

  — Clear

- Glass jars with caps

- Numbered marking tents or triangles

- Permanent marker (fine and chisel tip)

- Engineering paper (gridded)

- Awl or diamond-tipped scribing tool

- Small voice recorder (nice to have)

Once an investigator has the appropriate training and equipment the additional work can begin.

Procedures

We do not intend the following sections to offer any degree of formal training in arson investigation but simply to give you a perspective on what is involved. This should facilitate informed decision-making and planning in respect to starting or evaluating this function in your fire prevention bureau. If you want to conduct fireground investigations, you should look into other courses, training, and books on the subject.

Size-Up

Determining the origin of a fire requires a systematic approach. Your starting point should be your initial arrival on the fire scene (assuming that you arrive on the scene during the incident or shortly after during mop-up operations). It will be very beneficial in your investigation if you can reconstruct in your mind what the scene looked like prior to the fire department's arrival and where the first signs of fire were located. If the building has been completely consumed by fire you will need to reconstruct what it looked like and the location of its contents when the fire started. It also is important to know what the building looked like during the course of the fire and how it behaved. Talk to fire crews and document what they saw upon their arrival. Also, make sure they document in their reports what they observed individually. Keep in mind that what they initially saw might have been consumed by fire and will no longer be visible to you. They will be able to save you time during your reconstruction process. It may even be helpful to have them draw a sketch. Fire suppression crews may have left the scene or have been relieved by another crew. It is always a good practice for the fire investigator to attend the fire suppression crew's critique of the incident.

Figure 9.7 Air handling equipment loads add to the likelihood that a weakened and distorted roof will collapse.

Figure 9.8 Fire investigators need to examine the exterior of the building to check for signs of the fire originating outside the structure and burning in.

Figure 9.9 Be sure to observe whether roof openings are due to the fire itself or to suppression crews' ventilation efforts.

Talk to whomever reported the fire and document the time of the alarm and how it was transmitted. You should ask questions or observe for information about a number of concerns, such as: are there any injuries or fatalities? If yes, does anyone dislike the victims? If a fatality occurred, could the fire have been started to cover up evidence? Most likely, law enforcement agencies will be involved if a death has occurred in a fire. What were the weather conditions? Do all the things you see and hear from crews and witnesses correlate with the weather? (Closed or open windows, doors, etc.) Was lightning a factor? What was the wind direction and speed? Were there any unusual delays or obstructions to the fire suppression crews? Where did fire suppression crews make initial entry? Do you notice anything unusual about witnesses or bystanders at the scene? Did any broken glass seem not to be from the fire itself? What color of smoke did fire crews observe? This question can be important as certain types of materials produce certain colors of smoke. However, given the types of fuels available today, distinguishing them by the color of their smoke is getting more and more difficult.

Examining the Exterior

After you have sized up the scene, the next critical step is to determine whether the fire started on the exterior or the interior of the building. Safety is always a primary concern (**Figure 9.7**). During the scene examination and during the interview with the suppression crews, it is important to determine approximately how much water was used to extinguish the fire and what parts of the structure are not safe to enter. The firefighters will most likely be at the incident prior to the fire investigator's arrival. They will be able to explain what they encountered and how the fire scene initially looked prior to suppression activities and further consumption of the combustibles by fire. If the firefighter has some insight into the cause of fires and what has taken place in the past, he or she may be able to provide a critical piece of information that will help the investigator determine the cause of the fire. Essentially, this method utilizes the fire suppression crews as preliminary fire investigators. In fact, some fire departments do not have a designated fire investigator. Instead they use on-duty fire personnel to conduct the fire investigation.

As you examine the four sides of the structure, determine if the fire started or communicated to the structure form the exterior (**Figure 9.8**). Note if the fire ventilated through the roof on its own or if the suppression crews opened the roof as part of the ventilation process (**Figure 9.9**). Are there any unusual prints, tracks, or debris on the outside? Were the windows broken in or is glass on the exterior? Are doors and windows secured? Are any utilities cut off or disrupted other than for fire suppression? Look for anything that seems out of place either with what you judge or what witnesses state.

Examining the Interior

Determine where the most significant damage occurred based on the fire's highest temperature and longest duration. Trace the burn patterns back to the fire's origin. Look for uneven burning or localized deep char. Where is the most ceiling and roof damage? Find the lowest point of the burned area within the area of origin. Was the floor burned through, and if so, from the top or from the bottom? Once you have localized this fairly well, look for potential air movement or drafts that could have influenced the fire. Also try to determine the types of furnishings or objects in the area before the fire to see if they had any effect that would be inconsistent with the apparent burn (**Figure 9.10**). Contents removed. Look for heat flow paths. Are there multiple ignition locations? Do you see a traditional V pattern pointing to the low point like the one in the **Figure 9.11**?

Figure 9.10 Fire investigators need to check to determine if the contents of the building were removed at the time of the fire. *Photo courtesy of Mount Prospect Fire Department*

Figure 9.11 Fires can burn in what is commonly known as a V pattern. The narrow portion of the V can indicate the point of the fire's origin as shown in this photo. *Photo courtesy of Mount Prospect Fire Department*

Always examine the lowest point of burning. Accidental fires typically burn vertically upward leaving the floor and lower areas much less damaged than the upper levels of the room (fires do not typically burn downward, as heat travels upward). After you have dug to the lowest burn level, it may be a good time to use the pump can to clean the floor and lower levels away to see what is actually burned. Do not be afraid to dig (**Figures 9.12 and 9.13**). We

Figure 9.12 Fire investigators need to sift through debris looking for evidence. *Photo courtesy of the Mount Prospect Fire Department*

Figure 9.13 It is important to completely remove and examine the debris to check for signs of the origin of the fire. *Photo courtesy of the Mount Prospect Fire Department*

have seen valuable clues missed and incorrect decisions made simply because the investigator(s) were too lazy to work their way through the entire scene and surrounding area. To get to the bottom of the fire, you need to get to the bottom of the fire!

Indicators of fast propagating fires can be severe overhead damage in comparison to other parts of the room and distinct, sharp V patterns. Window glass may be crazed and have heavy soot on the interior. Small alligator scale charring patterns in wood could indicate a hot, short-duration fire. Look at concrete to see if it spalled near an area of ignition. This is typically an indication of an area that sustained a significant amount of heat.

Once you have isolated the point of origin, the next step is to determine the cause. To do this you must eliminate any and all natural or accidental causes before concluding that a fire is suspicious or incendiary. Many times the determining factor will be the process of elimination, which must be based on evidence. For example, you could eliminate any energized electrical sources if your investigation revealed the power to the building was disconnected at the time of the fire.

Look for any potential sources of accidental ignition, such as electrical heating devices, smoking materials, pinched electrical cords, overloaded electrical supplies, tripped breakers, or the like (**Figure 9.14**). Were any candles being used? Were painting, cleaning, or other activities taking place prior to the fire? How does the information from your initial scene interviews correlate to what you see with your own eyes.

Figure 9.14 Be alert to potential sources of accidental ignition such as the air compressor in the left rear of this photo.

The investigator must consider and eliminate all of these possibilities before making any other determination. Sometimes the fire's cause remains undetermined. That is not desirable, but it is certainly better than accusing people of something they did not do. Write the report to show the exact cause is undetermined, while ruling out any potential causes as in our electrical example above. Leaving the final cause of the fire as undetermined may open the door for reevaluation later if additional evidence becomes available. If the cause was intentional, the person who set the fire may set another and not necessarily in your jurisdiction. When the arsonist is finally caught, he or she may confess to setting other fires including the one you investigated. If you have already listed its cause as electrical, modifying your report will be difficult, even with the arsonist's confession. During the suspect's prosecution, the defense attorney will stop at nothing to discredit you and your initial findings, if only to confuse the issue. Remember, criminal issues must be proven beyond a reasonable doubt. To quote the defense attorney's famous admonition regarding a glove produced in evidence at the O. J. Simpson murder trial, "If it doesn't fit, you must acquit!"

If you suspect accelerants were used, then you must mark their locations, photograph the area, take good secured samples, and send them to a qualified lab. Document all of your findings. Many times, the collection of accelerant samples and other evidence may be better left to law enforcement agencies trained in this task. Fire departments often do not have the expertise to handle this type of situation. It is important that all investigators know their limitations and seek help from others. No one can be an expert in all aspects of fire investigation. Investigators may need the expert advice of electrical engineers, appliance professionals, or bomb experts, to name just a few.

Getting the results from evidence samples can take weeks to months in some cases. Some jurisdictions may be able to secure the use of accelerant dogs (**Figure 9.15**). (Another example of using experts as collaborative partners!). These dogs are phenomenal to watch and very good at what they do. If you have the opportunity to work with one, make sure you ask the dog's handler for special instructions before you do anything. The handlers are highly skilled at working their animals (partners) and operate very methodically. Most state agencies have access to these experts.

Remember, determining that a fire was not accidental is not always the difficult part; prosecuting the individual who set the fire is! Some of the biggest mistakes we have seen investigators make on fire scenes include:

- Failing to take enough photographs (Film is cheap.)

- Not digging and scraping to the bottom of the fire scene

- Not digging and scraping with care (Don't just shovel stuff out the window! Some of that "stuff" may be evidence.)

- Not documenting where the evidence samples were taken

- Failing to get and document accurate statements from witnesses

- Assuming something happened without making certain

Figure 9.15 ATF handler praising accelerant dog used in accelerant detection.

- Failing to write a comprehensive report

- Failing to seek the assistance of outside agencies

- Failing to seek the assistance of experts

After Origin and Cause, What?

If you have determined where and how the fire started and that it is suspicious or incendiary, you must proceed through another entire process. You need to determine if crime specialists are needed. It is a good idea already to have developed a solid working relationship with your district attorney. Prosecutors may want to be called to see the scene firsthand. They can often give you hints on what to do and what not to do, avoiding pitfalls later if the case does go to court. If a fatality is involved, what did the coroner or medical examiner determine as cause of death? Involve local, county, state, and federal officials if you need more help or if leads keep popping up that are beyond your capacity to handle. Do not ever be afraid to get help. Often, this networking among law enforcement agencies yields far more than going it alone.

Smaller fire departments usually do not have the experience and training of more experienced law enforcement agencies. Fire department personnel are generally pretty good at determining what caused the fire, while law enforcement personnel are experienced at collecting evidence, preserving the crime scene, and working to prosecute the offender. Establishing a working relationship between law enforcement and fire personnel enables a much more thorough and efficient investigation team.

> Never be afraid to seek help from other authorities or agencies.

Toward a Long-Term Solution

The crime of arson is interesting and complex. It is a killer. Set fires burn quickly, trapping tenants and endangering firefighters. Arson is a local problem. It is a crime with high potential for financial and emotional gain and very low risk of detection. Two major categories of arson are those motivated by financial gain, which are constantly weighed against the risk of loss vs. gain, and those motivated by psychological gain. The latter are far more difficult to prevent and control. What we are finding is an increasing trend of juvenile fire setters whose motives fall into the second category. We must continue our efforts toward juvenile fire setter prevention programs. To make policy makers at all levels aware of these trends we should provide them with better data so they can see the problem clearly. As a fire service professional, you should make it your mission to provide these data as clearly and effectively as possible, allowing decision makers to properly measure the problem's magnitude and our progress in controlling it.

The best way for you as a fire service professional to address a good fire investigation program is to strive to achieve the following goals:

- Develop good policies and procedures for everyone to follow.

- Integrate fire investigation functions into the mission of the fire department.

- Train everyone on the job about what it means to do good fire investigation.

- Get management's commitment to this process.
- Provide proper training and equipment.
- Develop arson task forces where appropriate.
- Gather and track good data.
- Develop an early arson warning system.
- Develop a progressive public education program citing all aspects of fire.
- Partner with community organizations.
- Develop relationships with law enforcement agencies and prosectors.
- Support advances in fire investigation technology.

By following these goals and attending to the details and complexities of fire investigation, you will have the basic tools to form a comprehensive program, providing a solid foundation for future fire prevention efforts. Keep in mind the need to ensure that staff and equipment are available for your use. You must do this well before an event takes place. We cannot and should not be solely responsible for fire investigations. We need to use all of the resources available and to share information in our mutual endeavor to prevent fires or control their spread.

Summary

The purpose of a fire investigation is to determine how the fire started and why it behaved as it did. The data collected from the investigation of fires can be a key element in addressing a community's fire problem. The data gathered in a fire investigation can be used for fire prevention.

Fire prevention bureau personnel can use fire investigation information to try to prevent similar events. One excellent method of using this information is through fire and life safety education. The information gained from a fire investigation can and should be used to educate and inform the public of potential fire causes. The best opportunity for presenting this message is when the media attention is greatest—just after an incident takes place.

The information can also be used to identify code modifications that will reduce the potential for similar fires. This is very similar to the case studies we reviewed in Chapter 2, "History of Fire Prevention." The only difference is that the lessons learned can be community specific. If many communities experience the same type of incident then it gains more attention, and more people benefit from finding the cause of the fire. At times this may even lead to a product recall on a national level.

An important level of fire investigation is determining if arson was the cause of the fire. Arson directly impacts the community where it takes place. There is the potential for the community to lose revenue as well as for the loss of life to a firefighter or innocent citizen. To combat arson effectively, it is essential for fire investigators to pool their resources and work with other agencies, such as law enforcement.

Chapter 9 Review Exercises

9.1   What is the purpose of investigating fires? _____
_____
_____

9.2   How is fire investigation a function of fire prevention?_____
_____
_____
_____
_____

9.3   What is a cause and origin investigation? _____
_____
_____
_____

9.4   What are some of the common mistakes made by fire departments
during a fire investigation?_____
_____
_____
_____
_____
_____
_____
_____
_____
_____
_____
_____

9.5   What is arson? _____
_____
_____

9.6   How does arson affect the citizens in a community? _____
_____
_____

9.7   What NFPA standards apply to fire investigations?_____
_____
_____

9.8   How are the methods of conducting a fire investigation similar to
those of conducting a fire inspection? _____
_____
_____

9.9　How can fire investigation be used for code development? Cite an example. _____

_____

_____

_____

9.10　Provide a list of information that could be collected during an investigation. _____

_____

_____

_____

9.11　Provide a list of tools and equipment that could be used during an investigation. _____

_____

_____

_____

_____

_____

_____

_____

_____

_____

9.12　What could be important data trend points to look at if you wanted to maximize your resources? _____

_____

_____

_____

_____

_____

9.13　What issues are safety concerns for fire investigators? _____

_____

_____

9.14　Outline ten goals that a fire investigations unit should strive to achieve. _____

_____

_____

_____

_____

_____

_____

_____

_____

NOTES

1. Tom McEwen, *Fire Data Analysis Handbook* (Washington, D.C.: U.S. Fire Administration, n.d.)

2. NFPA 1033, *Professional Qualification for Fire Investigator* (Quincy, Mass.: National Fire Protection Association, 1998).

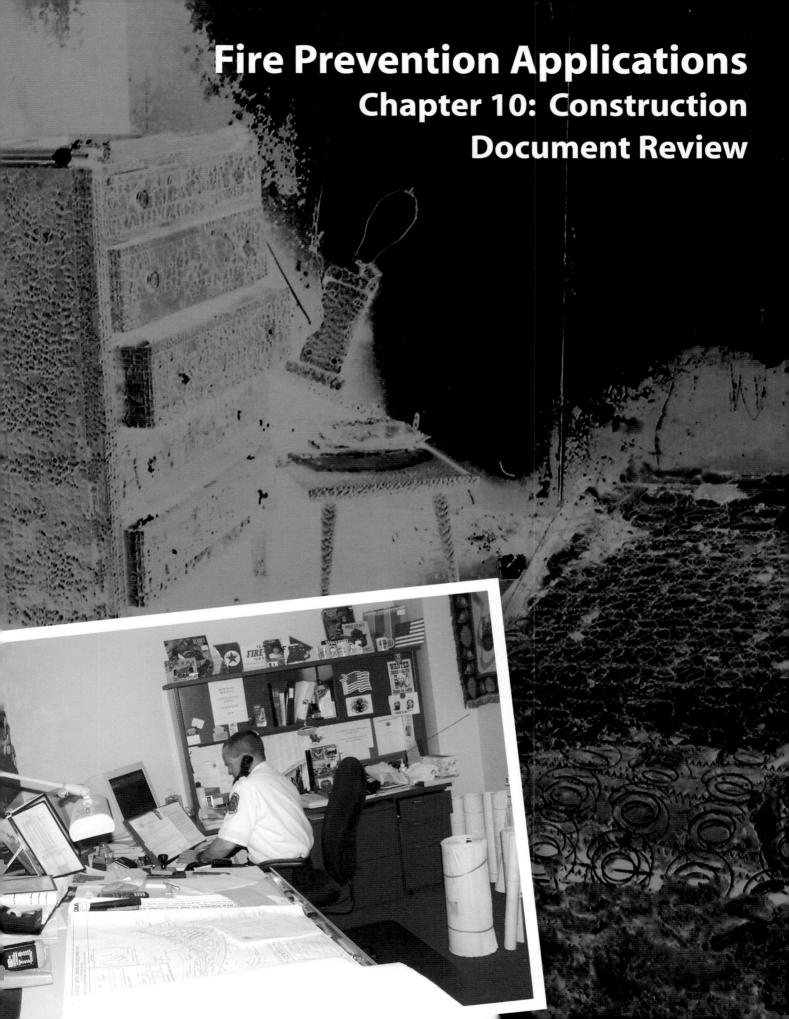

Fire Prevention Applications
Chapter 10: Construction
Document Review

FESHE COURSE OBJECTIVES

1. Define the elements of a plan review program.*

2. Identify the types of construction documents reviewed by fire departments.

3. Understand the development process and the fire department's role in it.

4. Understand the importance of the fire department's participation in the construction document review process.

*U.S. Fire Administration Objective

Chapter 10

Construction Document Review

Introduction

Buildings are constructed to protect people and their property from the elements. In suburban areas, the available large open-land parcels for construction are diminishing. Buildings are being constructed on smaller land parcels, and older buildings are being torn down to make room for new construction. Whether the municipality is growing rapidly or not at all, the fire department responsible for providing its fire and emergency services also should provide construction document review services (**Figure 10.1**).

This text's main theme is the need to ensure that fire tragedies of the past are not repeated. We have only one opportunity to ensure a building's construction features are adequate to prevent the spread of fire and include all of the required built-in automatic suppression systems. That opportunity occurs when the building is constructed or remodeled. The fire department should not see the construction document review process as just another unfunded mandate. The fire department should view construction document review as an opportunity to begin building a fire prevention coalition with the owners of the building and as an opportunity to identify potential hazards and risks that will impact the safety of the occupants and the firefighters who may be called there in the middle of the night to mitigate an emergency incident. Even small volunteer fire departments need to take an active role in construction document review. The fire department should consider construction document review one of the essential services it provides and a critical element of the fire prevention program. Making the right construction document review decisions

Figure 10.1 Fire department personnel must review construction documents for fire safety issues.

The construction document review is an opportunity to begin building a fire prevention coalition with the owners of the building.

pertaining to fire protection design will impact the safety of fire fighters and building occupants for many years to follow.

In many areas of the country the fire department may not have the authority or staff to enforce nationally recognized codes and standards (see Chapter 3). Architects and builders then can construct buildings as they see fit without the benefit of oversight. Architects do, however, have some legal obligation to ensure a building's design is safe. Constructing a building to meet the adopted building code indicates it meets the minimum safety requirements.

Difficulties arise when a developer who is unaccustomed to fire department input constructs a building in a location where the fire department actively reviews construction documents. The fire department providing construction document review faces confrontation from a frustrated developer or builder who indicates his construction method was approved in another location. Why is it not approved in this location? Most municipalities do not have the same codes. Many municipalities make amendments to the model codes. This also places the builders in a difficult situation. We recommend that municipalities require permits for construction only after the project has been through a construction document review process.

The construction document review process in most municipalities can become very political, which in turn may create pressures on the individual responsible for conducting it. The individuals involved in the construction document review process must be fair, accurate, and consistent in their review practices. Following these philosophies will not relieve all of the political pressures applied to the construction document reviewer but will provide a means to alleviate potential conflicts and accusations of selective enforcement.

A professor at Oklahoma State University once said, "Architects do not just design buildings, they design fires." As an individual's career advances in the fire service, he or she will see just how true this statement really is. The demands on architects and builders to meet construction deadlines and to be under budget are enormous. In almost every construction situation, the owner, contractor, and architect encounter significant economic penalties if the building's scheduled completion date is missed or if additional costs are incurred that are outside the initial scope of the project.

Methods are available for contractors to ensure they complete a project within budget and on time. Unfortunately not all contractors or architects follow these methods. Some individuals will cut construction costs by using substandard material or by cutting corners and not using approved construction methods. Some builders untrained in the benefits of code requirements for certain materials to be UL listed, can improve their profit margin by substituting the type of material used. This practice can save the builder substantial costs if a product appears to be similar. The owners of the building may not be getting what they actually intended to purchase and the product will not perform as needed. A good example of this is substituting a normal caulk found in most hardware stores for caulking that is UL listed for fire-stopping. This is where the fire department's service to the owner is very beneficial.

The individuals involved in the construction document review process must be fair, accurate, and consistent.

In most situations, the owner of the building wants a safe structure, architects want to design a building that complies with codes, and the contractor wants a quality product. Fire departments can actually say, "They are working on behalf of the owner of the building." The fire department is basically a consumer advocate in this instance. Providing the owner the opportunity to learn this early in the project design process helps to establish a rapport with the owner. Keep in mind; the owner of the facility will be around to deal with the fire inspectors for years to come, long after the architect and contractor have completed their work.

The owner of a facility will be around to deal with the fire inspectors for years to come, long after the architect and contractor have completed their work.

Architects do not often see firsthand the devastation of fire and may not always comprehend the significance of constructing a building to comply with nationally recognized standards. Although architecture curriculums now cover fire safety more than they have in the past, many still do not spend a lot of time emphasizing this issue. The architects also do not have the opportunity to see the impact of a simple change of occupancy or see the implications that performance based design can have on the fire inspection process well after the building construction is complete and occupied. The building's occupancy may change from its original design, and the parameters of a performance-based design will impact the fire department throughout the life of the building.

The construction document review process is one of the few fire department activities that incorporate all three of these principles of fire prevention—education, engineering, and enforcement. Fire department personnel involved in the construction document review process educate building owners, developers, and architects on the importance of fire protection. Many times fire department personnel can explain the code's intent and the reasons for its development. They can accomplish this through comparing the occupancy under construction with similar occupancies that have had fires. Fire department personnel use engineering skills during their review of the construction documents. These skills range from reviewing site drawings to ensure fire department access to reviewing hydraulic sprinkler calculations. The enforcement of the codes and standards is the foundation of the construction review process. One reason fire department personnel participate in construction review is to ensure that buildings are designed and constructed in accordance with the codes and standards the fire department has adopted.

The Construction Document Review Team

The person responsible for fire department construction document review needs to establish a relationship with all of individuals involved in the construction document review process. These people all have vested interests in the process, and understanding them will help fire personnel to work with them as a cooperative team.

Building Officials

Building officials are involved in the construction document review process and have a number of concerns beyond compliance with the building code.

Of all the people involved in construction review, the building official's participation and close working relationship with the person responsible for fire department construction document review is the most critical. The building official is usually responsible for enforcing a building code that contains many requirements to assist and protect firefighters during a fire. The scope of the building code is to ensure the safety of a structure's occupants is provided for during fires and similar emergencies. Keep in mind that many of the model codes' requirements were developed as the result of significant fires. A major intent of the building code, which is enforced by the building official, is to prevent the spread of fire. His or her role at times parallels the role of the fire official, and sometimes their duties may overlap. The building official's role is to ensure protection of the structure's current and future occupants and owners and of the surrounding property and to oversee changes in the building design.

Insurance Rating Bureau

In some instances, the insurance rating bureau and/or insurance companies can be involved in construction document review. They have an interest in the classification of risk and evaluation of the construction to determine the insurance premiums. Many of the insurance carrier's requirements during the construction document review process will be stricter than those of the local fire or building department. The insurance requirements are based on the risk or loss potential of the building or its operation. Insurance providers develop their requirements based on national code as well as on the industry's loss experience with similar occupancies and buildings. Many times the loss potential is so great that the insurance company will require protection above and beyond the national codes.

State Fire Marshals

State fire marshals enforce codes adopted by their state. Their role in the construction document review process will vary from state to state depending on the type of occupancy and on jurisdictional constraints upon their own offices as well as upon the local fire department. State fire marshals typically are responsible for enforcement of state codes in occupancies such as state owned buildings, schools, nursing homes, and hospitals. Some state laws may exclude fire departments from having jurisdiction in these types of occupancies. In these instances, local fire departments may have the opportunity to conduct a cursory review, but the final approving authority will be the office of the state fire marshal.

Fire Department

Traditionally, municipal building departments were actively involved in construction document review, and the fire department's fire prevention role began after the building was constructed. The fire prevention codes enforced by fire departments were, and in some cases are, considered maintenance codes. Once a building is constructed, the fire department is left with enforcing the maintenance of the built-in fire protection systems and egress components. The fire department also usually is responsible for ensuring the building is used as designed. This maintenance posture does not provide adequate predesign and construction input and leads to inappropriate or poor fire protection design. For this reason, fire departments have begun to take a more aggressive and active role in development and design rather than just maintenance. Today, for a number of reasons, more fire departments have taken a larger role in construction document review process.

Becoming actively involved in the construction document review process is the best opportunity for fire departments to eliminate hazards or protect those hazards that cannot be eliminated. During this process fire department personnel can make the biggest impact on the building's overall fire protection features. The decisions made during construction document review are long lasting and most likely will be in place for the life of the building or the duration of the occupancy of the facility. It is critical, therefore, that fire departments employ individuals capable of conducting thorough and accurate construction document reviews. We have only one opportunity to ensure the building is constructed in accordance with adopted codes and standards. That opportunity is during construction document review.

> Becoming actively involved in the construction document review process is the best opportunity for fire departments to eliminate hazards or protect those hazards that cannot be eliminated.

Progressive fire departments will ensure fire department personnel are involved in the construction document review process for a number of reasons including:

- Enforcement of codes for construction practices (elimination of construction deficiencies)

- Firefighter safety

- Occupant safety

- Property conservation

- Environmental conservation

- Preincident planning

- Opportunity to build a fire prevention coalition with the owner of the facility

- Identifying performance based design criteria requiring fire department monitoring during the life of the building

Other entities that may be involved in the process as members of the construction document review team are:

- *Engineering.* The municipal civil engineering department typically has construction document review responsibility for items pertaining to drainage and easement issues. This department may also be responsible for flood control.

- *Public works.* The municipal public works department typically has review responsibility for issues such as water, sewer, roads, and improvements on the public right-of-way.

- *Zoning.* The municipal zoning department focuses on ensuring buildings and their associated uses are constructed in a permitted area zoned for such use.

- *Health.* The heath department in a municipality is typically responsible for issues that directly impact its citizens' health. This may include those health items associated with restaurants or sanitation issues.

- *City manager's office.* The city manger's office is responsible for protecting the interest of the entire municipality and will take an active role in a variety of issues.

The Construction Document Review and Permit Coordination Process

Although the procedural details of the construction document review process may vary from municipality to municipality, some elements of the process are consistent. Municipalities may have procedural guidelines on how to submit the documents for review or who is responsible for reviewing them. For instance, some municipalities have a department responsible for economic or community development that may oversee the entire construction document review process. In most municipalities, construction documents are submitted to one department and then routed for review comments to the other departments that comprise the construction document review team. The easiest way to explain a typical construction document review and permitting process is to break it down into steps as shown in **Figure 10.2**. The following sixteen steps briefly summarize how a building is constructed and how the fire department and other construction document review team members are involved.

Step 1: Determine Need

The entire construction document review process actually begins when the owner, potential owner, or occupant of a building determines the need for constructing a new building or renovating an existing building.

Step 2: Contact Design Professional

After determining a need, the owner or occupant contacts a design professional, such as an architect, to develop conceptual drawings based on that need. However, this may not always be the path owners or occupants choose. They may simply hire contractors to begin the work. This may be acceptable in some situations, but not using a design professional can delay the project. The design professional is responsible to ensure the design of the project meets all required codes and is constructed safely with quality workmanship. The architect may also monitor the construction process to ensure it is being constructed in accordance with the design. Architects also are available to solve any issues that may arise as part of the construction process. This is extremely important during renovations of existing buildings. Typically these issues become labor intensive among the AHJ, the contractor, and the designers. Architects are trained professionals and should always be used in

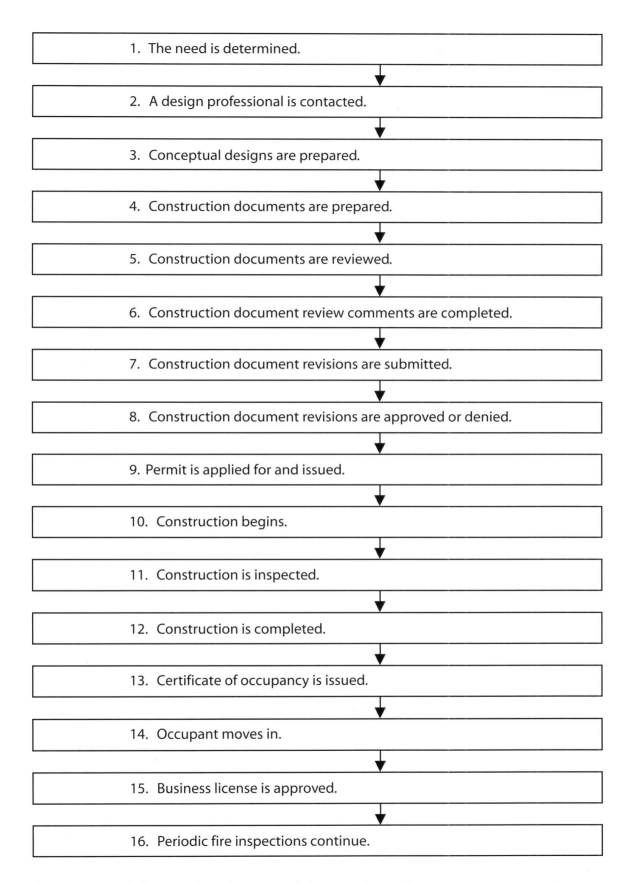

1. The need is determined.

2. A design professional is contacted.

3. Conceptual designs are prepared.

4. Construction documents are prepared.

5. Construction documents are reviewed.

6. Construction document review comments are completed.

7. Construction document revisions are submitted.

8. Construction document revisions are approved or denied.

9. Permit is applied for and issued.

10. Construction begins.

11. Construction is inspected.

12. Construction is completed.

13. Certificate of occupancy is issued.

14. Occupant moves in.

15. Business license is approved.

16. Periodic fire inspections continue.

Figure 10.2 The typical construction review and permitting process follows these sixteen steps.

Fire department personnel who are contacted by a building owner who is contemplating a renovation should always seek the advice of an architect.

✔ **conceptual design**
preliminary document that is not intended to be used for construction or permit approval

✔ **preconstruction meeting**
meeting during which the people involved in a building project review the conceptual designs

the construction process. Fire department personnel who are contacted by a building owner who is contemplating a renovation should always seek the advice of an architect.

Step 3: Preparation of Conceptual Design

The first document presented to the municipality for comment may be only a **conceptual design**. Conceptual designs are preliminary documents and are not intended to be used for construction or permit approval. These drawings may include a sketch of the site and the proposed building, along with sketches of exterior elevations and rough outlines of the interior space. Conceptual drawings typically serve as a means to facilitate a meeting of the construction document review team with the owners and their design professional. These conceptual design review meetings, or "**preconstruction meetings**," provide the architect, other design professionals, and owner the opportunity to ask the construction document review team specific questions regarding the project. The fire department can respond to the civil engineer's questions regarding fire department access needs. If a civil engineer is part of the construction document review team, other specific design questions pertaining to the actual road construction could be discussed. The preconstruction meeting is an excellent opportunity for everyone involved in the project to meet all of the individuals from the design team and construction document review team. The architects and designers benefit from such a meeting because they will reduce or eliminate design mistakes, and the construction document review team benefits because ensuring their concerns are addressed in the initial design will most likely shorten the review time.

Many times the experienced design professional understands the importance of seeking the fire department's and other review team members' input early in the design phase. Depending on the nature of the project, the fire department may comment on the conceptual site plan or the interior layout. These comments would be very preliminary and even somewhat vague. For instance, the fire department may indicate that the drawings do not reflect a fire lane along one side of the building. The interior details may not show a separate room for the fire command station. Seeking the construction document review team's input avoids project delays and begins the establishment of a working relationship. When the construction document review team can offer a service to meet with the owner and design professional before final construction documents are completed, the entire review process is most often greatly improved.

Step 4: Construction Document Submittal for Review

Fire department personnel need to review the entire construction document package. It will include:

- Architectural drawings
- Structural drawings
- Mechanical drawings

- Electrical drawings
- Site, landscaping, civil, utility drawings
- Plats
- Fire Protection Drawings
  — Sprinklers
  — Standpipes
  — Fire detection and alarm

The construction documents provide details of two types of fire protection systems, active and passive. Passive fire protection systems would include the roof, floors, walls, ceilings, doors, egress, and vegetation management. Active fire protection includes fixed fire suppression systems (such as automatic sprinklers), standpipes, special fire suppression systems, fire detection systems, and smoke control systems.

Some elements of the construction documents require more fire department involvement than others, and the construction features reviewed can vary from fire department to fire department. This variation occurs because some fire departments may only review fire suppression and fire detection related issues and leave the remaining items to another member of the construction document review team, such as the building department. Many of the items overlap in the construction document review process. This only reemphasizes the need to establish a cooperative working relationship with other construction document review team members. Such a relationship will allow the fire department to express their concerns informally to the other team members, who then can communicate the issue formally to the design professional.

Figure 10.3 Floor plans are a familiar type of architectural drawings.

Architectural Drawings

Architectural drawings provide a significant amount of detail that may require fire-department review. In some situations, the architectural drawings may be an inclusive submittal that contains all of the construction documents. However, the actual architectural drawings provide details of nonstructural elements such as fire resistive construction features, exit components, occupancy classification, occupant loads, occupant load calculations, travel distance to exits, door schedules (door details), door hardware, and

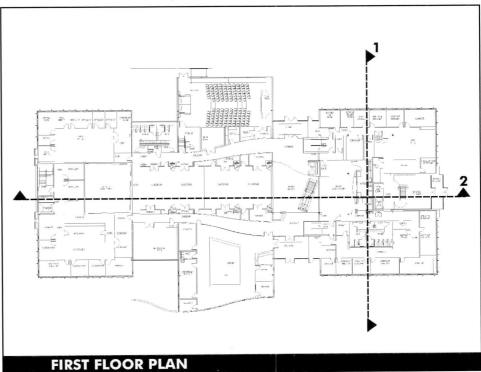

FIRST FLOOR PLAN

the building's fire suppression features. The architectural drawings do not provide the details of the fire suppression and detection systems. These are usually listed among the architectural features to be provided and submitted later.

The **floor plans** are also included in the architectural drawings (**Figure 10.3**). Floor plans indicate the room uses or occupancy of each room. Important elements such as generators, fire pump rooms, hazardous storage rooms, and transformer vaults are just some of the typical details shown on the architectural drawings. The drawings are very detailed and even show the location of furniture and equipment as well as reflected ceiling plans highlighting the locations of lighting fixtures, air ducts, and other items found on ceilings.

Fire Department's Concern During Architectural Document Reviews Comprehensive architectural drawings offer the greatest amount of construction detail. The fire department representative responsible for construction document review will spend a great deal of time reviewing the architectural drawings.

Those fire departments responsible for reviewing egress components also will spend a considerable time reviewing the architectural drawings. Fire departments are concerned with items such as the building's occupancy classification. (This classification is noted on the architectural drawings and identifies the building's intended use.) Fire departments ensure compliance with items such as flame-spread ratings for interior finishes, fire stopping details, construction of hazardous storage rooms, and details of any proposed hazardous operations.

Structural Drawings

Structural drawings provide details on how the building is put together (**Figure 10.4**). Essentially, the structural elements are the critical components of the building that hold it up or keep it from falling down. The structural drawings provide details of the load bearing walls, roof, floors, and ceilings, structural steel, and other components.

✔ **floor plan**
detailed drawing that indicates the dimensions and use of each room structural drawing drawing that provides details on how a building is put together

✔ **structural drawing**
drawing that provides details on how a building is put together

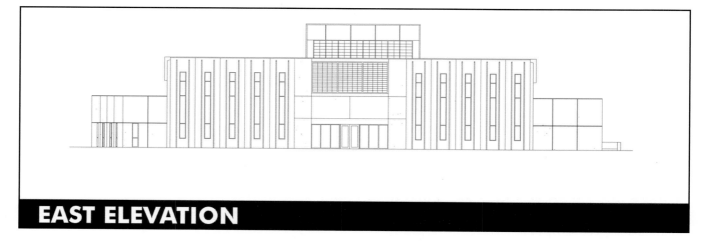

EAST ELEVATION

Figure 10.4 Three types of construction drawings are (a) elevation views, (b) section views, and (c) detail views. *All three courtesy of C. H. Guernsey & Company*

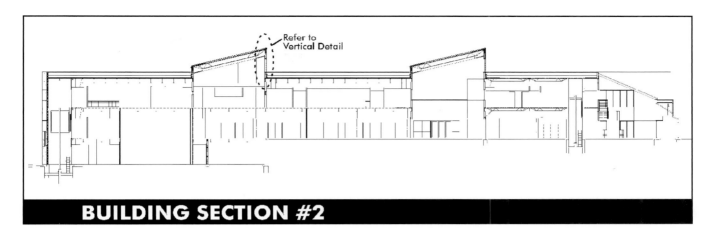

BUILDING SECTION #2

Refer to
Vertical Detail

Figure 10.4b

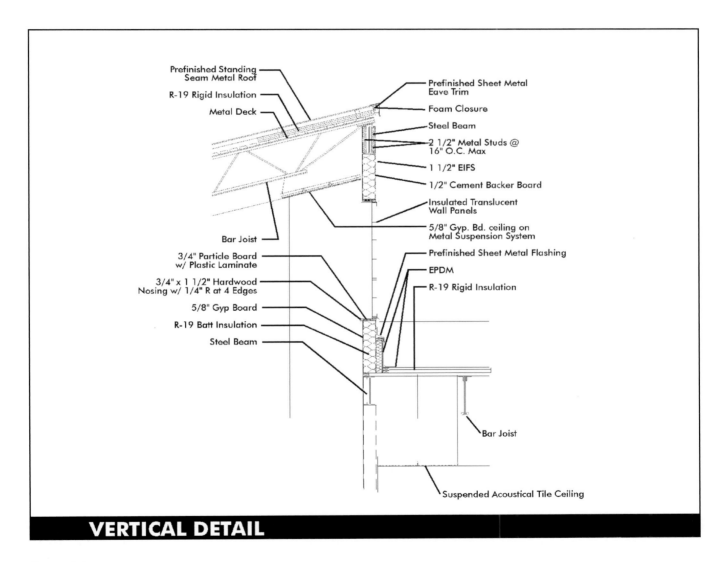

Prefinished Standing
Seam Metal Roof

R-19 Rigid Insulation

Metal Deck

Prefinished Sheet Metal
Eave Trim

Foam Closure

Steel Beam

2 1/2" Metal Studs @
16" O.C. Max

1 1/2" EIFS

1/2" Cement Backer Board

Insulated Translucent
Wall Panels

5/8" Gyp. Bd. ceiling on
Metal Suspension System

Bar Joist

3/4" Particle Board
w/ Plastic Laminate

3/4" x 1 1/2" Hardwood
Nosing w/ 1/4" R at 4 Edges

5/8" Gyp Board

R-19 Batt Insulation

Steel Beam

Prefinished Sheet Metal Flashing

EPDM

R-19 Rigid Insulation

Bar Joist

Suspended Acoustical Tile Ceiling

VERTICAL DETAIL

Figure 10.4c

Fire Department's Concern During Structural Document Reviews Fire departments review construction drawings for code compliance as well as for preincident planning and firefighter safety. Elements of the structural documents pertain to both firefighter safety and preincident planning. Fire department personnel will review items shown on the structural drawings, such as firewalls, parapets, openings in walls, roof construction, and type of construction and roof access. These passive fire protection elements are critical during a fire. When a fire does occur, this type of information can help the fire officer make tactical decisions and determine how long to continue an interior fire attack or whether to place firefighters on the roof for ventilation duties.

Mechanical Drawings

The mechanical drawings reflect many of the elements of the building's mechanical systems, such as plumbing, heating, air conditioning, and sometimes specialty features such as refrigeration, compressed air, oxygen systems, inert gas systems, swimming pools, kitchen hood exhaust, or others (**Figure 10.5**). In some instances, the mechanical drawings show the building's fire suppression system. For the purpose of this section and for clarity, we will consider the fire protection drawings to be a separate document.

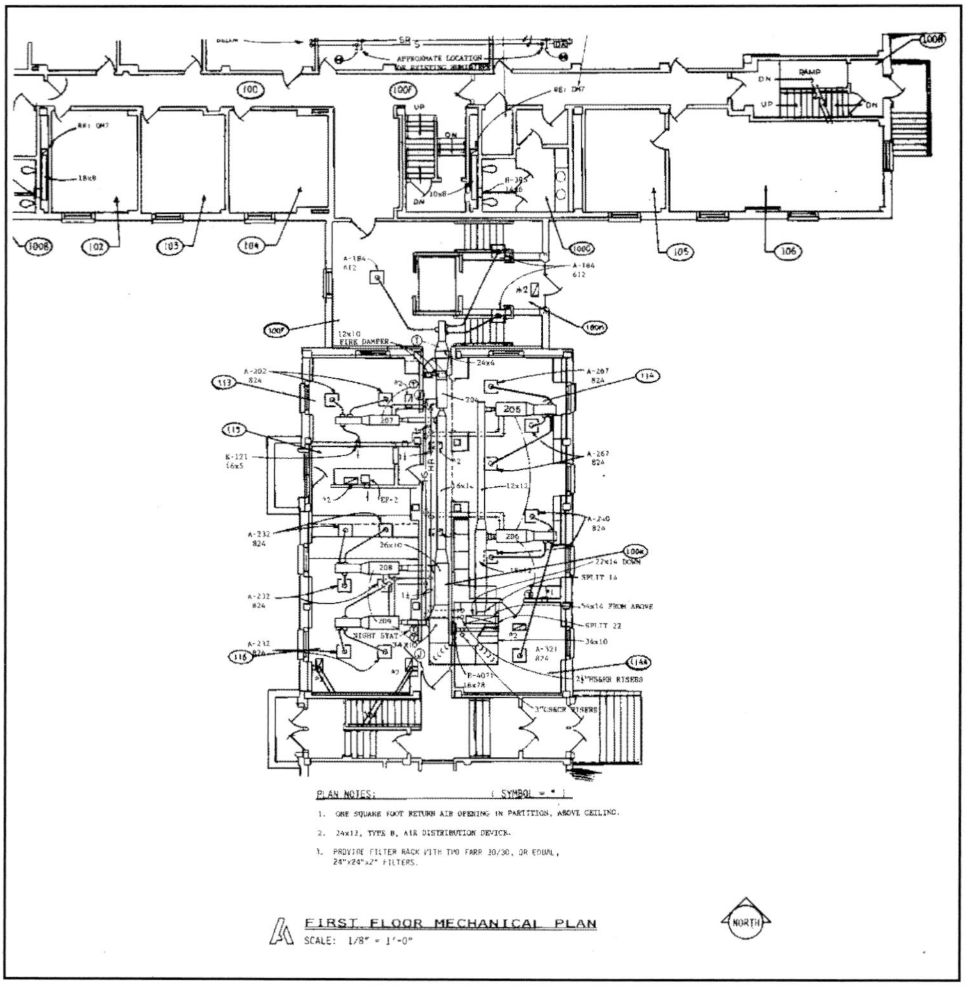

✔ **mechanical drawing**
drawing that indicates the elements of the building's mechanical systems, such as plumbing, heating, air conditioning, etc.

Figure 10.5 A typical mechanical plan.

Fire Department's Concern During Mechanical Document Reviews Some items on mechanical drawings significantly affect fire fighting activities, and fire departments must consider them even if mechanical reviews are not among their responsibilities. For example, the building's ductwork may contain provisions for smoke removal or smoke control. The ability to control a building's ventilation system can be critical to mitigating structural fires, particularly in large buildings, such as malls or high-rises.

Another important element on most mechanical drawings is the building's plumbing details. Fire departments will review the plumbing details if the building has automatic fire sprinkler protection. The water service that supplies the automatic sprinkler protection is shown on the building's plumbing drawings. Other automatic sprinkler details, such as the backflow prevention device, may also be shown on the plumbing details.

Examination of the various mechanical and plumbing chases that run throughout the building also provides invaluable information on how fire or products of combustion may travel or affect the rest of the building.

Electrical Drawings

The electrical drawings reflect the details of the building's electrical system (**Figure 10.6**). The power supply for the building and the associated wiring diagrams are typical details in these drawings. Some electrical drawings include the building's fire alarm drawings. This is typically done for subcontractor bids rather than for formal fire detection and alarm system reviews. Since this is not normal practice, we will discuss fire alarm drawings in further detail later in this chapter when we explain the fire protection drawing submittal.

✔ **electrical drawing**
drawing that reflects the details of the building's electrical system

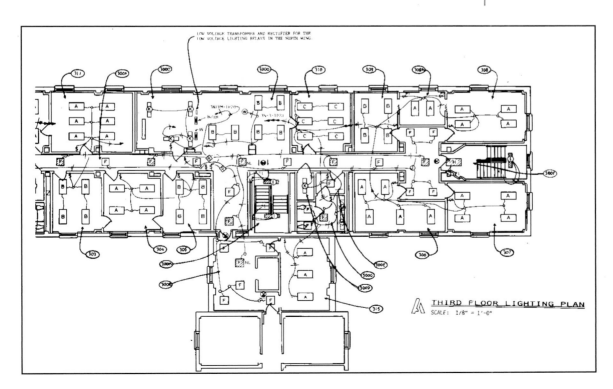

Figure 10.6 A common electrical system drawing.

Fire Department's Concern During Electrical Document Reviews The fire department may review the electrical drawing details pertaining to the installation of the electrical fire pump, emergency generator, emergency lighting, exit lighting, egress lighting, and location of transformer vaults. Fire department personnel assigned to construction document reviews typically do not have the expertise of an electrical engineer. However, they need an understanding of how to locate these items' location on electrical drawings and must understand basic electrical drawing symbols and details.

For larger complex facilities or those with special electrical systems, fire department personnel assigned to the construction document review should seek the assistance of the team member who is responsible for the comprehensive electrical review. The National Electrical Code, which is adopted by many municipalities, is a published by the National Fire Protection Association.

Site, Landscaping, Civil, and Utility Drawings

✔ **site drawing**
drawing that indicates a variety of details concerning topography, landscaping, and civil engineering details

The site drawings for the building are composed of a variety of details pertaining to a number of areas (**Figure 10.7**). Most details on the site plan concern civil engineering. For example, the site plan will include details pertaining to the grade of the land for storm water retention and detention needs. Road construction details are included as part of the building's site plan as well. Details pertaining to the building's utilities such as water, sewer, natural gas, and electrical supply from the public utility are shown on the building's site plans.

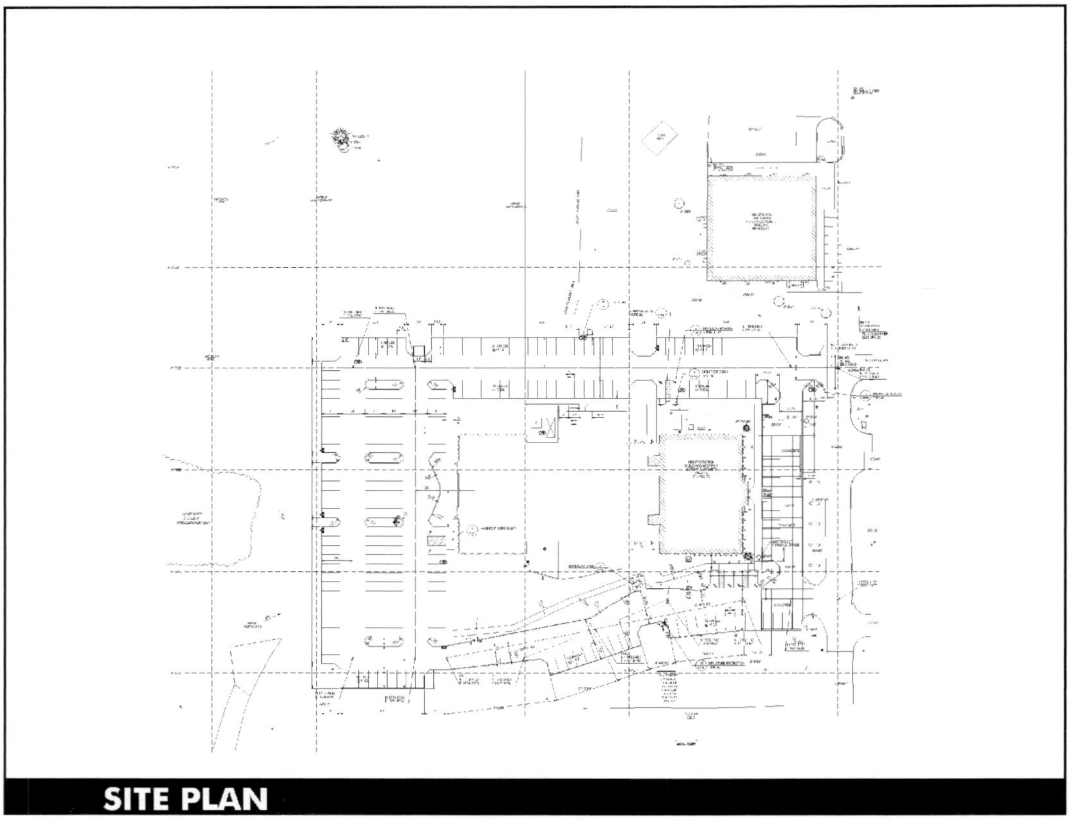

SITE PLAN

Figure 10.7 A site plan. *Courtesy of C. H. Guernsey & Company*

The site plan also shows comprehensive details of the topography of the land and site of the facility including the landscaping features. The only building details shown are the structure's shape and location on the site. Although the site plan does not reflect any building construction details, it does contain two of the most critical elements of the building's fire protection features, access and water supply. Fire departments must be provided with the necessary tools to do their job in an emergency. Those tools include access to the building and an adequate water supply. It is important that newly constructed buildings contain these features. Fire department personnel should not be hindered by poor access to the building or an inadequate water supply.

Fire Department's Concern During Site Document Reviews The fire department will focus on fire department access, hydrant locations, and vegetation management. During the review of the site drawings, details such as street widths, dead-end streets, and turning radius all pertain significantly to the fire department's access. In addition to building access, considerations may include access to fire hydrants, ponds or other bodies of water, and fire department sprinkler or standpipe connections. During this portion of the review process, the fire department may determine that the building needs fire lanes to ensure fire department access during an emergency operation. The person responsible for the construction document review should understand the fire department's apparatus to ensure that access will be adequate to accommodate them; fire lanes are of no benefit unless fire department personnel and their apparatus can use them.

Another important aspect of the site drawings is the utility details pertaining to the water supply and hydrants. The fire department will review the documents to ensure the provision of an adequate number of hydrants designed in accordance with the adopted codes. The fire department may consider discussing the water supply details with the Insurance Service Organization (ISO). The Insurance Service Organization evaluates the water supply as part of its grading of the municipality. The required fire flow for the structure determines the size of the water mains. Here it is important to consider not only the proposed structure undergoing construction document reviews but future structures anticipated as well. Fire department personnel need to work closely with the construction document review team's civil engineering and public works members. They review the site plans in great detail and can offer expertise in areas pertaining to road construction and utility installation.

Other important features involve the landscape plan, which can be part of or separate from the site plan. This is particularly important if the building is within the wildland/urban interface. Vegetation, landscaping materials, steep slopes, grade, and so forth all play parts. For example, if you are looking at a large apartment or town home plan, rescue may be severely hampered if slope and vegetation prevent the placement of ground ladders. The ability to advance handlines for fire suppression must also be considered, particularly if a wall is blocking access.

From a wildlands fire perspective, vegetation types and proximity to the structure are very important. This may involve examining the slope adjacent to the structure. In some cases when the structure is located high on the property, 200 feet of clear space or well-managed vegetation may be necessary if possible. Other issues may be the types of trees, proximity of bushes and shrubs, and so forth. It may also be beneficial to suggest the types of plants best suited for planting, such as those that are high in water content and naturally resistant to fire. The proximity of decks to combustible vegetation is also important.

Plats

Plats are legal documents prepared by a land surveyor. They contain the legal description of the property as well as any legally binding easements (**Figure 10.8**). The dimensions of the lot lines are shown along with the associated property lines.

✔ **plat**
legal document illustrating the legal description of a property as well as any legally binding easements

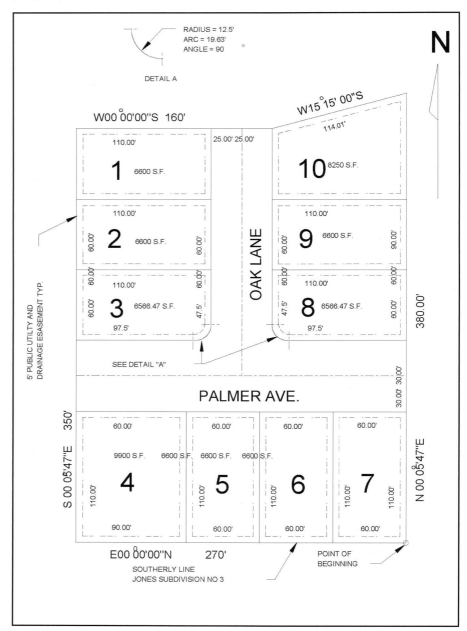

Figure 10.8 A typical plat.

Fire Department's Concern During Plat Document Reviews The fire department should review the plat to ensure that it reflects any easements pertaining to fire department access. When property is being subdivided to construct additional buildings, the fire department may review the plat to assess the new structures' impact on the department's ability to access the site and provide fire protection. In some situations, the plat may reflect existing farmland subdivided into a major development that will have many implications on the fire department's ability to provide service.

✔ **fire protection drawing**
drawing that indicates the systems and elements pertaining to a building's fire protection systems

Fire Protection Drawings

The fire protection drawing submittal will contain a variety of different systems and elements pertaining to the building's fire protection systems (**Figure 10.9**). The types of fire protection drawings submitted may include the following:

- *Sprinklers.* Detailed drawings and calculations pertaining to the building's automatic sprinkler system and fire pump where applicable. Sprinkler piping details, sprinkler locations, and sprinkler riser details are all reflected on the sprinkler drawings. Depending on the design of the sprinkler system, fire pump details may also be reflected on the sprinkler drawings.

- *Standpipes.* Detailed drawings and calculations pertaining to the building's standpipe system. They show the system's piping arrangement and hose valve locations. Depending on the design of the standpipe system, they may also show fire pump details.

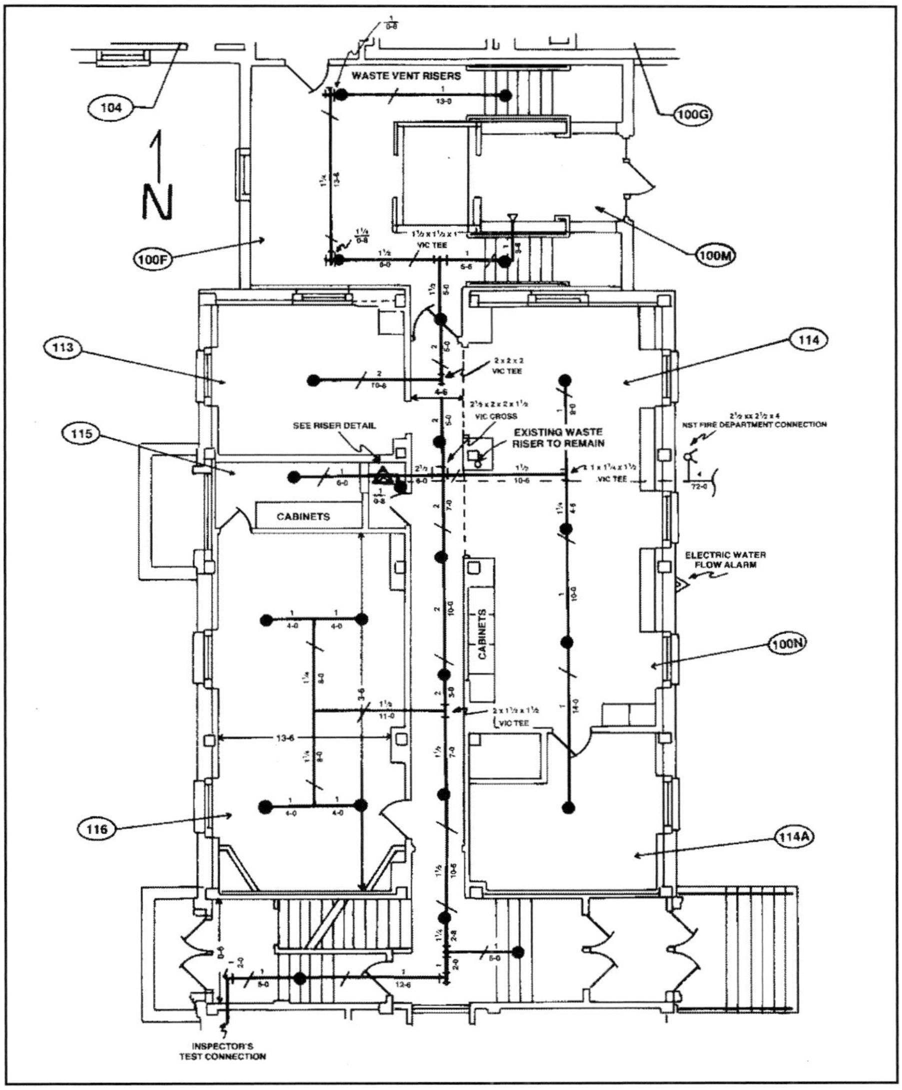

Figure 10.9 A sprinkler system drawing.

- *Detection and alarm.* Detailed drawings and calculations of fire detection initiating devices and indicating devices including power load and performance and battery calculations. These drawings will show location and placement of devices, types, numbers, and the like.

Fire Department's Concern During Fire Protection Document Reviews The fire department may have the greatest involvement in the review of fire protection drawings. The review will focus on the drawings' compliance with the adopted codes, standards, and ordinances. The National Fire Protection Association publishes fire codes pertaining to fire protection systems. In addition to reviewing the fire protection construction documents for compliance, the fire department will need to review the location of the fire protection system components, such as sprinkler risers, fire alarm control panel, and voice evacuation panel. The location of these system components must accommodate fire department operations. For instance, most fire departments will enter the front of the building for fire alarm activation. Ensuring that the fire alarm panel or a remote annunciator is in the front entrance of the building will help responding personnel locate the fire alarm panel.

Step 5: Construction Document Review

Taking part in the construction document review provides the fire department the opportunity to ensure that newly constructed or renovated buildings meet the adopted codes. Because the construction document review is one aspect of code enforcement that can create conflict, it must be performed in a precise and systematic fashion. Fire department personnel responsible for reviewing construction documents must be able to read blueprints, be knowledgeable of the adopted codes, and be able to communicate fire department concerns professionally and diplomatically. Many fire departments employ fire protection engineers to review their construction drawings. In some municipalities, an outside agency or third party performs the construction document review.

Step 6: Generating Construction Document Review Comments

After the construction documents have been reviewed, the next step is to communicate the results to the owner, tenant, design professional, general contractor, and key construction document review team members. Again, individual design team members often have overlapping responsibilities. For example, a review of hydrant placement may have some impact on the public works review team member. Depending on the nature and scope of the project, communicating the review comments to the entire construction document review team may be prudent. Some organizations send all of the review comments from every team member as a single communication. This may work for some municipalities but not for all.

Most important is to communicate the results of the construction document review in writing. The review comments must be clear and concise to enable the design professional to respond if requested. An effective review comment will identify the following three elements:

1. The deficiency. What is the problem with document under review?

2. The code and code section of the deficiency. Where can the design professional go to find more information?

3. What is needed to correct the deficiency. What must the design professional do?

The review comments will also indicate if the construction drawings have

Because the construction document review can create conflict, it must be performed precisely and systematically.

The results of the construction document review must be communicated in writing.

been approved for permit or if they have been denied and must be resubmitted. If there are no review comments, this should also be communicated. Many fire departments will include the code requirements for ensuring the fire department is present for witnessing the acceptance testing of any fire protection systems.

Just how important an effective preconstruction meeting can be becomes apparent during the development of the construction document review comments. If the design professional and other individuals associated with the project have had the opportunity to discuss the project and meet the review team, many of the review comments will have been addressed in the submittal. If either the design professional or review team members have concerns, they then can contact an individual from the preconstruction meetings to help answer their questions. Many times the ability to communicate verbally can reduce the bureaucratic snares associated with the construction document review process. If the issue is resolved verbally, it should be noted as such in the construction document review process. This will avoid potential conflict in the future. Documentation is very important.

Rest assured, communication breakdown will always result in poor product and time delays and will likely upset customers and staff. Make every effort to communicate as effectively and completely as possible.

> Communication breakdown will always result in poor product and time delays and will likely upset customers and staff.

Step 7: Construction Document Revision Submittal

If the construction documents are not approved for permit, then the design professional may have to submit revised drawings and begin the review process again at Step 4. This typically means that the designer will get the plans back with appropriate comments and notes as well as a rejection notice or stamp of some type. The designer must then address the discrepancies, make the necessary changes or provide the missing information, and resubmit the plans. Keep in mind, generally speaking, the fire department's job is not to design but to review and ultimately to approve the design.

Step 8: Construction Document Revision Approval or Denial

When the construction documents have been approved, review comments are generated that indicate approval for the permit. In some cases, the construction documents may have been conditionally approved, or what we term "red lined." This may include approval based on trust and assurance that appropriate changes will be made, or it may be based on an item's being addressed at a future date prior to completion of the project.

Step 9: Permit Application and Issuance

When all of the construction document review team members have approved the construction of the project, a permit will be issued allowing work to begin. The format of permits varies from municipality to municipality. Some jurisdictions issue a separate permit for individual construction stages or

The fire sprinkler work being conducted on this site is covered by

BUILDING PERMIT

Address   Permit Number

Contractor   Owner

WARNING

No building, structure, or portion thereof shall be used or occupied until all the provisions of the Village Code have been complied with and a Certificate of Occupancy issued.

Any person who occupies or permits occupancy is in violation of this law and is subject to a fine up to $500 per day (Section 21.217 of the Mount Prospect Municipal Code).

THIS NOTICE SHALL REMAIN POSTED UNTIL THE CERTIFICATE OF OCCUPANCY HAS BEEN ISSUED.

Call (847) 818-5253 forty-eight hours in advance to schedule necessary inspections.

Figure 10.10 A permit to begin construction of a building.

systems. For example, **Figure 10.10** reflects a permit to begin construction of the building. **Figure 10.11** shows a permit to begin the installation of the automatic sprinkler system. Most municipalities assess fees with building permits. They may range from development fees to construction document review fees. Once the fees are paid, a permit is issued for construction.

Step 10: Construction Begins

The fire department's involvement does not stop when the construction documents have been approved and a permit has been issued. Fire departments will continue to be involved with the project while it is under construction. Assurance that water supplies are provided as soon as combustible materials are present or construction is started is one example. The fire department will want to ensure they have access to the construction site should the need arise for emergency personnel to respond to the site. If the review process has successfully identified items to be corrected, very few changes for noncompliance should be needed during construction. Prewire tests, prehydrostatic tests, or any number of other inspections may also be required before the real "guts" of the construction inspection take place. Familiarity with the facility by stations and engine companies is also an important aspect to be considered.

STILLWATER
1895
Heritage • Service • Pride

PERMIT CERTIFICATE

Date / Time: 09/08/04   08:32

Occupancy Name: Headquarters Fire Station

Address: 1506 S Main ST
Stillwater, OK 74074

Phone:

The following permit has been issued:

Permit No. 001280

Issued To: John Doe, USA Sprinkler Company

Type: SP INST. Automatic Fire Sprinkler Installation (New)

Issued: 09/08/04

Effective: 10/08/04

Expiration: 10/08/04

It is the contractor's responsibility to ensure that conditions are in accordance with applicable State and Local Fire Codes and Standards. Please contact Stillwater Fire Department for more information.

_____   **Date**

Installer / Contractor:

_____   **Date**

Inspector: Trent Hawkins

* This permit must be available on-site while inspection, testing, or maintenance is being performed.

Office of the Fire Marshal · 1510 South Main Street · Stillwater, OK 74074
Phone (405) 742-8308   Fax (405) 747-8050

Figure 10.11 A permit to begin the installation of an automatic sprinkler system. *Courtesy of Stillwater, OK Fire Department*

Step 11: Construction Inspection

While the building is under construction, fire department personnel as well as the other construction document review team members will conduct a variety of inspections. On-site fire inspections ensure the construction site is safe from fire and verify the work being performed conforms to the approved drawings. Most municipalities require a job copy or approved copy of the construction documents to remain on the construction site. If a discrepancy should arise between what is being constructed and what was approved, the fire inspector can view the approved set of construction documents as well as the construction document review letter. Conflicts can arise during the inspection of the facility while it is under construction. The field conditions may have necessitated changes that were not noted on the drawings, such as as-built issues or changes from the initial design. If the contractor or design professional did not consult the construction document review team prior to making the changes, there may be issues to address later that can cause project delays and escalate construction costs. This is just one of the many reasons that frequently visiting the construction site is important and conducive to the project's progress. The construction site visits also allow the parties involved to discuss issues that may have arisen. The fire department as well as other members of the construction document review team may need to inspect parts of systems before they are concealed behind walls or ceilings. This is especially true for some components of the fire protection systems.

The last inspection performed is the final acceptance testing of the fire protection systems. The fire department does not conduct the acceptance tests. They are performed by the contractors with the fire department as a witness. The fire protection system installer is responsible for conducting the tests. The fire protection system installer should have conducted troubleshooting tests before contacting the fire department to come and witness the final test. The fire protection system installation should be 100 percent complete when the contractor asks the fire department to be present at an acceptance test.

Step 12: Construction Complete

When construction is completed the fire department and other members of the inspection or construction document review team may be called to conduct a final inspection. The final inspection will verify the project was completed according to the approved drawings. If the fire department had not visited the site as indicated in Step 11, there could be a number of very costly issues to address after the work is completed.

Step 13: Certificate of Occupancy Issued

A certificate of occupancy is issued to the occupant when the building has been determined to be safe to occupy and has been inspected to meet the code requirements. The certificate of occupancy ensures the building's fire protection features are operable. This is typically issued by the building department.

On-site fire inspections ensure the construction site is safe from fire and verify the work being performed conforms to the approved drawings.

Step 14: Occupant Moves In

The occupants can move into the building once they have received the certificate of occupancy. In some situations occupants move into the facility prior to final approval by the municipality. These occupants may face legal action by the municipality. Moving into a building without final approval from the municipality is an unsafe practice. On some occasions, temporary certificates of occupancy may be issued to allow this, but typically only after all fire/life safety systems are installed and tested.

Step 15: Business License Approval

Some municipalities require occupants of commercial occupancies to obtain a license to conduct business. The requirements for when and if a business license is required will vary from one municipality to another.

Step 16: Periodic Fire Inspections

When the building has been completed and occupied, periodic fire inspections are conducted to ensure modifications have not been made without the benefit of the construction document review process and to identify any changes in hazards associated with the operation of the facility. The frequency of the periodic inspections will vary depending on the hazard and its potential to cause large loss of property or life. The documentation generated in the construction document review process becomes a very useful reference source for fire inspectors when they conduct their periodic inspections.

Significance of a Good Construction Document Review Process

One of the most important aspects of the construction document review process is to ensure the building is constructed in accordance with the adopted codes, standards, and ordinances. Periodic fire inspections are needed to ensure the building and its operation continue to meet the fire codes. It is expected that the owner of the facility will need to make changes to both the building and the operation of the building. In fact, during the life of the structure a variety of uses may take place in the building. With this in mind, providing thorough documentation is paramount to enable any member of the fire prevention bureau to determine what the building was originally designed to be used for and what fire protection systems were provided. We know that sprinklers have a success rate of over 96 percent. One reason for the limited failures that do occur is that the system is not designed specifically for the hazard it protects. This usually does not result from an error in the construction document review process but from a change in occupancy.

What is important for anyone in the construction document review process is to create sufficient documentation to revisit the project in 10 or 15 years and clearly understand the code requirements when the building was constructed based upon its original design. When fire department personnel become active in the construction document review process, they have the opportunity to build a relationship with the building owner or tenant. This should be a positive relationship that lays the foundation for building a part-

> The construction document review process should create sufficient documentation to revisit the project in 10 or 15 years and clearly understand the code requirements when the building was constructed based upon its original design.

nership in fire prevention. The contractor will leave the site after the project is complete, but the owner or tenant will be involved with the fire department during fire inspections for years to come.

Summary

The fire department's role in construction document review is another essential component of its overall fire prevention efforts. The construction document review provides an opportunity for the fire department to begin building a fire prevention coalition with the owners of the building. It also offers an opportunity to identify potential hazards and risks that will impact the safety of the occupants and the firefighters who may be called there in the middle of the night to mitigate an emergency incident.

The fire department is part of a team of individuals with a vested interest in the construction document review process. The individuals may include representatives from the city manager's office, public works, building department, zoning department, economic development department, engineering department, and many others depending on the size of the project and the organizational structure of the municipality. The fire department provides input to an array of construction documents that may include site or civil drawings, zoning drawings, plats, architectural drawings, mechanical drawings, fire protection drawings, and electrical and mechanical drawings.

For the construction document review process to prove successful, all of the parties involved must work together during the developmental process that begins with the conceptual drawing and ends with the occupant obtaining a business license. An important element for fire departments to remember during the construction document review process is that the building's occupants as well as firefighters will rely heavily on the effectiveness of its life safety features long after the first certificate of occupancy is issued. As part of the construction document review process, the fire department will help to ensure the life safety features are in place during construction. The final step of the construction document review process is to ensure the fire and life safety features are maintained by conducting fire inspections at the facility for the life of the building.

Chapter 10 Review Exercises

10.1 Explain the fire department's role in the plan review process and why it is important. _____

_____

_____

_____

_____

_____

_____

_____

10.2 Identify three individuals who may have a vested interest in the construction document review process and explain why they would be involved in construction document review. _____

_____

_____

_____

_____

10.3 Identify five reasons why fire departments are involved in construction document review.

_____   _____

_____   _____

_____

10.4 List each type of drawing typically found in the construction document review package and describe the fire department's possible concerns with each. _____

_____

_____

_____

_____

_____

_____

_____

_____

10.6 What are preconstruction meetings? _____

_____

_____

_____

10.7 Why are preconstruction meetings beneficial? _____

_____

_____

_____

_____

10.8 What is the intent of conceptual drawings? _____

_____

_____

_____

_____

10.9 What is a certificate of occupancy? _____

_____

_____

10.10 What three elements must good plan review or construction review comments have? _____

_____

_____

_____

_____

10.11 What are fire protection drawings? _____

_____

_____

_____

10.12 What are the steps in a thorough development review process?

_____

_____

_____

_____

_____

_____

_____

_____

_____

_____

_____

_____

_____

_____

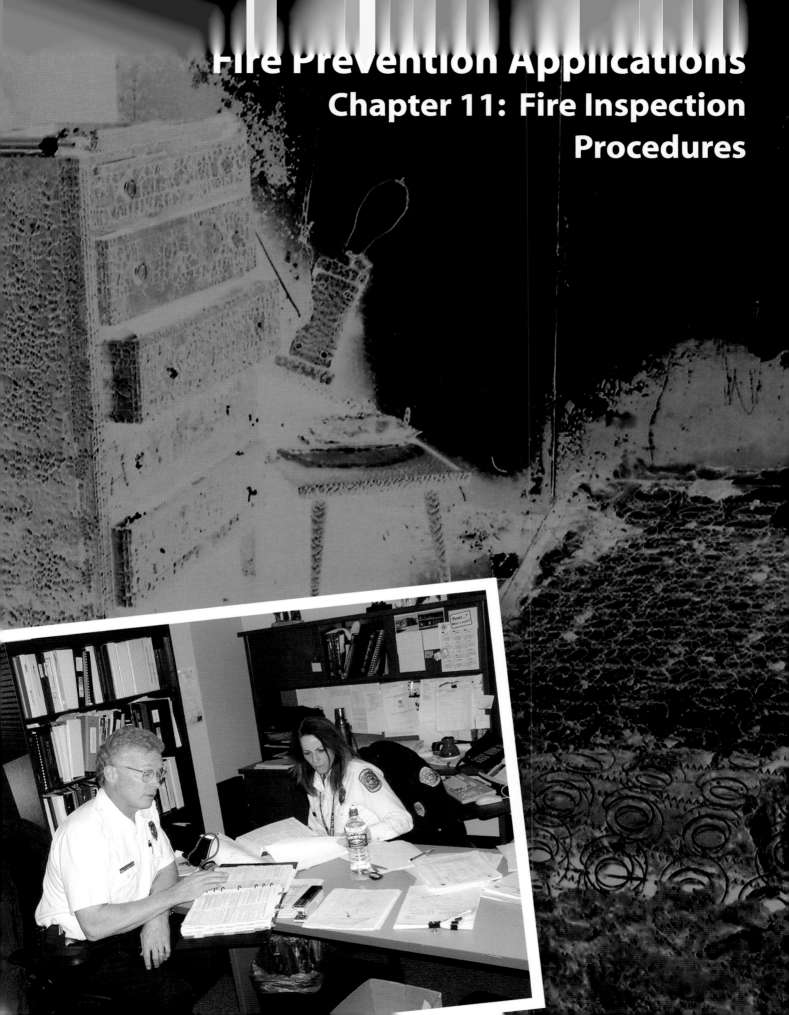

FESHE COURSE OBJECTIVES

1. Identify the goal of a fire inspection program.
2. Define the elements of a fire inspection.
3. Identify methods to conduct a fire inspection.
4. Determine what constitutes a "good fire inspection."
5. Identify methods for compliance of inspection findings.

Chapter 11

Fire Inspection Procedures

Why Conduct Fire Inspections?

One of the fundamental tasks of a fire prevention bureau is to conduct fire inspections. When the term fire prevention bureau is mentioned, the average citizen usually thinks of fire inspections. The purpose of conducting fire inspections is not to write violations or issue citations for court appearances. Two of the primary reasons for fire inspections are to identify and correct hazards or conditions that could cause a fire to start or contribute to the fire's spread and to determine conditions that will endanger occupants and firefighters during a fire. Once these conditions have been identified, they are then communicated to the property representative in a manner conducive to educating the individual, not reprimanding him or her. Fire inspections are a means to educate the general public on the importance of fire prevention and to eliminate hazards or conditions that will contribute to the development or spread of fire. You should view them as a service provided to the community by the fire department, and you should conduct them in the same manner that anyone would provide any other excellent service to a customer.

> Two primary reasons for fire inspections are (1) to identify and correct hazards or conditions that could cause a fire or contribute to its spread and (2) to determine conditions that will endanger occupants and firefighters during a fire.

The ability to explain the history or the reasoning behind determining that a condition is unsafe helps to make the occupant understand the danger. In most cases, once fair-minded people understand the reasons, they have an easier time addressing the issue. Nobody likes to do anything just because a code book says so! Not that fire prevention is an easy sell; it can definitely be tough at times. Simple things such as using the term deficiency instead of violation may help achieve compliance. Whenever you can, always try to keep word choices positive rather than negative. Keep in mind, what you do and say will impact the safety not only of the occupant but of visitors to the occupancy and of the firefighters who will be called there in the middle of the night to extinguish a fire or deal with any other emergency.

Everyone presumes that when they enter a commercial building it is safe to do so. The citizens rely on safe buildings just as they rely on a fire engine or ambulance to be available to take care of their emergency needs.

Implementing Inspections

How does a fire department begin to conduct fire inspections? The establishment of a fire inspection program may result when the fire department's governing body (city government, for example) annexes property or when a fire department's strategic planning identifies the need to take a more active role in fire prevention by conducting fire inspections. Whether the fire department is new to the art of fire inspections or has been conducting them for some time, one thing is certain: the fire inspector must be professional and credible in the performance of his or her duties.

Do not think of the term professional in the sense of whether a firefighter is paid or volunteer but in the sense of performance. Many "professional" fire inspectors in volunteer fire departments conduct inspections without pay. The fire inspector in the 21st century will continue to evolve into one of the most technically competent and professional members of the fire service. The number of fire inspectors and the amount of fire prevention activity within fire departments will likely increase throughout the 21st century. More fire department personnel will likely take an active role in fire prevention as the importance and successes of fire prevention activities are emphasized. They probably will perform these functions in addition to their suppression or emergency medical service duties. One thing is certain, it does not matter whether you are a volunteer, paid firefighter, full-time or part-time inspector, sworn or civilian; conducting fire inspections is one of the fire department's most important functions and must be taken seriously. The success of fire inspections is at times difficult to measure, but they must be conducted thoroughly and accurately just as a paramedic would provide emergency medical treatment to a patient. Many still argue the value of fire prevention activities, inspections specifically, cannot be measured. We propose that you determine the net worth of your community, which includes all structures and property that could conceivably be destroyed by fire. Tax rolls will provide this data. From that total subtract the amount of fire loss you incurred last year. The difference is the amount your fire prevention and mitigation efforts saved your community in the previous year. If anyone disagrees, tell them to prove you wrong. They cannot prove you wrong any more than you can prove them right.

Step 1: Analyze

Why are we starting a fire prevention inspection program? Chapter 4 discusses the need for the fire prevention bureau to be involved in the fire department's strategic planning process and to ensure that fire prevention activities are part of the overall mission of the organization. One of the fundamental planning steps is to determine the level of service to be provided. This is most effectively done through the policy makers who oversee the government entity. These officials may be either elected or appointed.

The establishment of the fire inspection program must be derived from the need to provide the service. This need may have been recognized as a result of the strategic planning process or a catastrophic loss. A fire inspection program should not be used for revenge, for political motives, or for selective enforcement. The inspection program must be established for the protection of the community served by the fire department.

Step 2: Determine the Enforceable Regulations

The first step in establishing a fire prevention inspection program is to identify the laws that assign the fire department the duty to conduct fire inspections. The fire department's authority may originate from local or state government agencies (see Chapter 3). Once the fire department has determined its authority to conduct inspections, the next logical step is to learn what codes and standards can be enforced (**Figure 11.1**). The codes are the inspector's rulebook. A look at the codes adopted by the governing entity may reveal they are not the most recent editions published. Or it may be discovered that there are less stringent state or federal codes that can be enforced. This may require the fire department to adopt a different edition of the code, another code, or a combination of both with amendments. (This is something that could be brought forward at the next fire department strategic planning meeting!) For the purpose of this discussion the code itself is not necessarily as important as what is or is not enforceable.

The fire inspection program must be established for the protection of the community served by the fire department.

Figure 11.1 Various books, codes, and standards will be required to provide proper guidance and legal enforcement.

Step 3: Determine Inspector's Level of Training

The next step is to determine the level of training required for conducting inspections. The National Fire Protection Association offers courses on-line that individuals can complete at their own pace. *Fire Inspection and Code Enforcement*, sixth edition, published by Fire Protection Publications (Oklahoma State University), is an excellent resource for learning about fire inspections and code enforcement. The principles of this text create a foundation for the inspector or fire prevention bureau manager to build upon. Many junior colleges and professional organizations offer courses and seminars in code enforcement.

Conducting a fire inspection for the first time in any occupancy takes time and extra effort. This is true even if other inspectors have inspected the occupancy previously. An inspector may conduct a fire inspection and identify conditions that are in violation of the adopted codes. The condition may have existed for years without being identified by previous inspectors. Situations like this make educating the occupant about the severity of the deficiency difficult. If it was not serious enough for other inspectors to identify, how does it become serious now? This should also be a good indication to the fire prevention manager that previous inspector training was inadequate. Depending on the severity of the deficiency, the occupant may not be able to correct the problem immediately, and the inspector should be prepared to allow a reasonable amount of time. Having the ability to explain why correcting a problem is important will help significantly in having the occupant remedy the deficiency and in establishing good will.

> The ability to explain why correcting a problem is important will help significantly in having the occupant remedy the deficiency and in establishing good will.

For example, the Life Safety Code requires exits to be enclosed with rated walls and doors. If the occupant of a building removed the doors on a basement exit stair entry to move material easily to a storage area in the basement, an inspector might assume this was approved as part of the construction process and is acceptable. More inspections might occur without ever identifying or correcting the deficiency. When a new inspector visited the occupancy and identified this condition as a deficiency, the owner/manager might be upset that it was not previously identified. Instead of confronting the occupant, the inspector could offer to research the question and get back to the owner. The inspector then would determine that doors were originally required by code and installed. Upon returning to the occupancy, the inspector should explain why the doors are needed: they would prevent fire spread from the basement to the second floor; they would provide a safe passage for the occupants to exit; and they would ensure firefighters had an enclosed and protected area in which to extinguish a fire. The inspector now has explained the dangers of the deficiency and the benefits of correcting it instead of just reciting verbiage from the code book or giving the impression of enforcing some made up version of the code. It may take time to have the violation corrected but the end result will be compliance.

Remember too that inspections provide an opportunity to educate (remember, be careful with that word) or make others aware of what you are trying to do as a fire service professional. "Sell" your issues. It is easy be a badge-heavy thug and make people do things just because you can. Don't do that! Find issues that need to be corrected, explain why correcting them is important, and be flexible when you can. Remember, any time you put pen to paper or open your mouth, you are costing this business owner money. It is one thing to tell warehouse owners they have to take down the top row of crates because they are stacked too close to the ceiling. It is quite another for the owners to lose over a third of their inventory capacity. We are not saying that you should not enforce the code but that you should think about what you are doing. Sell the reasons for the requirements. Sometimes the decision needs to be shared by more than just you and the business owner. Work with your clients, don't browbeat them. You have authority and responsibility, but you must not abuse your position.

The goals of the fire inspection are to ensure the building is safer than when the inspector entered it and in compliance with the adopted codes and to educate, or increase the awareness of, the public about fire safety practices. Achieving these goals may not happen overnight. Educating the occupant about practicing fire safety can help to ensure the property owner/manager will eliminate potential hazards without requiring the fire inspector's presence. If the occupants gain an understanding of the hazards associated with their property, they may be more willing and able to take corrective action on their own. Fire safety is not just the fire department's responsibility. It is best accomplished through partnerships with the community. One of the best ways to develop these relationships is through the fire safety education that takes place during a fire inspection.

To achieve compliance, the fire inspector needs to be able to help prioritize any list of deficiencies to be corrected. The challenge for the inspector is determining if the deficiency identified is serious enough to warrant immediate attention or if the corrective action may be delayed a reasonable time. Mastering this takes time and experience as an inspector.

Step 4: Establish Organizational Fire Inspection Policies and Procedures

Now that the need and the legal right to conduct fire inspections have been determined, it is prudent to develop organizational policies and procedures for conducting fire inspections. The level of detail in the policies and procedures will vary dependant on the size of the fire prevention bureau as well as on the size of the community served.

Most fire departments have developed standard operating guidelines (SOGs) for suppression and emergency medical services. Similar types of guidelines are needed for fire inspection activities. An important consideration is that the guidelines are not developed as a means to "police" or "control" the inspection process within the fire department but as a means to provide guidance for the inspection staff. It also provides and promotes continued focus on mission and purpose. Some of the guidelines may result from ordinances or laws. For instance, a local ordinance or state law may require all day-care occupancies to be inspected twice a year. A corresponding guideline for the frequency of conducting inspections would list day-care centers as being inspected twice a year.

Procedural guidelines also will assist in the enforcement of codes in situations where it becomes necessary to pursue legal action. The guidelines may state that a regular inspection form is used on first inspections. If the violation persists, then an order notice is issued. If the violation again continues, the guidelines would indicate the forms to use when issuing a citation or summons and when it could be issued, and then they would detail the court appearance procedures.

One of the best ways to build fire safety partnerships is through the education that takes place during a fire inspection.

Fire Inspection Priorities

To determine when to inspect what, you need a good understanding of your local fire problem. Good fire protection practice would dictate inspecting all commercial code-regulated occupancies or properties once a year. Smaller departments can generally accomplish this because the inventory is manageable, but relatively few large departments can do so. For these larger departments, prioritization is key.

To prioritize your inspection targets, first you should identify your fire problem (**Figure 11.2**). As an example, in Colorado Springs, Colorado, in 1997 William H. Wallace analyzed community risk.[1] Wallace concluded that the number-one cause of fires was unattended cooking in private dwellings followed closely by the same problem in apartments. Since formal fire inspections do not typically address single-family homes, the department looked to apartments. Those are commercial structures, which the department has the authority to inspect. Ultimately the department may decide to mount an aggressive public education campaign and offer free home inspections to single-family homeowners while targeting multifamily residences, or apartments, for mandatory inspections.

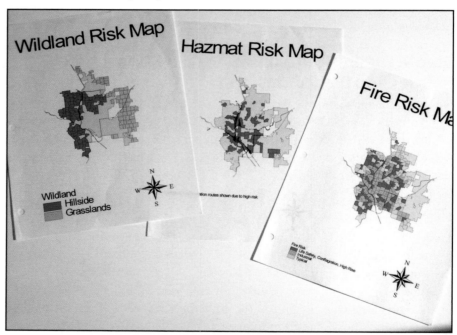

Figure 11.2 A good fire prevention program should first identify what the community risk problems are and where they occur. These maps show the locations of particular types of risks.

The intent of a fire prevention bureau or division is to mitigate the threat of fire. In the interest of doing that, determine the type of occupancies in your jurisdiction where fire incidents are most prevalent. If they are regulated by your department, prioritize them from highest risk to lowest. Finally, identify the number of occupancies in each group and devise a plan or schedule to attack the problem.

Some departments put occupancies on cycles. The first year they may inspect apartments and schools, the second year hospitals and care facilities, and the third year high-pile storage warehouses and malls. The following year they may start over or plug in another occupancy if trends show a problem in a specific area.

For initial targeting, follow the same order as for operational considerations. What is most important? Life safety. What is second? Property conservation. So identify those locations with high life loss potential or exposure. Next take those with high property values or large economic impact. Next may be those locations identified as high hazard such as hazardous materials storage or use locations. The others will rank low, so public education and public information releases alone may be sufficient to deal with problems.

Figure 11.3 Training and preparation are very important. Do your research ahead of time.

Preparing for Fire Inspections

Many times, quality fire inspections follow careful preparation and homework before the inspector even leaves the fire station. Just as fire department operational personnel should spend a great deal of time preplanning for fire incidents, fire inspection personnel should take ample time to prepare for a fire inspection (**Figure 11.3**). Likewise, just as firefighters spend time learning about the hazards they may encounter in a particular building, fire inspectors should spend time looking in reference material for background information about the hazards or deficiencies they may encounter in a particular type of occupancy (**Figure 11.4**). Doing this homework will make the inspection go smoother. Most all of the code requirements are based on the occupancy classification of the building.

Just as operational personnel should spend a great deal of time preplanning for fire incidents, inspection personnel should take ample time to prepare for an inspection.

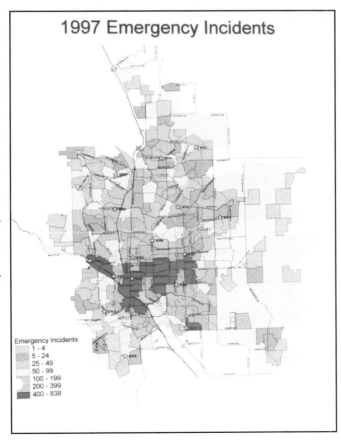

1997 Emergency Incidents

Emergency Incidents
1 - 4
5 - 24
25 - 49
50 - 99
100 - 199
200 - 399
400 - 838

Figure 11.4 Certain GIS mapping applications may help target specific areas or items to enforce or communicate with more efficiently.

Occupancy Hazards

One of the first things to consider is the hazard associated with a particular occupancy. Where can you find such information? A number of references are available, including the following:

- Factory Mutual Data Sheets, Factory Mutual Corporation
- *Fire Protection Handbook*, National Fire Protection Association
- *Fire Inspectors Manual*, National Fire Protection Association
- *Fire Protection and Code Enforcement*, International Fire Service Training Association
- *Industrial Fire Hazards*, National Fire Protection Association

These resources provide a guide to some of the typical hazards that inspectors may encounter during an inspection. They offer insight into the conditions that may warrant correction by the owner. Your research should not only identify typical hazards associated with the occupancy but also determine why these conditions create fire hazards. Much of that information will provide a short synopsis of fires that started or rapidly spread as the result of a condition identified as a hazard. Keep in mind, the inspector will have to sell the need to correct the condition. Convincing the occupant that a condition can contribute to the spread or ignition of a fire will be easier if the inspector can clearly cite examples of past fires that the condition caused in similar occupancies. The reason something needs to be corrected is more convincing if the inspector can cite details of how it can contribute to a fire's starting or spreading. The inspector can gain this information either through experience or readings or a combination of both. Do not be too upset if the occupants still are not happy with your explanation. You are costing them money to fix the problem. You are not paying for the changes, they are. Do not shirk your duties, but do not take it personally if they listen with empathy and still think your requirement is stupid. Besides, they will likely tell you they never had to comply with it before, and they very well could be right.

Specific code requirements may address the hazards of an occupancy. Determining process operation hazards before the inspection can help prepare the inspector for their presence during the inspection. Process hazard(s) may also require the inspector to review codes or standards applicable to the process hazard. For instance, if an occupancy contains a dipping and coating operation, the inspector should become familiar with NFPA 34, *Standard for Dipping and Coating Processes Using Flammable and Combustible Liquids*.

History of Occupancy

Earlier we identified the importance of selling the need to correct a deficiency and overcoming the "it has always been that way" response. An invaluable tool for doing this is the ability to review what has occurred at the occupancy in the past (**Figure 11.5**). It is important that the inspector know as much history as possible about the occupancy before conducting the inspection. Additionally, it is a good practice to follow up fires in regulated occupancies with a top-down inspection. This means doing a thorough inspection immediately after any fire to identify problems as they were and use that leverage, while the embers

It is a good practice to follow up fires in regulated occupancies with a top-down inspection "while the embers are still hot."

Figure 11.5 Researching the past history of an occupancy gives good insight as to what you may find.

are still hot, as it were, to motivate the owner/manager. Some aspects of the occupancy's history to consider include:

- History of fires at the occupancy
- Number of fire alarms or requests for service
- Past fire inspection and fire prevention deficiencies noted
- Outstanding fire prevention deficiencies not corrected
- Construction permits for building alterations
- Use of the facility in the past (Is the use of the occupancy different than at the time of the last inspection?)
- Results of most recent annual fire alarm testing
- Results of most recent annual fixed fire suppression system testing
- Results of most recent annual fire pump testing
- Written correspondence, such as complaints from citizens, suppression personnel, and letters of inquiry
- Fire prevention permits

As inspectors become more experienced they realize the importance and benefits of documentation.

An important consideration for fire inspectors is that they must constantly provide documentation that will enable any inspector to pick up where another left off. This documentation may not seem important at the time but may play a critical role later down the road when a deficiency needs to be corrected, particularly by someone else.

Fire Inspection Public Relations

Most citizens encounter fire department personnel not through fire responses to their home or business but through fire inspections or emergency medical service responses. In fact, a busy fire prevention division will likely have more face-to-face contacts than the emergency operation's division will. In some circumstances, fire prevention inspection personnel will be the only fire department personnel who have any opportunity to make a lasting impression on citizens. The fire inspection provides the fire inspector with an excellent opportunity not only to educate the general public about the importance of fire prevention but also to sell the fire prevention division's excellent services (**Figure 11.6**). When the fire inspector performs in a diplomatic and professional manner, the entire fire department is portrayed as professional and diplomatic. How the inspector talks and dresses and even the inspection report he or she produces will dictate the image of the inspector and his or her fire department.

Figure 11.6 Take the time to explain and "sell" your fire prevention message to those you are working with.

The inspector's ability to deal with the general public is just as important as his or her knowledge of the applicable codes. If the inspector cannot communicate his or her knowledge of the code to the occupant in a fashion that is neither condescending nor overly authoritative, obtaining voluntary compliance will be difficult if not impossible. The fire inspector should constantly seek voluntary correction of any deficiencies found during the inspection. This holds true even with trying to achieve voluntary compliance for minor deficiencies such as a missing or malfunctioning exit light.

The inspector's ability to deal with the general public is just as important as his or her knowledge of the applicable codes.

Government entities in general can have difficulty enforcing compliance issues simply because they are part of a governing body. Many individuals resent being forced to do anything mandated by government. As the inspector begins to build a rapport with the occupant, the ability to see from the occupant's viewpoint helps to achieve this goal of voluntary compliance. For example, conducting an inspection when the occupant's fiscal year is ending may contribute to the occupant's resentment and resistance to voluntary compliance because his or her money is running low. If the inspector is able to discuss the occupant's concerns of fiscal restraints, the occupant may comply voluntarily at the beginning of the next fiscal year. Of course, delaying compliance on a fire code issue requires careful evaluation and approval from the fire department's highest-ranking officer. However, even the best fire inspector will still encounter conflicts with the occupants. Resolving these issues requires conflict management skills that will improve over time as the inspector encounters them.

Managing conflict can be difficult. Many people cite three ways of dealing with conflict:

1. Domination

2. Compromise

3. Integration

One expert on resolving conflicts, Mary Parker Follett, has suggested that **compromise** is the popular way to resolve many issues. Each side gives up something and they reach an agreement. While sometimes necessary in other situations, this likely would dilute fire code requirements, which is not always a preferred choice among code enforcement professionals. **Domination**, Follett believes, is a victory over an opponent. One side is the victor and one side is the loser. In this instance, she proposes nothing is ever resolved, it is merely postponed. This likely would be a poor choice for fire code enforcement. Follett goes on to say that the most sophisticated approach to resolving conflict is **integration**. This is where a mutual solution is found and both sides achieve their goal to some degree with neither being wrong or bad. Probably the best choice for resolving conflict, this allows the inspector to enforce the code and the owner to accomplish his or her objective.

Some fire departments have implemented means for occupancies to conduct a self-inspection program. These departments set the criteria for determining if a business is suitable to participate in the self-inspection program. The criteria may be based on the size of the facility, occupancy of the building, and/or results of previous fire inspections. Some departments set a time limit for how long the occupancy can participate in the self-inspection program and provide mandatory training for participants. The occupant of the business conducts the inspection and provides a copy of the inspection report to the fire department. The fire department may then stop by to verify the occupant's findings or may accept the inspection report as submitted without visiting the location.

✔ **compromise**
method of resolving conflicts in which each side gives up something in order to reach an agreement

✔ **domination**
method of resolving conflicts in which one side is the victor and one side is the loser

✔ **integration**
method of resolving conflicts in which a mutual solution is found and both sides achieve their goal to some degree with neither being wrong or bad

Conducting the Inspection

The general principles of conducting an inspection are the same no matter who is responsible for the task: it must be organized, systematic, and methodical. Beyond that, there are a variety of methods or techniques to conduct an inspection. The inspector needs to chose a systematic method that fits his or her needs and to follow the same format for every inspection. Repetition helps avoid mistakes and will assist in keeping the inspector on track during the inspection. Depending on the complexity of the inspection, it may become easy to be overwhelmed or distracted.

Whenever possible the fire inspector should call the contact person for the facility and schedule the inspection. This will help to ensure the contact person can spend time with the inspector. The inspector can also use the phone call making the appointment to explain exactly what he or she will be looking for. If deficiencies from the last visit are still outstanding, the inspector should let the contact person know that he or she will want to see if the deficiency has been corrected or that progress has been made to address it. The inspector also should indicate any documentation that will be useful or required for the inspection, such as fixed suppression testing, fire alarm testing, or material safety data sheets.

The inspector should consider if any other individuals should also be present at the inspection. Many times the actual owner of the property will not be the contact person for the inspection. In a number of instances, the building is leased to a tenant, who may not be responsible for all areas of the building's maintenance and upkeep. This is particularly likely in situations where multiple tenants occupy a single building. In circumstances such as these, the inspector should schedule the inspection so that both the owner and the occupant are present.

Some building owners may become frustrated if they are inspected by multiple entities over a short period of time. In some communities the health department will inspect restaurants; the housing or property maintenance division will inspect multifamily occupancies; and so on. Fire inspectors may wish to coordinate their inspections with those of any other entities that may be required to inspect the occupancy. This demonstrates the desire to limit interruptions to the business and not have multiple inspections at the same level of government (i.e., city, town, county, etc.). The potential drawback of conducting simultaneous inspections is that the occupant may become overwhelmed and frustrated dealing with multiple inspectors, each of whom has his or her own specialty. The occupant may even have a sense of being "ganged up on."

Once the inspector has made an appointment for the inspection, an important element in establishing credibility is being punctual. Very possibly inspectors may be delayed in their appointments or may be called to assist at an emergency incident. During these situations, at least making a phone call to cancel or reschedule the appointment for a later date is imperative. In many cases, a department secretary can make the phone call to the occupant and explain the circumstances. When scheduling, inspectors need to ensure adequate travel time between inspections and allow enough time to conduct a thorough inspection. Hurrying to finish one inspection in order to proceed to the next is not usually conducive to providing a quality inspection service.

Many circumstances warrant just dropping in for the inspection. For example, engine companies that are assigned to perform fire inspections usually do not schedule those inspections. The engine company cannot know exactly when it can conduct the inspection if it must still respond to emergency calls. Frequently when fire personnel assigned to an engine company visit a location unannounced for an inspection, the owner may ask them to come back at another time or day. Likewise, it is not uncommon for fire inspectors to visit a location unannounced. Frequently fire inspectors will drop in on small businesses to conduct inspections, especially when a number of businesses are in close proximity and the inspector can go from one occupancy to the next.

Fire inspectors in the 21st century are equipped differently than their predecessors. The age of electronics assists them tremendously but also adds to their equipment list. For example, in addition to the traditional fire department uniform and identification an inspector's equipment typically includes:

- Digital organizer
- Laptop or tablet computer
- Electronic rulers or measuring tape
- Rechargeable flashlight
- Cellular phone
- Pager
- Pen
- Clipboard
- Inspection forms
- Digital camera

And of course there are old-fashioned overalls for extremely dirty areas.

The inspector can choose between a couple of systematic inspection approaches. The most important thing to remember is to inspect every interior and exterior area of the building as well as the grounds of the facility.

The most important thing to remember is to inspect every interior and exterior area of the building as well as the grounds of the facility.

Upon arrival at the site, it is a good idea to spend a few moments driving around the facility and becoming familiar with the building's layout. This is also a good way to see if the facility is accessible for emergency vehicles. This is not the exterior inspection but only a tool to become familiar with the building and surrounding areas and to make some mental notes regarding the height of the building, exterior housekeeping practices, and notable construction features.

Unless otherwise requested by the owner of the property, the inspector should enter the premises at the front door or the main entrance to the facility.

The inspector should identify himself or herself and proceed to meet with the contact person. In most all situations, inspectors will want a building representative to accompany them during the inspection. Often more than one person will accompany an inspector. Greeting these people with a positive attitude is important. The contact person accompanying the inspector may have had a bad experience with an inspector in the past as well as naturally being a little apprehensive about what is going to take place. During the initial contact or opening remarks, the inspector explains what he or she is going to do. This is also a good time to emphasize the philosophy of working together to resolve any deficiencies. Good inspectors will also indicate that they understand it can take time to correct any deficiencies and that together they will establish a "game plan" to address concerns. Voluntary compliance is always better than pursuing legal action.

Some inspectors start on the exterior of the building, others start on the interior. Where the inspector starts does not matter, as long as he or she is thorough and systematic. During the inspection, the inspector must take the time to explain any deficiency to the occupant and to explain any corrective action needed. In some cases, the inspector may recommend the occupant contact an architect or engineer to help in correcting the deficiency. The inspector should offer to assist by meeting with the architect or engineer to discuss the deficiency further and in greater technical detail. The inspector can indicate to the owner how the fire department will provide this service and that the fire department is looking out for the best interest of the occupant. In most cases, the occupant may not have the technical understanding needed to correct the deficiency.

Interior Inspections

Three common systematic approaches are used to conduct an interior inspection. They include:

1. Start from the roof and work down to the lowest level.

2. Start from the lowest level and work up to the roof.

3. Follow the manufacturing process from the point where the raw goods enter the facility to the point where the finished product is placed for shipping or storage.

Some fire inspectors prefer to inspect each area in a clockwise direction, a counterclockwise direction, from front to rear, or vice versa. No one method is necessarily better than another. The important point is that the inspection is systematic. Occupants might not show the inspector an area of the facility unless the inspector specifically asks to see it. As the inspector visits an area, he or she should look for doors, stairs, or fixed industrial access ladders and ask what is located in the areas to which they lead. The inspector should request to enter these and all other areas. In documented circumstances, building occupants have used restrooms to store hazardous materials, not considering that the inspector would ever look in a restroom!

If the inspector has elected to follow the manufacturing process from start

Voluntary compliance is always better than pursuing legal action.

to finish, a systematic approach is still warranted. This method is conducive for the building's contact person to rush the inspector through the process. The inspector needs to stop along the way and ask questions about the process and the facility. For instance, questions pertaining to the types of materials used in the process may lead to where the materials are stored and handled.

The inspector's most valuable tool for achieving voluntary compliance is the ability to develop a rapport and level of trust with the building contact.

The inspector's most valuable tool for achieving voluntary compliance is the ability to develop a rapport and level of trust with the building contact.

Exterior Inspections

The inspection of the exterior of the facility should be done with the same systematic approach as the interior. The building's exterior is an important fire protection feature that is the first to be utilized by responding emergency personnel. For example, fire department vehicle access, fire hydrants, sprinkler connections, and building addresses are all exterior features that if not maintained and in good working condition, may cause difficulties when fire personnel first arrive for an incident.

Inspections may need to examine structures or conditions that are not usually thought of as fire department concerns. These could be inspections of single-family developments, making sure roadway width is appropriate as designed and pavement or overlay meets the required specifications or inspections of vegetation management in the wildland/urban interface. These inspections must be carried out according to local laws or regulations but should be handled in the same fashion as described above.

Fire prevention personnel provide a service not only to citizens but also to fire suppression and emergency services personnel. A significant but sometimes overlooked function of the fire inspection is to ensure fire department personnel can handle any emergency as safely as possible. Of course, fire fighting will continue to be a dangerous job; however, inspectors must evaluate the building's conditions and hazards to minimize risk to firefighters. Items such as open floors or such as doors or stairs fixed in a permanently closed position may pose a threat to firefighters in a smoke-filled environment.

Fire Inspection Evaluation

The types of inspection forms used will vary from a multicopy paper form to electronic documents (see Chapter 14). Some fire departments will use a checklist. Others will use some other type of simple form. Some feel that check sheets may keep the inspector too focused on checking boxes rather than looking for and discussing fire prevention deficiencies.

Fire Inspection Steps

The inspection process is relatively simple but should not be underestimated. The legal ramifications of improper procedures can be costly and painful, if not for you then for your boss or your boss's boss. We recommend the following guidelines to complete a good fire inspection:

The legal ramifications of following improper inspection procedures can be costly and painful.

- Contact the business owner if possible to schedule an appointment for the inspection. Sometimes surprise inspections are beneficial and necessary, but avoid them when you can. No business owner likes to be surprised.

- Arrive on time. Time is money to a business owner or operator. Treat this time as a very valuable commodity to them. Show respect.

- Look professional, act professional, and be nice (**Figure 11.7**). You are representing not only yourself, but also your organization and the fire service as a whole. Generally people will react the same way they are treated.

Figure 11.7 Inspectors need to be professional in appearance and demeanor at all times.

- Introduce yourself and explain the purpose and objectives of your visit. If the business owner hands you off to someone else, never leave until you make an effort to close your inspection with the owner or operator of the business. They are responsible and accountable; let them share in your efforts.

- Ask questions if you have them. Important information can come in bits and pieces. In fact, you will likely find problems you did not know about, as long as you are methodical.

- Be systematic. Whether you start inside and work your way out or start at the top and go down or vice versa does not matter. Just be consistent, every time. Conducting inspections is like playing an instrument; you will develop a rhythm. Do it the same way every time and you will find yourself being more consistent and organized from one visit to the next.

- Never stop at verbally requesting a correction of a code violation. Make every request in writing. We cannot begin to tell you the number of times we have had to start over because someone forgot to record exactly what was wrong or what needed to be fixed. If it is a dangerous violation, it is worth writing down. If it is a violation worth noticing, it is worth writing down. This not only helps you, but also helps the business owner, the inspector who has to follow you, and the attorney who has to defend you three years from now. Write everything. You can never have too much documentation. Is this hard? Yes, but protecting everyone involved is worth the effort.

- Sell, sell, and sell. Sell every fix you have to a problem. Let the occupant know why and how it affects everyone. Generally, the problem exists for you because no one in the occupancy understood that it was a problem to begin with. You are the messenger of fire-safe behavior and issues. Be thoughtful.

- Always take the high road. Why get into a spitting contest? If you are right and the occupant is resistant, write it up and explain how to appeal through your local appeals process. Smile and say thank you. Do not be confrontational.

- Make sure you praise the positive conditions. Everyone likes to be told good things or to be complimented. Take the time to share with occupants the things they are doing right.

Record Keeping

Documentation is very important. All activities of the inspector should be well documented in a format that allows easy recall. Record keeping may be done on paper, although most departments are capable also of maintaining documents in a computer database. Most inspections require some type of signed verification of notice received, and many jurisdictions require a copy of this signature. Your department's legal authority can tell you how to handle these records. Records are an essential component of the fire prevention bureau's work and should be organized in a systematic fashion that enables easy retrieval. Because the volume of records on an occupancy continues to grow throughout its life, a method to archive the documents or to separate the documents into categories may be beneficial. One efficient filing system is similar to that found in many doctor's offices. The files are color coded to meet the needs of the fire prevention bureau. For example, orange tabs may indicate documentation for the building's construction projects, blue tabs may indicate sprinkler information, and so on. One method of filing is not necessarily better than another. The system must be user friendly and meet the needs of the department by making files easy to locate and easy to access without having to dig through mounds of paper shoved into a file. Chapter 14 further examines the use of information technology for managing the fire prevention bureau's records.

Summary

One of the most important fire prevention bureau functions is inspections. Inspections are important because they provide an opportunity to identify and correct hazardous conditions that could start a fire or contribute to the severity of a fire endangering not only the occupants but firefighters as well.

For a fire department to serve the public properly some key elements must be established and implemented prior to beginning an inspection program. If a program is already established, it may be a good idea to review it to determine if any of those elements are lacking or need adjustment. These elements include:

- Analyzing the level of service the community needs and wants

- Determining and codifying enforceable regulations

- Determining the level of training inspectors will need

- Establishing organizational fire inspection policies and procedures

Next the inspection priorities must be established. This means identifying those risks and hazards that are the biggest threat to your community and fire department and dealing with them at the appropriate level of detail and frequency to address the risk. Then personnel must prepare for conducting the inspections. This may include very detailed research of various occupancies, processes, loss history, past inspection history, and so forth.

Once the appropriate research has been conducted, the inspection can begin. One important thing to remember is that any time you open your mouth or put pen to paper during an inspection, you cost the business or property owner money. That is your job and it is your responsibility. You are there to identify problems and have them corrected. However, never forget that what takes two minutes to document may take up to a hundred thousand dollars to fix.

Working with business owners often requires a series of stiff negotiations and reasonable compromise. We must always honor the intent if not the letter of the code; however, we must be empathetic and understanding enough to work with individuals in achieving compliance. When initiating the inspection, make sure your appearance is neat, your demeanor is professional, and your attitude positive. As far as the technical aspects of the inspection, you may follow any number of systematic approaches to going through a property or building. The key is to remain consistent so you do not overlook or forget things. Also, make sure you allow a reasonable amount of time for the owner to abate the hazard or correct the violation. The decision on when something must be done is really the inspector's. However, it should be a negotiated agreement with the owner/manager unless there are extenuating circumstances, such as a resistant occupant or owner.

Document, document, and document. Never conduct an inspection without following up on the proper documentation. This will be vital if an issue ever comes up in court, and it will be equally important if the occupancy suffers a fire. All records will be culled and examined. Any department that does not have good record keeping not only will be viewed as an embarrassment but could incur legal or civil responsibility due to litigation.

Chapter 11 Review Exercises

11.1 List the elements of a fire inspection. _____

_____

_____

_____

11.2 Is credibility important for a fire inspector? Why or why not? _____

_____

_____

11.3 Why should a community have a fire inspection program? _____

_____

_____

_____

11.4 Identify the steps to conduct a fire inspection discussed in this chapter. _____

_____

_____

_____

_____

_____

_____

_____

_____

_____

11.5 What constitutes a good fire inspection? _____

_____

11.6 What is a self-inspection program? _____

_____

_____

11.7 What are the advantages and disadvantages of a self-inspection program?

Advantages: _____

_____

_____

Disadvantages: _____

_____

_____

_____

11.8 Why is an efficient method to document inspections an important element of a fire prevention program? _____

_____

_____

_____

11.9 What skills should a fire inspector possess? _____

_____

_____

_____

_____

11.10 How should a fire inspector prepare for an inspection? _____

_____

_____

_____

11.11 What equipment does a fire inspector need to conduct an inspection?

_____

_____

_____

_____

_____

_____

11.12 Discuss the fire inspection guidelines identified in this chapter.

_____

_____

_____

_____

_____

_____

_____

_____

11.13 Define a reasonable time frame for gaining compliance. _____

_____

_____

_____

11.14 Why is it important to have a good set of operational policies or guidelines for an inspection program? _____

_____

_____

11.15 What is the goal of an inspection program? _____

_____

11.16 What is meant by the dictum, "Sell fire prevention"? _____

_____
_____
_____

11.17 How do you prioritize those occupancies or facilities you choose to inspect? _____

_____
_____
_____
_____
_____

11.18 List ten items that are important to glean from the history of a facility.

_____
_____
_____
_____
_____

11. Is technical knowledge of the codes more important than customer relations? Why? _____

_____
_____

11.20 What are three ways people tend to deal with conflict?

_____
_____
_____

11.21 Is it better to conduct your inspection from the outside in or from the inside out? Explain your answer. _____

_____
_____

NOTES

1. William H. Wallace, *Community Risk Issue: Structure Fires* (Colorado Springs, Colorado: Colorado Springs Fire Department, 1997).

2. This discussion of Mary Parker Follett's ideas is based on Donald F. Favreau, *Fire Service Management* (New York: Donnelley, 1969).

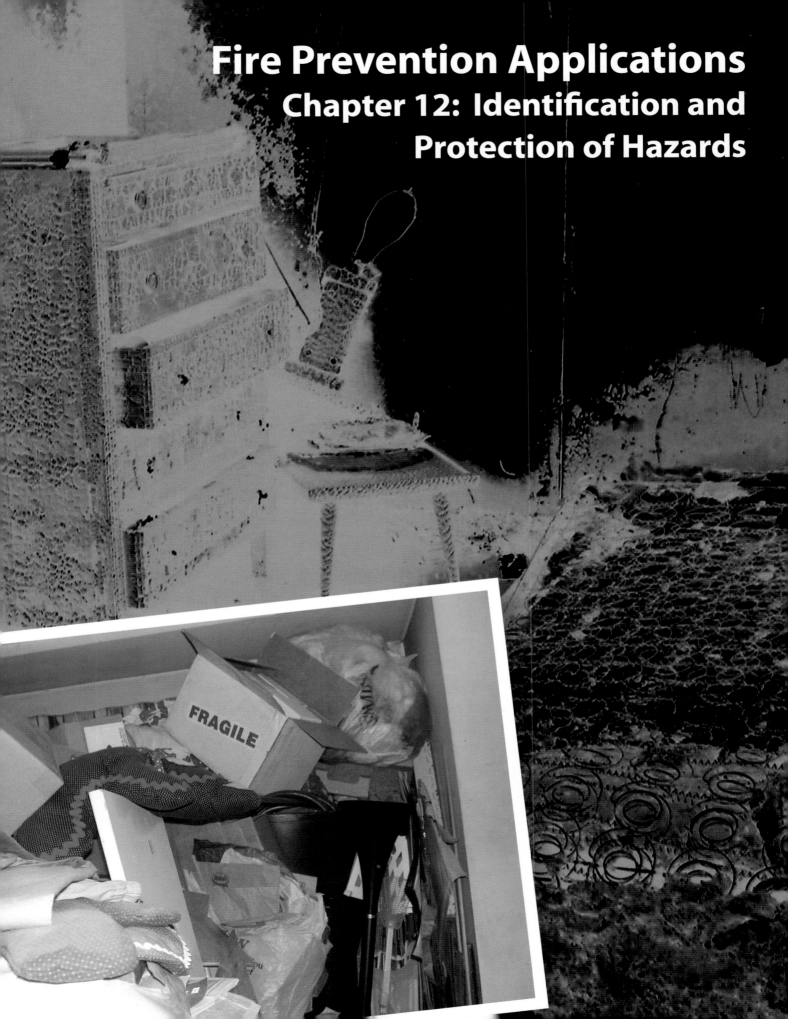

Fire Prevention Applications
Chapter 12: Identification and Protection of Hazards

FESHE COURSE OBJECTIVES

1. Identify the types of hazards.
2. Identify basic engineering methods to control a fire.
3. Explain the difference between active and passive fire protection.

Chapter 12
Identification and Protection of Hazards

Types of Hazards

The term **hazard** has a number of definitions. None of the definitions is especially specific, particularly in the context of fire prevention. To frame this chapter's discussion, we will define a hazard as a condition or element that provides a source of ignition for a hostile fire or that contributes to the spread and severity of a hostile fire. **Hostile fire** is a term for any unwanted or destructive fire.

Historically, the distinction between common hazards and specific hazards has been a subject of much discussion. **Common hazards** are typically referred to as those hazards that are common among many occupancies or locations (**Figure 12.1**). An example would be the storage of flammable or combustible liquids such as paints, lacquers, or cleaners, which can be located nearly anywhere. **Specific hazards** are those hazards that are isolated to specific operations or locations,

✔ **hazard**
a condition or element that provides a source of ignition for a hostile fire or that contributes to the spread and severity of a hostile fire

✔ **hostile fire**
any unwanted or destructive fire

✔ **common hazard**
hazard that is found among many occupancies or locations

✔ **specific hazard**
hazard that is isolated to particular operations or locations

Figure 12.1 Unfortunately many homes and businesses can be dangerous firetraps not only to occupants but also to neighbors and fire crews. This photo from the Spokane Fire Department shows how fire loading can impact a simple residential structure.

Figure 12.2 High-rise dwellings such as these condominiums can pose a significant risk.

Because the perception of dealing with events in a particular type of occupancy differs among departments, the perception of the hazard will differ, too.

such as cryogenic oxygen storage tanks at a hospital. These installations are not common to all buildings but instead are specific to occupancies or locations with particular needs.

Another method of identifying hazards is by occupancy type. This method can be inefficient as different localities and jurisdictions may perceive hazard types differently. An example could be a small town with a single high-rise protected by only a couple of fire stations. This high-rise could be the community's most significant target hazard (**Figure 12.2**). New York City, however, may not consider high-rises that significant as they have a tremendous number of these buildings and a large department that can handle such fires. Because the perception of dealing with events in these locations is different, the perception of the hazard is different, too.

This chapter will not delve into the specifics of hazards within buildings or processes as numerous texts already do this including the *Fire Protection Handbook,* from the National Fire Protection Association, and an excellent resource, the *Fire Inspection and Code Enforcement* manual, from the International Fire Service Training Association. We will instead look at a more global picture of what hazards are. This more holistic approach should be taken to overall hazard identification and protection. It is not merely a review and analysis of the single exit sign that is nonfunctional in a motel hallway, but more global in the perspective of how the entire motel is viewed and protected as a hazard and risk within the community.

Identify the Target

Assume for a moment that you are the fire marshal of a mid-sized American city. Assume you recently have been placed in this position and sitting before you is the opportunity of a lifetime. You have an excellent staff, you work for a progressive fire department, and the community likes your department's performance and has for a number of years. What do you do now?

One of the first things you must do is define exactly what fire hazards you are trying to protect others from. That's a big task. If you are stuck, list the top five causes of structure fires in your community. For purposes of illustration, let's list five that are common to many communities.

- Unattended cooking
- Arson
- Electrical shorts
- Children playing with matches
- Smoking

Now that we know the cause, or rather how your structure fires are starting, let's determine the types of structures or occupancies where these fires are occurring and this time list only the top three (**Figures 12.3 and 12.4**). Once more for purposes of this example, let's list the following occupancies, which again are common to many communities:

- Private dwellings

- Apartments (multifamily)

- General business offices

Figure 12.3 Typical hazards generally can include less threatening buildings, such as single-family dwellings.

Now let's readdress the question. What are you trying to protect others from? The answer to this question will define your community's target hazards. The data in the example may indicate that your community does not know how to cook well, that you have bad people running around town using fire as a weapon, and that your public is at risk both at home during the night and at work during the day. This methodical approach makes identifying the hazards fairly straightforward.

Many references list specific conditions related to hazards in particular operations or occupancies. While these are vital to your overall fire prevention mission, you must first deal with your immediate problem, the community signs and symptoms you have just identified.

Identifying hazards begins with a good origin and cause determination.

Remember that without scrupulous data collection and analysis you will be shooting in the dark. How can you look at your problem if you cannot see it? The origin and cause investigation is crucial to good fire prevention efforts. So, identifying hazards begins first with a good origin and cause determination.

Strengthen your data collection if you want to hit the target and truly make a difference. In Chapter 14 we will discuss using technology to your advantage when collecting and using data.

Think Strategically in the Target Identification Process

Think back to Chapter 4, "Development and Implementation of Fire Prevention Bureaus." It discusses the importance of strategic planning's role in

Figure 12.4 Increased risks may include such things as multi-family dwellings, particularly if your department will have access or water supply issues.

establishing the fire prevention bureau. What does it mean to think strategically in the target identification process? Some people have compared it to viewing the world through a telescope, looking way down the road to see where you are going and understanding why you need to be there. So, thinking strategically in identifying your target means knowing very clearly your direction, your objectives, and the methods and resources you will use to attain your goals and planning for the resources you need to have available to accomplish your goals (**Figure 12.5**).

Figure 12.5 Be sure to keep your library complete and up-to-date and to utilize all of the resources available when making decisions.

Done regularly, strategic planning allows you to deal more dynamically with changes in identifying targets. People, technology, and hazards change all the time. We need to be dynamic and adjust to those changes by thinking long term. Thinking strategically will keep our fire prevention efforts appropriate to our jurisdiction's ever-changing circumstances.

Develop a Target Protection Plan

How do you get started? Let's return to our previous scenario, in which we determined that single-family dwellings, multifamily dwellings, and businesses were our target occupancies. With this in mind we start our plan.

The planning process consists of seven main steps.

1. Create and/or gather the team who will do the work. The team should include stakeholders from the identified hazards.

2. With the team, create or reaffirm your mission statement.

3. With the team, establish the strategic goals you want to accomplish for the specific hazards identified. These goals should be realistic and appropriate.

4. With the team, establish the specific strategies you will use to accomplish the goals.

5. Print the document and have everyone sign it to affirm their agreement with and commitment to its content.

6. Implement and evaluate, just as you would any program management cycle.

7. Make adjustments as necessary based on the evaluation.

Nothing will happen without a high-quality team. Even if you are in a small department and you are the sole chief, fire marshal, inspector, and dog catcher, you will need help reducing the risks. You will need a team, small though it may be. Involving all of the potentially affected stakeholders in the process from its inception is the best way to develop good synergy and cooperation. If you have nay-sayers, give them the opportunity to "own" part of the solution. That way, they cannot object later on if the idea was in part theirs.

> No matter how small the department, developing a target protection plan requires a high-quality team.

Identify Your Resources

Once you have worked out all of your strategies, you need to identify how to work on them. Think outside the box. Do not lock yourself into looking only within your department (**Figure 12.6**). What other stakeholders in the community will benefit from this program? We identified apartments as a target hazard. Do you think the local apartment management association has something to say about their members' property getting burned up every week? Sure they do! Involve them. Consider all potential interested parties and benefactors. Look for funding sources such as grants and fund-raising organizations to help you. Include local civic centers, YMCAs, any place where owners or occupants of your target hazard may live, work, or play. People will help if they know what to do and have direction. By establishing your strategic plan, you will show them you are serious and assure them they can participate knowing they are part of an organized effort.

Figure 12.6 Hard discussions often need to take place when trying to determine the best priority for the best work you need to perform for your community. Often that can lead to days ending like this.

Involve Your Team

Brag about your team. Use as much publicity as possible. Get your fire and life safety educators, your public information officers, and your chief involved. Good press gives the effort a great boost. Let the team see their progress regularly. Show them off and they will do wonders for you and the effort. This is especially true for organizations outside the fire department. They love to be recognized standing by a fire truck or the chief of the department or even you, the fire marshal. Have fun and celebrate the successes, no matter how slight. Once the ball gets rolling, it will pick up speed.

Reevaluate the Plan

Without following through by re-evaluating your target protection plan you will lose credibility and likely waste energy doing unproductive things.

Getting everyone motivated to do the work and take off only to see them fall flat on their faces because no one did any follow-up is probably the saddest way for planning to end. Planning is just like a batter swinging at a baseball: follow-through is very important. Without it you will lose credibility and likely waste energy doing unproductive things. No plan is perfect. Be ready to make mistakes. Always look for better ways of doing things. Don't be afraid to blunder. Those who do not blunder usually are not doing anything.

Solutions for Control

When you have finished your plan and have provided for reevaluating and revising it as needed, the hard part is done. Now you just use your knowledge of fire protection issues as a tool to solve the problems you have identified. When we examine methods to protect a hazard or a series of hazards, we are assuming a fire will occur. We need to think of where the fire will most likely occur and how the fire will progress. We also need to consider the fire's impact on any occupants who are present.

The best, although maybe not the cheapest, method of dealing with identified hazards is engineering. Eliminating as much of the "human factor" as possible will keep incidents to a minimum. Remember the three *E*s: engineering, education and enforcement. As a species, human beings have engineered solutions to natural or manmade problems ever since we came into existence. Down through the ages, engineering has been in the forefront of history. Its task is to put knowledge to practical use.[1] The objective of fire protection engineering is to find ways of preventing or mitigating hostile fires. In this chapter we will concentrate primarily on mitigation as we addressed prevention issues previously. Because of our limited resources for prevention and the recognition that prevention will never be 100 percent successful, we have to plan and design so as to mitigate damages when fire occurs.[2]

The engineering method of choice boils down to picking the right tool for the job. As stated previously, there may be numerous tools for the job. Years ago in middle school we watched a film in shop class that used a Neanderthal character called "Primitive Pete." Primitive Pete was the film's example of what not to do with tools. One of the memorable scenes was when Pete began using a flat-blade screwdriver as a hammer. While the nail did go in the wood, it ruined the screwdriver, bent the nail, and failed to attach the pieces. Choosing the wrong fire protection systems can end much the same way, with the even more disastrous results of larger property loss and potential loss of life.

Choosing the wrong fire protection systems can have disastrous results: large property loss and potential loss of life.

You can use many different approaches and systems, and some will work in more than one scenario. However, a select few generally are best for any given situation. It becomes paramount, then, that as a fire protection professional and as a manager of a fire prevention bureau, you must become the resident expert in understanding the best approach for a given application.

Keep in mind, you must accomplish this regardless of your education and background.

Let's analyze the ways we can mitigate fire situations. For our purposes, we will use Webster's definition of the term **mitigate**: to make less harsh or hostile or to make less serious or painful. Hostile fires generally occur due to one of three main causes: men, women, or children. That said, we need to recognize how we as human beings behave in our living environment. On average, we sleep nearly a third of our lives, we work nearly a third of our lives, and we do other things the other third. Our behavior in relation to hostile fire is much different, depending upon which of these three phases we are in at the time of the fire. Keep these phases in mind, reflecting on how they interact with the engineering controls we will discuss next. After we talk about engineering aspects we will discuss behavioral issues that deserve specific discussion by themselves.

✔ **mitigate**
to make less harsh or hostile or to make less serious or painful

Some basic engineering designs used in controlling fire can be divided into two types: active and passive. Some examples of each are:

- Active
  — Suppression and control (automatic fire sprinklers, hood and duct extinguishing systems, etc.)
  — Detection and alarm (smoke detectors, building alarms, etc.)
  — Fire department emergency response (last resort)
- Passive
  — Product manufacture and performance control (automatic shutoff timers on coffee makers, ignition pilot control on water heaters and furnaces, etc.)
  — Compartmentation (fire walls, fire doors, fire and smoke dampers, etc.)

Suppression and Control

Suppression and control is the best all-encompassing method of achieving a fire protection and life safety goal. By using automatic fire suppression methods, we not only benefit from early automatic detection that rapidly alerts occupants for evacuation and summons emergency services, but we also take an active step toward controlling a hostile fire during its incipient stage.

Suppression and control is the best all-encompassing method of achieving a fire protection and life safety goal.

From an engineering perspective, many different types of suppression systems are available. They all work in basically the same way; it is the extinguishing agent that typically makes each of the systems different. Also, specific hazards require specific types of components; some examples are:

- Automatic fire sprinklers
- Deluge systems
- Water mist systems

- Clean agent gases

- Dry chemical agents

- Foam

For more than a century, automatic fire sprinklers have protected millions of dollars in property and have, in fact, saved many lives (**Figure 12.7**). These systems have also provided significant alternatives to designers and builders as trade-offs for more hazardous designs. Automatic fire sprinklers have also allowed storage or hazardous processes that otherwise would have been impossible. This has provided far greater flexibility for better technology and newer construction products than ever before imagined.

Figure 12.7 A sprinkler in operation.

All of these systems are relatively complex, and you should study them in detail. We strongly recommend the IFSTA text, *Fire Detection and Suppression Systems* (3rd edition) for more information and a fuller understanding of how these systems and devices are utilized and function. Water systems provide the best all-around protection; however, they have disadvantages that may warrant using a different system. Clean agent systems such as carbon dioxide or FM 200 are excellent choices for computer or other high-tech applications. These and similar agents replaced Halons 1301, 1211, and 2402, which were identified as ozone-depleting gases and banned. The Montreal Protocol on Substances that Deplete the Ozone Layer, an international agreement, required a complete phase out of the production of ozone-depleting agents by the year 2000.[3] This agreement has forced many manufacturers to research alternative extinguishing agents such as FM 200 and Inergin.

In some applications, dry chemical extinguishing systems are the best choice for ease of installation, cost effectiveness, and reliability. Dry chemical systems are especially good for dip tanks, painting, or other coating-process hazards. As the expert, you should become familiar with all the systems and their agents to make the best choice possible for protecting the particular hazard.

Although all of these systems do an excellent job of automatically protecting hazards during an unwanted fire occurrence, you must remember that they will be effective only if they are:

- Matched for the appropriate hazard

- Designed properly

- Maintained regularly

- Kept current for the hazard present

Similar to a computer data base, where information technology folks say, "Garbage in, garbage out," automatic fire protection systems only work as well as they are engineered: "Bad design, bad performance."

Automatic fire protection systems only work as well as they are engineered: "Bad design, bad performance."

Detection and Alarm

Fire detection and alarm are important elements of fire protection. Detection systems may initiate fire suppression system operation, equipment shutdown, and door closure, not to mention the notification of fire suppression forces for quicker response (**Figure 12.8**). The alarm may go to a distant monitoring agency for notification at a corporate level, an on-site monitoring location, or simple notification of the occupants within a building or area.

The two principle means of detection are:

- People

- Automatic devices

When they are awake and in an area where they can see or smell a fire starting, people are some of the best detection devices available. For example, people are the principle means of detecting wildland fires. Although sleeping people will not generally detect products of combustion, those who are awake generally are alert to the scents of combustion byproducts and to visible smoke and flame. In these instances people can be relied upon to activate manual alarm devices such as pull stations, public announcement, or other means of notification, assuming devices are available.

The drawback is that while this human detection element does a good job of identifying hostile fire, it is not always effective at protecting lives even while people are awake and alert. Many of the larger fire loss events (dollar and life loss), occur during the hours people are awake, at work, or out and about. While human detection appears to be fairly reliable, our reactions do not necessarily coincide with our senses. The point being, when not asleep or incapacitated, people do a good job of discovering fires; they just don't know what to do about them.

The second means of fire detection is automatic. This may be done in any number of ways:

- Smoke detectors

- Heat detectors

- Suppression system activation by fusible links

- Ultra violet or infrared

- Sound (although still being researched, some sound-sensing security systems have detected fire)

- Gas-sampling detection

Figure 12.8 This manual station simultaneously initiates an alarm and actuates the suppression system.

When not asleep or incapacitated, people do a good job of discovering fires; they just don't know what to do about them.

These methods all provide good early warning and notification, but each is tailored to fit a relatively specific situation or fire event. Excellent resources are available that provide greater detail on system performance and design criteria. One example is the International Fire Service Training Association's *Fire Detection and Suppression Systems* (3rd edition). We will not go into detail on these systems' operation but instead will focus on the big picture of overall strategy. Again, however, we strongly recommend that you research these systems as you are the community and department expert. If you wish to use automatic detection as a means of hazard protection, be certain these systems are installed in accordance with the applicable National Fire Protection Association standards.

Whether a fire detection and alarm system relies on people or automatic devices, its purposes are the same:

- Alert occupants of the condition requiring appropriate response (evacuation, fire suppression response, or other)

- Initiate mechanical operations (smoke removal, elevator recall, fire door activation, notification appliances such as horns and strobes)

- Transmit a signal to initiate emergency fire response

Remember that a firefighter's basic training prioritizes two fundamental tasks in this order:

1. Life safety

2. Property conservation

Engineering methods must conform to the same ranked priority. If people can get out of harm's way, "stuff" can be rebuilt. Life safety is most important and is the objective that our society and we as fire protection professionals aim to achieve above all else. Note that in our priorities of outcomes from detection, emergency response is last. This is not to say it is not important; however, in keeping with this book's overriding theme, response after an incident has occurred is our last resort and therefore the least preferred option. The message: control hostile fires before you have to rely on response. It truly gives the best bang for the buck.

Fire Department Operations

The lowest ranked element of active protection for hazards enlists the help of our operations division or emergency responders. It is not ranked low because of resource capabilities or expected performance. It is ranked low because it comes into play only when a significant event has already occurred and we are trying to mitigate it by preventing a larger event such as a conflagration.

Conscious risk management decisions allow us to rely on reactive remedies rather than on engineered solutions. While the three *E*s (engineering, education, and enforcement) are our motto, if you will, one mechanism in the engineering approach is emergency response (**Figure 12.9**). The reality is, calling 911 to report a fire and waiting for the responders' arrival is no different than installing a very slow-acting suppression system. You lose quick

Controlling hostile fires before you have to rely on response truly gives the best bang for the buck.

Figure 12.9 This department is reacting to a fire problem rather than having prevented it on the front end. Fire prevention efforts must become more prevalent if we are ever going to reduce losses significantly.

response, small-fire containment, and automatic notification. However, for a community that pays several hundred thousand to a million-plus dollars a year for a fully staffed fire station, this equipment and trained staff should count for something. For that reason, it is natural to expect this mechanism to have to perform and to do so reliably. That expectation should be clear and well defined, however, as one part of the engineered systems approach.

From a code enforcement perspective, fire prevention efforts should take into account all important aspects of fire fighting. Buildings, processes, or conditions that fire prevention bureau reviews should be code compliant and devised to minimize the risk to fire crews and other responders. Higher risk in some circumstances is unavoidable and acceptable. Firefighters do not perform their duties expecting always to be totally safe and protected; however, they do expect reasonable safety while they do their job going into places that other people are fleeing. Our success as fire prevention experts not only rests on the design and installation of various systems or mechanisms to make fire fighting easier but also in training and educating the line firefighter in those aspects. We are the experts and therefore should share our knowledge with those we work with and rely on to provide an important component of our fire protection system. We expect the fire suppression folks to have a fire prevention attitude. In return we fire prevention folks must think like the fire suppression folks who will be in a smoke-filled environment at 3:00 A.M. trying to decipher the fire alarm control panel that was inadvertently placed in a closet.

To use suppression resources properly, all fire prevention staff must be intimately familiar with the equipment, training, policies procedures, and capabilities of their emergency crews. They must continually factor integration and application of this combined resource into all engineering and educational

> From a code enforcement perspective, fire prevention efforts should take into account all important aspects of fire fighting.

applications of hazard protection. In a fire department systems approach, we are all in this together.

Product Manufacture and Performance Control

Products that we use and misuse every day of our lives play an important part in fire protection efforts. Thankfully, in this country, we have various independent testing laboratories like Underwriters Laboratories and Factory Mutual. These agencies test various items (power cords, heating devices, etc.) following specific test procedures and criteria. If an item meets the test criteria and passes the test as designed, it is then listed or approved (Chapter 2). A testing agency's stamp indicates the item passed whatever test it was submitted for. Do you see the problem yet? Often only one of the product's many components may have been submitted for and passed the testing process.

Example One: You go to the store and buy decorative lights for the winter holiday season. You look on the box and, voila, it has a U.L. stamp. You assume that it is U.L. approved (which it is not—U.L. only lists, they do not approve) and that it must be safe. However, if you were inclined to do further research in the U.L. directories, you may find that for this particular string of lights U.L. tested only the electrical cord for electrical protection from power loss through poor insulation (which could lead to shorts), improper connections of the wires to the blades that go into an outlet, or an incorrect ratio length of a wire's length to its diameter (so as not to overheat based on the projected electrical load). However, the out-of-country manufacturer decides to install cheaper bulbs that use more power and burn hotter than initially planned. Since the bulb may not have been part of the required test, changing it may not impact the listing. So, you thought you had a good set of lights, but it is actually unsafe because the increased current flow will heat the wires and the bulbs will overheat because they are different than initially designed. While the box has a listing stamp, it does not contain the product that actually was tested.

Example Two: Your chief decides he wants a window in his office door, which requires a one-hour rating. It currently has that rating because it is solid and has a U.L. listing stamp. The chief tells the light-duty person who is imprisoned at headquarters to take the door out to the shop and have a nice window installed so he can keep an eye on who goes in and out of the fire marshal's office. Upon the door's return, you ask the chief if he bought a new door. He replies, "No," and tells you the shop put in this nice window so he can watch you. You inform him that he cannot do that because the door is required to be rated. The chief informs you it has been and shows you the U.L. stamp. You kindly but carefully explain that the U.L. listing stamp was provided when the door was tested as a solid door, not with the window. He gives you a "chief" kind of look and then firmly urges you to note that the glass is wired and therefore it does not void the listing.

We will avoid the ugly parts of the rest of this story, but suffice it to say that the type of glass, the mounting frame, and other materials used were not specifically tested by U.L., and therefore the door cannot keep its original listing. The door has been changed and the listing is void.

These are hypothetical examples and would be highly unlikely to actually occur. However, they present pictures of what potentially could happen. For a good understanding of procedures and listing or approval criteria used by Underwriters Laboratories or any other testing agency, contact the organization directly and read their literature. Our experience has been that whenever you contact a testing agency you will get helpful information about the product and the testing procedure as well as learn a great deal from a friendly person.

In addition to the numerous testing labs, many watchdog groups, such as the Consumer Product Safety Commission, regularly identify problem products, assist in issuing recalls, and verify testing procedures to be sure they match the criteria. Our point is that products are comparatively safe in America but you must be mindful of which products are actually listed in part or whole and what that listing means. Do not assume anything! As a fire safety professional you are the one responsible for determining whether things are safe or not safe.

> As a fire safety professional you are the one responsible for determining whether things are safe or not safe.

Generally the applicable code will specify using or installing only those products that are listed by some outside testing agency, at which time you, as the authority having jurisdiction (AHJ) then approve their use or installation. Learn this process well as lives and property may hinge on it. You would be surprised at what things get used for aside from their intended purpose.

Hazard protection by product manufacture (for example, not selling children's sleep wear unless it is made entirely of flame retardant material) and performance control (for example, designing products and instructions to meet specific safety standards) is widespread. As a result of numerous large lawsuits, companies in the United States are generally very careful about what they produce and sell. When people in this country are hurt physically or financially, they are quick to hold manufacturers or producers accountable, as they should. This has created a fairly reliable fire-safe market that deals in products and goods. Independent testing and certification is the cornerstone of these lawsuits, along with aggressive stances by consumer protection agencies and advocates. So while not foolproof, you can reasonably rely upon a general understanding of product control and independent laboratory testing for addressing this means of engineering control.

Figure 12.10 Double swinging fire doors are among the more common types of fire-door assemblies.

Compartmentation

Compartmentation is critical to the survival of any building. It deals with our ability to engineer and install passive (and in some cases active) protection features to prevent fire spread. These features include: firewalls, fire doors, fire fire-resistant glazing, penetration protection, smoke and fire dampers,

✔ **compartmentation**
the use of passive (and in some cases active) protection features to prevent fire spread

and smoke management systems. The objective of compartmentation is to restrict hostile fire to one area rather than allowing it to migrate or propagate to another location. This is done through the use of rated assemblies that meet and have passed various test criteria (**Figure 12.10**). An **assembly** speaks to a particular type of construction method that details specific types of materials, their specific manufacturing or installation details, and components such as specific screws, nails, ceiling tiles, and drywall (an assembly typically is viewed as a wall, a ceiling/floor, etc.). You can obtain a detailed explanation of this from the IFSTA *Fire Inspection and Code Enforcement* manual and the IFSTA *Building Construction* manual as well as in from Francis L. Brannigan's *Building Construction for the Fire Service*.

In this day of computer and communication wizardry, communication and power cables are being fed through buildings from top to bottom and side to side. The holes that are punched in building assemblies to accommodate these cables violate the assemblies' integrity. Much as a chain is only as strong as its weakest link, fire barriers are only as effective as their performance integrity. Maintaining the integrity of these systems or assemblies is essential to providing adequate protection for evacuation and safety of occupants. Without careful adherence to requirements and specifications as spelled out in the listed assembly testing criteria, you can have no confidence in a system's ability to withstand a fire.

Collapse is also a major consideration. The intent of any structural assembly is to withstand thermal insult and remain structurally sound, thereby resisting collapse. If collapse does occur, it should not contribute to the additional destruction of anything more than what is already affected. The intent of compartmentation is to hold a fire in check. This must be done, relative to the design constraints, regardless of the anticipated fire's effect. Drywall is a good example of our progress over time. Because of its inherent flame retardant properties, this low-cost, easy-to-install product has done a tremendous job of containing hostile fires to their rooms of origin long enough for firefighters to arrive and extinguish them. Before drywall's invention, fires moved easily into voids in walls and ceilings, advancing rapidly unchecked throughout the building. In many cases, flames moved so fast that the fire department was powerless to stop their spread until the fuel was all consumed, meaning the building burned to the ground. We must consider all other products and options that facilitate the same end result. New products will come out and old ones will remain. Careful attention to how they are installed and used will provide a much greater arsenal for fire protection.

Occupant Safety

Intertwined with the proactive approach of compartmentation are certain reactive measures that play an important part in hazard protection and mitigation for occupants. These measures fall under the general category of occupancy evacuation. Protecting lives is the fire department's most important operational priority. To do this, people must be made aware there is a problem and then know what to do to protect themselves and others (**Figure 12.11**). Assuming that a structure has good consumer products and mechanical systems and an

Figure 12.11 Education and awareness for people in target hazards is a must. It is imperative that occupants know how and when to respond to a fire or other emergency incident. Frequent educational programs can assist with this.

adequate means of detecting hostile fire, the next step is getting people out of harm's way. The three principle methods for doing this are:

- Evacuating

- Defending in place

- Providing an area of refuge

Each of these methods involves specific expectations and uses. Sometimes a combination of methods may be used; however, combined methods generally are suited for specific types of occupancies. As the AHJ, you may find a need to integrate options and consider any of these methods for unique uses. Again, you are the resident expert.

Evacuation

As we have discussed previously, evacuation has two components:
- Notifying occupants

- Providing safe and unobstructed paths or methods of escape

Both of these components depend heavily upon the educational component of the three *E*s. Notification may be more important than you ever considered. After the first World Trade Center bombing, it took over eight hours for all the occupants to be evacuated from the upper portions of the buildings. Obviously the sooner people know of a hostile condition, the sooner they can leave. In large facilities accurate, prompt notification is especially important.

After people have been notified of a fire emergency, their next critical need is a protected path of egress. Protected path of egress basically means a hallway, corridor, or stairwell that is constructed to resist fire and smoke penetration for a minimum amount of time. This minimum time should be long enough to allow anyone who could be moving through the protected path sufficient time to get from harm's way to a safe area typically referred to as a public way. This is usually accomplished by providing a minimum of two ways out.

Most exiting systems (means of egress) are protected by a minimum two-hour construction. This means that the walls, floor, and ceiling assemblies are constructed in a manner that has been proven to pass a fire severity test based on the standard fire temperature curve. Keep in mind that while this test curve is a good scientific constant, it was created in the early 1900s. Today's phenolics, resins, and plastics were not available back then, and therefore could not be burned and tested for their effects on the outcome of a test fire. Thus, the test used today for certifying a two-hour wall is not necessarily representative of today's fire experience because fuels are different than when the original test was conducted.

Fires years ago burned hot for a long duration. Many fuel components today burn even hotter but for a much shorter period of time. How significant is this? It makes a difference in terms of time temperature curves, but as a basis for standard comparison and verification of performance, the results remain "close enough." As the fire protection professional, though, you must consider this difference if nontypical applications (which we see more and more of every day) come across your desk. As the lone professional, you must research and understand the differences and their effects.

While protecting occupants from fire and smoke exposure is important, the paths of egress must also be compatible with the occupants who must use them. If you have wheelchair-bound individuals, for example, five flights of stairs likely are not a good choice for emergency egress. Using elevators as a part of the emergency egress is not preferred, due to the compounding problems of moving people in a steel box down a chimney with fire directly below; however, in some cases elevators may be required. If a fire is above these occupants, it may not be unreasonable for them to evacuate using elevators. Understand, we are not endorsing elevators as a means of egress. What we are communicating are the variables from occupancy to occupancy and from occupant to occupant. The world is not perfect and neither will be your fire protection solutions. Think of your options, think of the expectations and the possible outcomes and use good practical judgment with the tools you have available.

Code books cannot be written for every type of structure, hazard, industrial operation, or process. You will need to determine the best method currently available and exercise good judgment. Remember, too, to be prepared to testify in court to why you did what you did and how it met the intent of the code requirements.

Defend in Place

The next element of evacuation is defending in place. Defending in place is generally thought of as a means of protecting people or processes without significant relocation or evacuation. This includes not only areas in buildings

---

Think of your options, think of the expectations and the possible outcomes and use good practical judgment with the tools you have available.

✔ **defending in place**
protecting people or processes without significant relocation or evacuation

but areas in the wildfire environment as well. Terrorism is another prime example of emergencies that might require defending in place.

Let's look at a wildfire scenario as an example.

Example: A large elementary school with some 500 children and around 45 staff is nestled in a residential neighborhood in the middle of an expansive wildland/urban interface. A fire occurs downslope of the school, moving quickly upslope, uncontrolled by the available fire fighting resources. Good emergency planning on the part of the school in cooperation with the local fire department has prepared staff, students, and parents to expect either evacuation or defending in place in the event of a wildfire emergency.

- *Evacuation* of the school's occupants is the method of choice if there is adequate time (one to two hours) to notify parents and secure transportation. (Buses do not just appear; they are on strict schedules. Likewise, parents may not be able to get from work to school quickly enough to get their children). The evacuation plan also calls for vegetation mitigation around the exterior of the school so fire crews will not need to remain in place trying to protect the property.

- *Defending in place* is the method of choice if there is an immediate threat (less than an hour) and people have insufficient time to leave the premises lest they become exposures themselves. Staff and students are instructed on how to behave. They move to interior portions of the noncombustible structure to get away from windows and doors. The maintenance staff shuts down all air intakes and closes all outside windows and doors. As for evacuation, vegetation management must be sufficient to protect the structure from damage in the absence of emergency crews. A tactical operations agreement with the local fire department assures that fire crews will respond to the school to establish an anchor for defending the site. This plan also incorporates careful education and participation of parents to understand that the children will be protected in the school and that they are not to try to get their children until advised by the local fire department. (This is very important yet extremely hard to achieve.)

Due to the proximity of the fire, fire crews respond to the location and set up a defensive perimeter in accordance with the plan. The staff moves the children to the core of the building, and the fire moves in proximity of the school. As expected, the heat pulse rises rapidly, consuming all vegetation downslope, throwing embers and flaming debris into the defending fire crews and the structure. Smoke begins to enter the structure through various cracks and openings, and the sound of the fire is deafening. Children begin to sob, teachers get anxious, and everyone has a hard time breathing. However, after about 10–20 minutes, the commanding fire officer enters the school and gives a good report that the flame front has passed. They are mopping up hot spots, but everything is okay.

Considerable training and behavior modification must take place to give people the necessary confidence that they can and will survive a fire even though it may seem to be bearing down on them.

This example of defending in place is applicable to many other settings, such as hospitals, nursing homes, prisons, high-rise buildings, and other locations where relocating or moving the occupants is not feasible. Defending in place requires careful preplanning and predesign work. To withstand a fire and its effects, various components must be included in the structure and regularly maintained. Also, a considerable amount of training and behavior modification must take place in order to give people the necessary level of confidence that they can and will survive a fire even though it may seem to be bearing down on them.

Performance expectations, such as time of tenability or survivability, must also be considered. Designers and planners should understand a fire's expected duration and what the defended location must be able to withstand. For example, if a fire in one portion of a hospital is predicted to last approximately twenty minutes, planners could feasibly design the defended portion to remain protected a minimum of two hours. This provides a level of safety, or safety factor, above and beyond what is typically expected and allows for an unpredicted event that may last somewhat longer due to unforeseen circumstances. Looking back to the school example, we can see that by using noncombustible construction, managing the surrounding vegetation, and working with the fire department, planners had considered how the fire would behave and knew that an intense fire exposure of 10–20 minutes was survivable. In this instance, things worked out fine.

When analyzing these types of scenarios, keep in mind, too, that bad events typically do not occur when things are going well. The "Murphy" who enforces "Murphy's Law" does not typically plan to make things go wrong when all is right. He waits until numerous things have already gone bad and then works his magic. That is why everyone calls on the fire service; we know how Murphy behaves and we try to fix things when they go wrong. As has been said, the fire service is in the bad-day business.

Provide an Area of Refuge

Defending in place requires an area of refuge. Planning and designing this area requires a lot of thought. Basically, this is an area or series of areas that are separated by sufficient fire resistive construction that we can move through or into for safety. An example could be a high-rise building where we encourage people to move above a fire floor rather than passing down through an active fire floor. This process can be contrary to many people's instincts. Another example could be a large warehouse or manufacturing facility where people may migrate to a different part of the facility to get out of harm's way.

This concept is not unusual and is widely used in warships. Anyone who has been in the Navy understands well the idea of compartmentation and isolation. If a fire is in one compartment, everyone who can do so moves to another compartment, and they close off the fire area letting it burn itself out. This happens while others are protected in areas of refuge, which may adjoin the fire compartment.

Performance-Based Design

Performance-based design is a relatively new concept and is being debated and discussed aggressively (see also the corresponding discussion of performance-based codes in Chapter 3). It centers on risk analysis, hazard assessment, consequence identification, and decision-making. Insofar as code books do not account for all types of structures, industrial operations, and processes that may be encountered, performance-based design is a tool to address unique or complex situations. While an in-depth understanding of performance-based design is well beyond the scope of this text, the following example offers a generalized illustration:

> A prescriptive code calls for a corridor in a commercial building to be a minimum of 44 inches wide. A performance-based requirement would state: the corridor must be wide enough to allow 65 people the ability to evacuate the building in the event of a fire, within 60 seconds, without suffering any ill effects from combustion byproducts or the fire itself.

As fire modeling and research data become more available and technology allows us more quickly to calculate an exhaustive number of variables, performance-based design will find more and more applications. It frees designers from constraints currently built into the codes by allowing them to design a product that performs equally well or better for very specific needs or objectives.

For local application, this process is very expensive, but in a broad sense many departments employ it every day. They probably do not think of it as performance-based design but as "alternate means and methods."

> *Example:* A designer proposes a new 15-unit, three-story apartment building. She is designing it for a developer who owns a piece of ground that is infill and landlocked. There is no good access for fire apparatus, and the water supply is old and cannot be improved reasonably. As the progressive fire prevention manager you are, you listen to issues and review your local ordinances to determine all of your options. Your review of the prescriptive code shows that since the building contains only 15 units, fire sprinklers are not required.

> But, because the building will be ordinary construction your water supply requirements demand 4,000 gallons per minute, and your city can provide only 2,750 gallons per minute at the site. You step back, put on your performance-based design hat, and suggest installing automatic fire sprinklers and a monitored fire alarm system. They agree and you have saved the day.

What did you do that was performance based? You examined your risk. You could have denied the whole project, right up until your mayor or city manager called you and your chief in the office and told you how to do your job. Your bosses basically let developers do what they want because "You are not going to control and stifle growth in this city!"

You realized that the apartments would be built one way or the other. Recognizing the limited water supply, you thought about how you could keep a fire to its lowest possible state until your crews arrived to fully extinguish it. Next you recognize that your crews have poor access and at best can get only one engine company close to the structure. One engine easily can provide 250 gallons per minute within the first minute or so, and that is pretty good if—again—the fire is kept at its lowest possible state for the first five minutes. You recognize that sprinklers are not required, but if they were you could rely on the sprinkler system to keep the fire in check for at least thirty minutes. The available water supply is plenty for a sprinkler system, even if it does not meet the fire code requirement for two engines to pump with. Thinking some more about the poor access, you realize that you could bring only one engine close enough to attack the fire, so you would not be able to use the additional water anyway. You want to get the earliest jump possible on any potential fire, and the only way to ensure doing so at 2:00 A.M. would be to monitor smoke detectors or the water flow device on the sprinkler system if they installed it. So you propose your idea and everybody wins.

You defined the risk, you conducted a quick hazard assessment, and you evaluated the various consequences. You then decided which solution would be best. Voila! You just performed your first nontechnical performance-based design process. But don't tell the people in fire protection engineering that. Tell them it was a process of working through "alternate means and methods!"

When applying the performance-based design approach, it is paramount to strive for a solution whose results will be equivalent to or more effective than the prescribed codes. Documenting very completely the entire process and *all* of the communication is imperative. The conditions and requirements identified in the performance-based design must stay in place for the life of the structure, and fire inspectors will need to verify that they do.

> When applying the performance-based design approach, it is paramount to strive for a solution whose results will be equivalent to or more effective than the prescribed codes.

Summary

Hazards are conditions that provide a source of ignition for a hostile fire or that contribute to the spread and severity of a hostile fire. In order to mitigate fire and explosion problems, these various hazards must be identified and eliminated or abated. Many texts discuss specific types of hazards such as improperly stored gasoline or exposed electrical wiring. However, our approach is more global in assisting fire officials to look at the "big picture" of occupancy type as opposed to specific individual hazards. We propose looking at the macro level rather than the micro level for global fire prevention work.

The principal part of your job is to mitigate threats to your community. While improperly stored gasoline is a threat, it would be very difficult to find every instance of that hazard in your community. So what we propose is looking at specific occupancies, or targets, within your community that are threats. Think strategically. Look at where you are experiencing fires currently and identify the hazards in those occupancies that aggressive fire prevention efforts can correct.

These efforts should not necessarily involve just your department personnel. They should also include the stakeholders who own or are involved with the occupancies. This establishes buy-in and involvement at the grass-roots level. That way you are not telling people what to do but assisting them in taking care of themselves.

The first step is developing a target protection plan. Then you must identify your resources. What can you bring to bear on the problem? What will you need to be effective? Always keep your team involved. People who are involved have a sense of ownership and do a much better job. Then constantly reevaluate your plan. Use a feedback loop to make sure you stay on top of changes in your target or modifications to your solutions. There are numerous ways to make the target protection plan succeed. Remember the Three Es: engineering, education, and enforcement. Both active and passive fire protection systems are a critical component of these three E's. Active measures include suppression systems, detection and alarm, and emergency fire department response. Passive approaches include product manufacture and engineering controls, administrative controls and compartmentation.

Occupant safety is our principle goal. If our occupants can get out of the structure or be isolated from hostile fire, then our principal mission of life safety is achieved. The procedures to accomplish this can vary but may include evacuation, defending in place, or providing an area of refuge. A major part of these procedures is making sure occupants know of the problem.

A newer and more difficult element of fire and life safety protection involves performance based design. This involves a process in which an architect or designer works with the local fire authority to craft outcome objectives regarding fire and life safety. The objectives can be as simple as "all occupants are able to leave the building before a fire event causes them harm or injury." With this objective in mind, then the designer and fire official establish goals by which this is to be accomplished. These goals may or may not be based on prescriptive fire code requirements. For example, if it is agreed that 100 people must leave a given space and get to the outside within 2 minutes in the event a fire starts and there is only a 15-inch corridor for all 100 people to escape through, the design is acceptable if it can be proven to work. This type of design may save designers and owners large sums of money on materials. In this example, current code would likely call for corridors to be a minimum of 44 inches wide. Allowing the corridor to be 15 inches saves time and money. However, be wary of the design costs. Often the cost of proving these elements' efficacy can be far more than simply meeting the default prescriptive design requirements. Also, for the fire official, future changes in occupancy may profoundly effect how the occupants will evacuate the structure. Therefore, the initial goals and objective of the design may be inappropriate for the new use, invalidating the original design.

As a fire protection professional, you must apply general principles to the community, not just to individual buildings. Identifying appropriate targets and problems will provide a much more visible and productive approach to your overall fire prevention effort. Explaining to a council member that

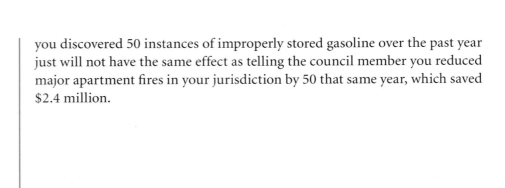

you discovered 50 instances of improperly stored gasoline over the past year just will not have the same effect as telling the council member you reduced major apartment fires in your jurisdiction by 50 that same year, which saved $2.4 million.

Chapter 12 Review Exercises

12.1 What is a hazard? _____
_____

12.2 What are the most common causes of residential fires nationally?
Use the Internet to contrast the causes this text identifies. _____
_____
_____
_____

12.3 What is meant by the term common hazard? _____
_____

12.4 What is meant by the term specific hazard?_____
_____

12.5 What does it mean to identify your target hazards? _____
_____
_____

12.6 List the seven steps of creating a target hazard identification plan.

1. _____

2. _____

3. _____

4. _____

5. _____

6. _____

7. _____

12.7 Identify the basic engineering elements used to control fire and explain how each works. _____
_____
_____
_____

12.8 Explain the difference between active and passive fire protection.
_____
_____
_____

12.9 List in order of importance the two tasks the fire service performs.
_____
_____

12.10 Are fire department suppression operations important? Why are they lowest in the priorities of overall protection of hazards? _____

_____

_____

12.11 How does product manufacture and performance-control impact fire protection? _____

_____

_____

12.12 What is compartmentation?_____

_____

_____

_____

12.13 Explain the concept of defending in place. _____

_____

_____

12.14 What are the two principle methods involved with evacuation?

_____

_____

12.15 What is the time temperature curve's drawback in current applications? _____

_____

12.16 What qualifies as an area of refuge?_____

_____

12.17 Define performance-based design. _____

_____

_____

NOTES

1. George C. Beakley and Herbert W. Leach, *Careers in Engineering and Technology,* 2nd ed. (New York: Macmillan, 1979), p. 3.

2. Arthur E. Cote and Jim L. Linville, *Fire Protection Handbook,* 17th ed. (Quincy, Mass.: National Fire Protection Association, 1991).

3. Ibid.

Fire Prevention Applications
Chapter 13: Wildland Fire Mitigation

FESHE COURSE OBJECTIVES

1. Identify the impact of wildland fires.

2. Identify the components of wildland and urban interface.

3. Identify agencies that take an active role in preventing wildland fires.

4. Identify methods to prevent wildland fires.

Chapter 13
Wildland Fire Mitigation

Wildfire and the Environment

Wildland fires have raged as long as the earth has had vegetation. The earth has undergone biological cleansing by fire on a regular basis. This process has been initiated by lightning, volcanic activity, and the like ever since fuel, air, and heat first combined. As man evolved and fire became a tool and weapon, wildfires—both accidental and purposeful—also became a product of human activity. Humans used wildfire to herd game and other humans. They also used it to clear dense underbrush to make game more visible and accessible for hunting. Fire's use in warfare is prevalent even today. Fire is part of the natural environment whether we humans have been present or not. Forest lands have burned for thousands of years as a result of these various causes.

In many parts of the world, humankind has altered wildfire's frequency and severity, which has forced it to progress in cycles, not necessarily managed the way Mother Nature would have preferred. This alteration has occurred due to clear-cutting to make room for crops and grazing, logging for lumber, fire extinguishment policies, urban sprawl, and carelessness, to mention only a few causes. While policymakers at the federal, state, and local levels argue about what is right for our country, we need to shift from the way we have been dealing with wildfire during the recent past. As technology has improved, so have our methods of identifying and dealing with wildfire. We will never be able to stop it, nor should we try as it is as much a part of nature as the trees and brush it consumes. Instead, we must try to understand it and work within its cycle as much as possible. The following chapter will help you understand more about where we have come from, where we are, and where we should go from here as fire service professionals.

> We will never be able to stop wildfire, nor should we try as it is as much a part of nature as the trees and brush it consumes.

What Is Wildfire?

A **wildfire** basically can be described as any hostile fire in the outdoors that is not prescribed or purposefully managed. Wildfires occur in every country and, unfortunately, as time goes on they are occurring with greater frequency and severity in many parts of the world. Each year, on average 200,000 fires burn more than 1.5 million acres of protected forest, brush, and grassland in the

✔ **wildfire**
any hostile fire in the outdoors that is not prescribed or purposefully managed

United States and Canada alone.[1] In 2001 and 2002 media accounts focused on wildfires in Australia; however, South America, Asia, and obviously, North America are no strangers to these events. Thousands of homes are destroyed each year as we move communities deeper into rural settings. People are moving to the mountains in record numbers to escape the hustle and bustle of the city (**Figure 13.1**). People as a whole either choose or are forced by lack of space to live in a natural fire environment. Many people are surprised at the tragedy and mayhem wildfire produces. People are actually mesmerized at

Figure 13.1 Homes continue to be built into the hillside. Heavy vegetation is a great risk to these structures and the folks who live in them.

the effects produced when nature unleashes her fury in wildfire events. Why? As we stated, fires have burned our countryside for hundreds of thousands of years. Driving on American highways and looking along the sides of carved out roadways you can see the black carbon line of historical evidence of "big burns" that occurred before the waters from floods and other geological changes covered the forest floor with silt and other debris.

Fire, left to its own course, used to be a good thing. Most forest fires were what we term ground fires. This means that fire generally traveled along the ground clearing forest floor debris (dead grass, twigs, deadfall, and other noxious organic substances) and making way for new growth. Small, heavily congested trees were killed, thereby thinning potential overgrowth and allowing mature tree stands to take hold, providing cover for smaller animals and birds. Only rare fire events were what we call stand replacement fires today. These fires generally occurred when the natural health of the forest ecosystem was diseased and overgrown due to too much vegetation growing in close proximity. When these fires occurred, flames moved from the ground into the crowns of the trees. They consumed everything in their path, from small ground-level plants to large ponderosa or fir stands. While not common, these fires were essential to reconstructing and realigning the vegetation that needed repair. It is important to keep in mind that while the human life span is around 75 years, the natural environment remains relatively unchanged for hundreds of thousands of years. An event such as this, while markedly tragic in our view of time, is but a small nuisance to Mother Nature. She utilizes this time to nurture, develop, and foster the ecosystem.

Our main mission in fire prevention is to protect people from the ravages of hostile fire. Wildfires raise issues that are not necessarily present in what we could term fire prevention's typical bread-and-butter operations. However, they can be addressed in much the same manner.

Historical Forest Service Issues

To begin solving our wildfire problem requires a look at its history. Fires were ravaging our forests at the turn of the twentieth century. In 1910, a Dr. Deckert noted, "devastating conflagrations of an extent elsewhere unheard of have always been the order of the day in the United States."[2] That same year the Forest Service lost around five million acres to wildfire, which was under their jurisdiction. This stirred great debate among government officials and the Forest Service, who began to throw considerable amounts of money and resources into a national fire fighting effort. Years of depression, drought, and inflation brought action on many issues. President Franklin D. Roosevelt's New Deal presented the opportunity for a massive manual fire fighting effort. This spawned a huge program called the Civilian Conservation Corps. With it came loads of federal money that played perfectly into the hands of the Forest Service's new philosophy and policies. So perfectly, in fact, that in 1935 Chief Forester Ferdinand Silcox initiated the **10:00 A.M. policy**, which mandated control of any fire by 10:00 A.M. the day it was reported or, failing that, control by 10:00 A.M. the day following, ad infinitum.[3] This policy led to tremendous advancements in strategies, tactics, and equipment, not to mention physical resources.

✔ **10:00 A.M. policy**
policy mandating that any fire be controlled by 10:00 A.M. the day it is reported or, failing that, by 10:00 A.M. the day following, ad infinitum

The United States Forest Service protects about 200 million acres of national forest and other lands. The Bureau of Land Management (BLM), the National Park Service (NPS), the United States Fish and Wildlife Service, and the Bureau of Indian Affairs control another 587 million acres. State and other local land under control of localized fire fighting resources makes up about 840 million acres.[4] In 2000, over five million acres were burned at a cost to the federal government of about $1.6 billion.[5] While this seems to be a small percentage of total area, the impact is gigantic. A significant amount of this expense went toward protecting homes and businesses—structures that have been designed and built in harm's way.

The 10:00 A.M. policy has recently come under tremendous scrutiny. The public and municipal fire service agencies are asking hard questions about the issue:

- Why are we fighting fires in the middle of the forest when nothing is out there but trees and grass?

- How do we protect an ever-increasing number of structures when

The policy of extinguishing fires as quickly as possible contributes to the wildland's poor ecological health basically creating a disaster waiting to happen.

resources are stretched thin fighting fire on some far away mountain well away from any populated area?

- Why do so many local fire fighting agencies commit so much resources at such low federal reimbursement rates?

Fueling this debate, the policy of extinguishing fires as quickly as possible has led to substantial overgrowth of vegetation, which is now being scourged by disease, drought, and insects. This only contributes to the wildland's poor ecological health. Basically, we have created a disaster waiting to happen.

Current Threats and Risks

We live, work, and play in a natural fire environment. Many believe this environment is presently out of ecological/fire balance. We are experiencing fires that grow much larger and much faster than ever before. This is due to the large volume of thick and diseased vegetation. Communities and businesses situated in or near this combustible tinderbox greatly exacerbate the perceived threat and risk. While the structures we protect are at great risk, the environment is equally endangered. The growing numbers of fires, burning with greater intensity, and the increasing thermal load of the surrounding vegetation are literally sterilizing the soil.

The wildland/urban interface is defined as that area of a community where forested land mixes with urbanized functions and structures. It is broken into three basic components:

✔ **interface mix**
rural area with structures scattered sparsely throughout

- **Interface mix.** This involves structures that are scattered throughout a rural area. It is typically an area where isolated homes are surrounded by undeveloped land. Usually few homes in concentration are at risk here, as the interface mix is similar to a sparsely populated mountain ranching community.

✔ **occluded interface**
isolated area of forested land or wildlands surrounded by homes or other structures

- **Occluded interface.** This is an isolated area of forested land or wildlands surrounded by homes or other structures, such as a large park or preserve.

✔ **classic interface**
area with homes and other structures, especially in small dense neighborhoods, pressed directly against the forest or wildlands

- **Classic interface.** This involves homes and other structures, especially in small dense neighborhoods, pressed directly against the forest or wildlands. A perfect example is Los Alamos, New Mexico, which was burned over in a wildfire in 2001.

These areas contain the most significant assets at risk. This is not to say that historical artifacts, such as the ruins at Mesa Verde National Park in Colorado, are not important. However, from a fire prevention standpoint, the elements of priority for our professional concerns are life, property, and resources.

Outside of communities, the major natural elements that are directly impacted by wildfire are:

- Water

- Wildlife

- Air

- Plants

- Timber

- Soil

Watersheds, which are becoming more and more critical to human survival are being polluted, costing millions to clean up and restore, particularly after a contaminating wildfire event. The water pollution created from wildfire is extensive and complex. Smaller organisms and the fish they support become poisoned and suffocated. Streams and creeks become obstructed and contaminated. Silt and sediment diminishes storage capacity in supply reservoirs. The destruction of forest canopy due to crown fires eliminates wildlife habitat for smaller birds, squirrels, and other animals on which predators feed.

Wildfires frequently produce thousands of pounds of airborne particles (smoke) that affect not only human health but the weather as well. Toxic gases, such as carbon dioxide, carbon monoxide, nitrous oxides, and other organic gases, not only harm animal life but also can contribute to global warming. Big fire events can paralyze the lumber industry. Trees do not grow old overnight and therefore must be established for many years before their lumber can be properly harvested. Forest soils, which once could be cleared of down and dead vegetation by relatively minor ground fire events, are now being turned to glass resulting in an inability to soak up moisture or rapidly spawn new vegetation.

Causes of Wildfire

The same conditions that cause most of our fire problem also cause wildfires. However, one more element, while not a direct cause, is certainly a significant contributor to catastrophic wildfire: interruption of Nature's fire cycle. We have clearly recognized recently the negative effects of removing fire from the natural cycle. This intervention is detrimental and disruptive to a wildland's ecology. Just a few of the many factors that influence a wildland's ecosystem are:

- Climate

- Topography

- Geography

- Vegetation

- Animal life

- Pollution

Defining a local ecosystem is complex, as it requires an examination of many elements. It depends upon events, objects, processes, and all the details of how they interact. An example could be a typical western mountain forest (**Figure 13.2, on next page**). If the forest is permitted to grow without fire, the vegetation will gradually become very dense and overgrown. Animal life

Figure 13.2 Vegetation is dynamic, not static. It grows and dies as the environment changes.

will dwindle, as the vegetation becomes too hard to navigate. Sunlight is reduced, thereby restricting the types of vegetation that will grow there. Plants, just like animals, are limited by the amount of nutrients they receive. Competition then becomes keen. Disease and insects become common, as they are among the few organisms that can survive this predicament. The insects and disease further stress the vegetation, making it even more susceptible to disease and parasites. The bark beetle is a good example. This beetle burrows into the bark of a tree, its host, and lays eggs. This damages the tree's natural protection (bark) and causes the tree to lose life-giving moisture due to the network of tunnels the beetles created as they spread throughout the tree. These numerous tunnels soon fill with a bluish fungus that blocks nutrients from feeding the tree. A healthy tree where drought is not present will form a plug of pitch or resin that in the colder months when the beetle is inactive will bubble outward forcing out the beetle and thereby saving the tree. However, when the tree is stressed and competition limits its moisture supply, the tree cannot protect itself and eventually succumbs to the beetle infestation, which it passes on to the next tree. Fire, in this example, would play an important beneficial role:

- Fire can influence plant community composition.

- Fire can interrupt and alter succession.

- Fire can change the amount, kind, and size of various vegetation types in a given area.

- Fire regulates vegetation (fuel) accumulation.

- Fire influences and improves the nutrient cycles and energy flow.

- Fire affects the wildlife habitat.

- Fire interacts with and controls insects and disease.

- Fire influences the productivity, diversity, and stability of the ecosystem.

When wildlands can proceed through their natural cycle, the fire resistivity of the forest improves; the balance of detrimental insects and disease is maintained, and wildlife interaction benefits the overall symbiotic relationship.

> When wildlands can proceed through their natural cycle, the fire resistivity of the forest improves.

Factors Determining Risk

The high intensity wildland fires of the last few years have forced a significant shift in federal directives giving priority to structures and community infrastructure over natural resources. This shift to address the "larger" risk is likely to quickly drain federal reserves and force more interdependence with state and local resources. The federal government will quickly be put in the position of forcing local communities to spend more money protecting themselves rather than depending on federal assistance.

Political and sociological factors also play a big part in the wildland/urban interface fire problem. Society is moving from a philosophy of "taking care of ourselves" to always depending on someone else. Our "don't-blame-me" culture causes extraordinary dependence upon governmental resources, whether federal, state, or local. This cannot be sustained and therefore is forcing all fire protection experts to foster leadership and cooperation.

From a fire prevention standpoint, this interagency cooperation is very important. The fire prevention message is difficult enough to convey in general fire safety issues but is compounded in wildlands because Americans in general do not perceive a risk from wildfire. The property owners who typically build in or adjacent to forested areas generally choose to do so because they want a more rugged lifestyle or desire a location that is "away from it all." This attitude is typical for those people who tend to show a little more independence and also who typically do not like being told what to do.

Much like those folks who live in hurricane alley, these people also have a belief that insurance companies will pay for their losses and therefore do not show much concern. In our experience, people who have survived or been closely involved with wildfire exhibit excellent fire-prevention attitudes, but generally this is short lived. After some time has passed, many of these same people develop an attitude that "It couldn't happen again; that was a once in a million years event." The amount of publicity surrounding wildfire events also puts a lot of focus on the fire service and the forest service. This is a major barrier to getting our fire prevention message across to the public we serve.

The factors that determine risk in the wildland/urban interface are relatively consistent throughout the country:

- What are the loss impacts to the community?
- What is the community's assessment of which losses are and are not acceptable?
- What is our ability to mitigate identified hazards?

To effectively deal with this risk, the fire service must determine what level of emergency they can reasonably contend with and then remedy those bigger emergencies in some other manner.

Wildfire Management

Once a community has determined its acceptable risk, elements of prevention and suppression should be readily identifiable to help target specific wildfire management schemes. This can involve a number of elements such as:

- Interagency cooperation
- Fire and life safety education
- Prevention tools
- Prevention and mitigation
- Suppression

Interagency Cooperation

Fire protection problems in the wildland/urban interface are very complex. The numerous political and bureaucratic barriers that must be dealt with include but are not limited to:

- Legal mandates
- Zoning regulations
- Fire and building codes
- Fire protection infrastructure
- Insurance grading and rating systems
- Environmental concerns
- Cooperative agreements

The wildland fire problem has increased steadily over the years. With an abundance of excessive vegetation and an ever-increasing populace moving adjacent to federal and state lands, the interaction among various agencies is unlike anything in the past. Federal agencies are being relied upon more heavily than ever before because their expertise at running campaign fires is renowned.

Federal officials, however, face the dilemma of ever-dwindling resources. At the time this book was written, the economy was on the brink of a double-dip recession. Expenses for war and homeland security were higher than ever in recent times. Tax cuts loomed as part of federal stimulus packages, and with all of this, massive retirements in the forest service command cadre coupled with limited funds to train and develop younger fire management officers had placed the federal managers in a critical predicament. The 2002 fire season brought several air-tanker crashes, which paralyzed air support for several weeks. The future of air support for fires is looking continually weaker.

How does this impact us as fire protection professionals? Without an effective and competent army to respond to and suppress wildfire, what are we going to do? We need to maximize our efforts and resources to provide the best prevention and protection possible. Most wildland/urban interface departments do not have the resources to respond. For a single agency to provide the necessary leadership in these catastrophic events is becoming more and more difficult. Local communities do not have the resources to combat large campaign events. The federal government also is losing the resources to respond. As a result, many smaller communities have to muster resources to combat these large conflagrations, while still subordinating command and control responsibilities to federal or state agencies. Conflicts between state and federal boundaries, not to mention those of municipalities and private land, all create huge logistical complications that should be worked out in advance. The best method for doing this is through proper fire prevention efforts, which will reduce the need for operational support.

Attempts to foster cooperation between the "structure guys and gals" and the "yellow shirts" are ongoing. Typically, these two groups have had very

The abundance of excessive vegetation and ever-increasing populace moving adjacent to federal and state lands requires greater interaction among agencies than ever before.

different missions and training. Wildland firefighters generally have not had tactical structural fire fighting training and structural firefighters typically have not been "red carded" (a training process equivalent to Firefighter I or II certification). While this effort at networking and building working relationships between the groups is important, much more needs to be done to unite the messages of fire prevention in a more cohesive nationwide program.

Fire and Life Safety Education

The forest service started a massive public education campaign with Smokey Bear in 1950. Smokey was a slightly injured bear cub found by a fire fighting crew in the Lincoln National Forest in New Mexico. The young cub was nursed back to health and placed in captivity, launching one of the largest forest fire prevention campaigns ever seen. This campaign is still in use today and is credited with preventing thousands of fires. In fact, considering the number of fires started by careless campfires or outdoor fire use (very small) vs. the number of people who recreate outdoors each year (very high), the number is amazing. If only our success was that good for cooking fires in buildings!

> Structural and wildland fire fighting messages must be united in a cohesive nationwide program.

In addition to fire prevention campaigns using Smokey, many more partnerships have been initiated to keep the message current and visible. Many communities have teamed Sparky with Smokey to emphasize the importance of fire prevention. Captain Bill Mills of Colorado Springs, Colorado, once even proposed developing a Mutant Ninja Turtle character named Sprakey to convey the message to the younger audience. While the world may not have been ready for that, the point remains: as fire service professionals, we need to keep current with the latest trends, the latest marketing strategies, and the latest fire problems to make sure we are adequately communicating our issues and solutions (**Figure 13.3**).

Prevention Tools

Wildfire cannot be explained, it can only be experienced. Nothing quite resembles the awesome power of these events. Three elements dictate how a wildfire will behave and move:

- Fuel

- Weather

- Topography

Understanding these three elements is crucial to understanding how to prevent wildfires. Humanity can change only one of them. To some extent,

Figure 13.3 This community FireWise trailer is a popular attraction among residents in Colorado Springs. Neighbors can go inside to see layouts of their neighborhood and what their individual ratings are and compare them with each other.

we might change a site by modifying its topography, but most communities or regulatory agencies prohibit any excessive ground disturbance that would impact the aesthetics of a hillside. For all intents and purposes then, we will consider fuel as the only factor we can control.

Weather is a natural phenomenon that has baffled mankind since our creation. It can and will do mysterious things. While our science and technology have allowed us to learn much about the weather, we have very little control if any over how it will behave. We can do a reasonable job of predicting what will be happening within a few hours or a day; however, changing the weather is out of our reach (since cloud seeding does not really pertain to the fire service, we'll leave its effectiveness for others to debate). Wind obviously has a major effect on the severity of a fire. We also know that large fires will create their own weather. El Niño, la Niña, and other weather patterns all have their effects, whether they be drought, flooding, lightning, or winds. Weather is a force to recognize and to prepare for, but we also must realize we can do nothing about it.

Topography is another significant factor (**Figure 13.4**). What happens when you light a wooden match and tip the flaming head downward? Ouch, right? Well, what happens when you build a house on the top of a steep slope? Ouch, again! Fire moves rapidly uphill. Although science can explain that, no one should need much explanation as it also follows the basic understanding that fire moves upward. So, flat land in Florida will not burn as severely as it would if it had steep similarly vegetated hills and slopes. In comparison to the Rocky Mountains, Florida has to contend with fuel and weather but not topography. Large mountains with steep slopes and drainages that are heavily vegetated can create massive firestorms that, without significant initial weather influence, can create their own weather.

From a fire prevention standpoint, it would not do us much good to recommend that people not live somewhere based on the weather. People generally choose weather as a principle reason *for* living where they do. Telling someone not to build a home at the top of a steep ridge overlooking a scenic valley or open meadow with beautiful pines and mountain mahogany surrounding them can be quite a struggle as well. Why do you think they paid so much for the property on that ridge top? The view. Why would they build down low where they could not see anything? They would not if they did not have to.

What about fuel? Can it be modified or mitigated? Yes, very easily. Does this mean that all vegetation needs to be clear-cut and removed from around a house or structure? Absolutely not!

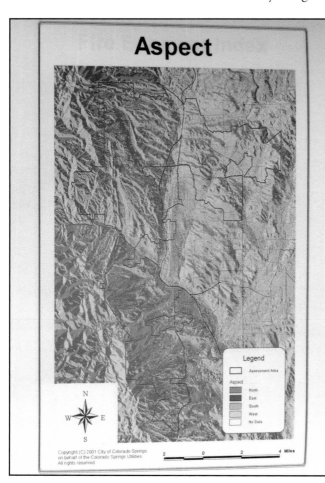

Figure 13.4a Different types of GIS mapping and identification can help identify problems to fix.

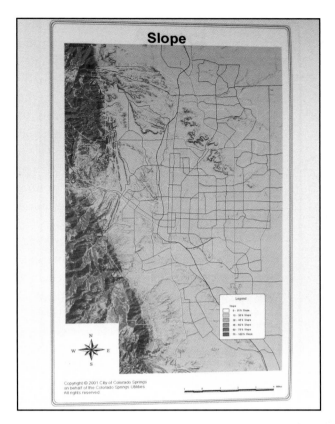

Figure 13.4b

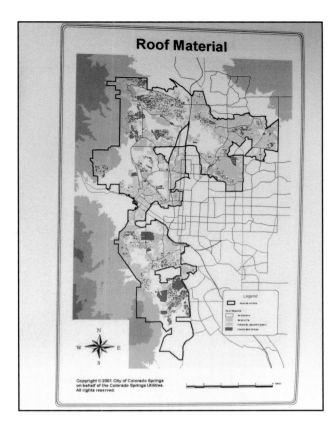

Figure 13.4c

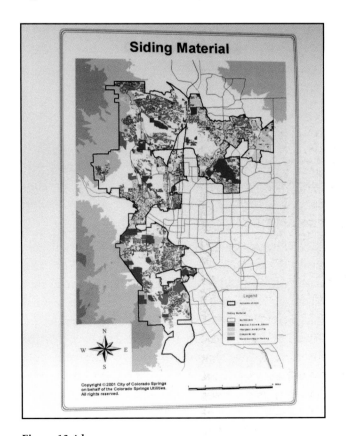

Figure 13.4d

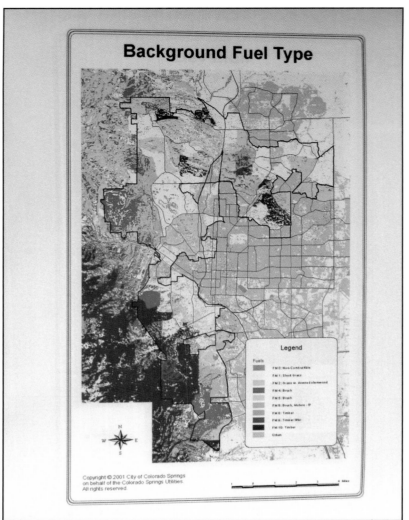

Background Fuel Type

Legend

Fuels
FM 0: Non-Combustible
FM 1: Short Grass
FM 2: Grass w. downed stemwood
FM 4: Brush
FM 5: Brush
FM 6: Brush, Mature - 8'
FM 8: Timber
FM 9: Timber Mixt
FM 10: Timber
Urban

Figure 13.5 Specific GIS risk maps detailing boundaries of dangerous topography and vegetation readily target those elements that should be focused on.

✔ **ladder fuels**
fuels that are configured so that a ground fire can become a surface fire and a surface fire can become a crown fire

In many wildland fires, structures are more of a problem than the vegetation that surrounds them.

Nothing can be done with a crown fire except to watch and wait until it drops to the ground.

Wildland fire models classify available fuels into 13 basic types of vegetation according to fire behavior and heat-release rates (**Figure 13.5**). We propose there are actually 14 types of fuels, with structures being the 14th. In many instances structures prove to be more of a problem than the vegetation that surrounds them. Structures also possess a tremendous amount of mass and in terms of mass-to-air-ratio fuel are a significant source of heat contributing greatly to conflagration outcomes. In fact, while much has been written about the Oakland Hills fire, we propose that it was not as much a wildland/urban interface fire as it was a conflagration from structure to structure. The way the structures blended into the surrounding vegetation made them as significant a fuel model or fuel package as the eucalyptus. Assuming for a moment that this is true, let's consider how to mitigate vegetation and then apply the same methodology to structures.

Vegetation can be grouped into three components for fire prevention or mitigation purposes:

• *Ground fuels (flash fuels).* Grasses or very light fuels that are easily ignited and spread fire rapidly; duff and roots

• *Surface fuels (intermediate fuels, brushy fuels).* Mountain mahogany, gambol oak, chaparral, or small trees

• *Crown fuels.* Branches, tree tops, high brush

In fire prevention, we work very hard to educate people to trim or interrupt ladder fuels. **Ladder fuels** are those fuels configured so that a ground fire can become a surface fire and a surface fire can become a crown fire.

Fires can be extinguished when they are on the ground or on the surface; however, when fire moves into the crowns, fire crews have to stand back and watch just like everyone else. Nothing can be done with a crown fire except to watch and wait until it drops to the ground. These fires, which are termed *stand replacement* fires, cause tremendous damage. Their heat release rate and heat output are so intense that hand crews, engines, or aircraft have no extinguishment effect. The education that we should provide would urge people to manage their vegetation to interrupt this ladder. Remove or strategically clump the brush and large surface fuels, and the ground or small surface fire will not get into the canopy starting a crown fire. This does not stop the fire but mitigates it; it prevents the fire from becoming impossible to combat or helps keep it relatively benign. Removing or greatly thinning one of the two lower fuels or pruning low hanging branches from large trees or brush will not allow fire to be drawn into the canopy as easily, thus preventing crowning.

Considering homes or other structures, we can do similar things. Why would we treat a home or other building in the wildland urban interface any differently? If we view the structure as a fuel source or fuel package, then we can address it like we do other fuels, managing it or mitigating it. As research physical scientist Jack D. Cohen points out, "Understanding how homes ignite during wildland/urban fires provides the basis for appropriately assessing the potential for home ignition and thereby effectively mitigating wildland/urban fire ignitions. Fires do not spread by flowing over the landscape and high intensity fires do not engulf objects, as do avalanches and tsunamis. All fires spread by meeting the requirements for combustion—that is, a sufficiency of fuel, heat and oxygen."[6]

Colorado Springs, Colorado, which has the largest wildland/urban interface in the state of Colorado, takes the approach of factoring this knowledge into home building. Developers have teamed with the fire department to provide several key elements that vastly improve new homes' survivability:

- Class A roofing ordinance (excluding solid wood material)
- Hardening the structure (noncombustible siding and soffits)
- Metal screens on all exterior vents
- Double-pane glazing (energy requirement)
- Vegetation (fuels) management
- Fire engine access for hose reach on all exterior portions of buildings

While this approach does not prevent a home from catching fire, it certainly reduces the possibility. Communication with the residents in those areas suggests a 50 percent improvement in a structure's chances for surviving a wildfire.

Our objective as fire safety professionals should not be to prevent wildland fires in total. Remember, fire is part of the natural environment. Since we choose to build homes in that environment, we should expect fires to threaten them periodically. This being the case, we should then engineer out what fuel sources we can and allow fire to move into and through a neighborhood without destroying homes along the way. Jack Cohen refers to the area around a home as the ignition zone. He writes, "Given low ignition potential and enough time, homeowners and or fire fighting forces can make significant reductions in the little things that influence ignition potential before wildfire encroachment. Then, if possible, homeowners and fire fighting resources can suppress small fires that threaten the structure during and after the wildfire approach."[7]

Prevention and Mitigation

Fire prevention and mitigation are the key to any structure's long-term survivability. The fire service alone cannot achieve this. Again using Colorado Springs, Colorado, as an example, over 51,000 addresses are in the wildland/urban interface. The City of Colorado Springs has a total of 18 fire stations (with two more on the way). This provides an on-duty force of just over 100 firefighters. Assuming there are no other emergencies, training, or public assistance requests to deal with, the department could throw 100 people per shift against a major fire. However, the department decided to utilize its emergency resources for what they are paid to do: respond to fires and other emergencies. Proactively then, they enlisted those who live in the affected areas to help by managing fuel (vegetation), thus keeping those fires that do occur small and relatively benign (**Figure 13.6**). This potentially created an army of 51,000 people or more. If only 10 percent actually participate, that still yields 5,100 people. Which army is better equipped, staffed, and able to communicate the issues? One hundred firefighters or 5,100 motivated citizens? Motivated citizens will win every time.

Education and awareness must compensate for our lack of resources to build a fire suppression army.

Figure 13.6 Neighbors likely want some assistance even if its just in the form of chippers and trucks to clear their yards.

The key is for the fire service to stop telling people what is good for them. This is an adult education issue and requires a different approach than Stop, Drop, and Roll. We suggest following these guidelines:

- Assume adults living in large homes in forested areas are educated, understanding, and responsible.

- Assume that these same adults do not know much about the natural fire environment or their actual risk.

- Assume that they want to do the right thing if they are informed, if they have the capability, and if they can measure progress by themselves, for themselves.

- Be factual, be truthful, and make clear all expectations about survivability and fire suppression capabilities. *Do not* exaggerate the issues.

Once you have communicated clearly the information that adults need to make good decisions, they will honor your attempts and generally do all they can do to help themselves. In Colorado Springs, neighbors motivate neighbors. Why would you want to act as safely as possible, protecting your property and family, while living next door to a person who has not learned about the issues and therefore does not care? You are likely going to go have coffee with that neighbor and share a little insight and maybe a little peer motivation.

Remember, think of this as adult education, not as government telling little people what to do. Government should provide factual information about problems, solutions, and resources, but this does not mean the government can provide those solutions and resources. Government just has to help answer questions that the ordinary person cannot.

Suppression

As with all good fire prevention programs, a systematic approach is critical. Engineer, educate, and enforce those things that facilitate the best emergency response capabilities. Even in the best of worlds we are giving structures only a "fifty-fifty chance" of survivability on their own if and when a wildfire does occur. But we are also helping people to help us. By providing good, survivable space and smart prevention/mitigation measures, we are also giving our fire suppression crews an opportunity to interrupt a hostile fire's advance on a structure (**Figure 13.7**). We give our crews the best chance possible for protecting the property because we already designed and factored in effective prevention and mitigation measures. Ultimately, we must use a systems approach. Without limitless funding, prevention and mitigation alone are not enough. We need to rely reasonably on fire suppression forces. Practicing these methods will go a long way toward ensuring the system's overall effectiveness.

Paradigm Shifts in Wildfire Management

In this chapter we have called for several paradigm shifts in the ways we think about and deal with wildland/urban interface fires. Where these shifts already have been made, they have proven successful. They include:

- Structures provide as much fuel or more than the trees surrounding them.

- Education and awareness must compensate for our lack of resources to build a fire suppression army.

- We must quit telling everybody what is good for them. Give them the information and help them to understand the information; then they will make good, informed decisions.

- Accept decisions with which you may disagree. Remember, you work for the public, not the other way around. Sometimes people want to accept greater risks. As long as they know the potential outcomes, why not let them? Just do not put firefighters in harm's way. And, of course, if someone's behavior becomes a fire risk to others who do not share the same beliefs and values, then we have to do something to change it. That is why they pay us.

Once you have communicated clearly the information that adults need to make good decisions, they will honor your attempts and generally do all they can do to help themselves.

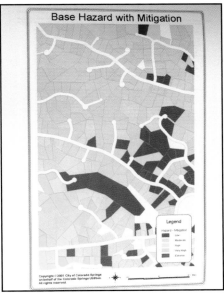

Figure 13.7 a & b The intent of a good wildfire mitigation program will be to move properties from more severe risk to lesser risk as seen in these two maps. Movement from red to yellow or green is a positive step indeed.

Summary

Wildfire is any hostile fire in the outdoors that is not prescribed or purposefully managed. Wildfires are becoming a significant cause of annual fire loss throughout our country. As our forests and wildlands become more dense and overgrown, and as more and more developments encroach the losses will continue to rise.

The philosophical and scientific basis for forest and vegetation management and wildfire control has a long history. However, most agree today that our aggressive posture of extinguishing wildfire has prevented much of the natural vegetation management that occurred from "frequent" fire. This has led to overgrown vegetation and to dead and diseased forests threatening our communities with huge unnatural fuel loading that contributes significantly to our wildland disasters.

Watersheds are also becoming a major exposure due to wildfire. As more and more people move and populate the west, water is becoming a more vital and valuable resource. The ponds, lakes, and estuaries from which we receive our water are easily destroyed or disrupted for many years if a wildfire event moves through them. This causes significant drought and water shortage issues for our communities, not to mention the death and destruction of the aquatic life these areas support.

Wildfire is generally impacted by three major components:

- Fuel

- Weather

- Topography

The issues affecting and determining risk are hugely varied. They depend greatly on the community where you live, as various values on the risk are readily apparent. Obviously, people moved into the mountains to be away from "civilization" in some sense and likely to be away from regulation or at least for the perception of being away from regulation. Thus the issue of how to mitigate wildfire risk can quickly stir controversy.

Various prevention measures are available, and depending upon the area of the country, some are emphasized more than others. Those we believe to be most important are, in order:

1. Noncombustible roofing

2. Hardening of the structure

3. Vegetation management

4. Defensible space

We will never have enough fire suppression capability to completely protect our communities from wildfire. Those departments that have this problem must be smart in applying prevention and risk management strategies that maximize their efforts by involving the community. No matter how you divide it, you will always have more citizens than firefighters. Use the public to your best advantage. They are inexpensive, and if you motivate and engage them, they will do most of the work for you.

Chapter 13 Review Exercises

13.1   What are wildland fires?_____

_____

13.2   Explain why preventing wildland fires from occurring is or is not a
worthwhile fire prevention function._____

_____

_____

_____

_____

13.3   Identify and define the three components of the wildland urban
interface._____

_____

_____

13.4   List the natural elements that wildland fires impact._____

_____

_____

_____

13.5   Identify those agencies that need to take an active role in preventing
wildland fires._____

_____

_____

_____

_____

_____

13.6   What are annual operating plans? _____

_____

_____

_____

_____

_____

13.7   Name at least two methods of preventing wildland fires. _____

_____

13.8   Explain how fire is part of the natural fire environment. _____

_____

_____

_____

_____

13.9   What is the "10:00 A.M." policy and why is it significant? _____

_____

_____

_____

_____

_____

13.10   What are the three priorities in addressing wildfire concerns? _____

_____

_____

_____

13.11   List five key resources that are impacted by wildfire and explain how.

_____

_____

_____

13.12   What three main factors determine how wildfire behaves?_____

_____

_____

_____

13.13   What are the three main factors that determine risk in the wildland/
        urban interface? _____

_____

_____

_____

13.14   Why are collaborative interagency relationships important? _____

_____

_____

_____

13.15   Which of the three wildfire components can human efforts reason-
        ably mitigate? _____

_____

13.16   List and describe the three main vegetation components._____

_____

_____

13.17   Define a stand replacement fire._____

_____

_____

_____

13.18 List the four key guidelines for providing adult education about wildfire mitigation.

1. _____

_____

2. _____

_____

3. _____

_____

4. _____

_____

NOTES

1. *Fire Protection Handbook,* 17th ed. (Quincy, Mass.: National Fire Protection Association). p. 8-220.

2. Stephen J. Pyne, *World Fire: The Culture of Fire on Earth* (Seattle: University of Washington Press, 1995), p. 187.

3. Ibid., p. 195.

4. *Fire Protection Handbook,* p. 8-221.

5. Stephen F. Arno and Steven Allison-Bunnell, *Flames in Our Forest: Disaster or Renewal?* (Washington, D.C.: Island Press, 2002), p. 70.

6. Jack D. Cohen, "Wildland-Urban Fire: A Different Approach," Missoula Fire Sciences Laboratory, Rocky Mountain Research Station, Forest Service, U.S. Department of Agriculture, 2002.

7. Ibid.

Fire Prevention Applications
Chapter 14: Using Technology to Improve Fire Prevention Efforts

FESHE COURSE OBJECTIVES

1.   Identify technological advancements that can improve fire prevention efforts

2.   Understand the elements needed for technology to be useful

Chapter 14

Using Technology to Improve Fire Prevention Efforts

Technology and Change

Our world is constantly changing both in the home and in the workplace. How we deal with those changes will determine how we survive the workplace as well as our home life. Some changes are occurring so fast that it is difficult to keep up, especially in the world of technology. Fifteen years ago, who would have thought fire inspectors would be carrying cell phones, pagers, personal digital assistants, laptops, printers, and digital cameras? Is all of this stuff really necessary or is it just a collection of toys and gadgets?

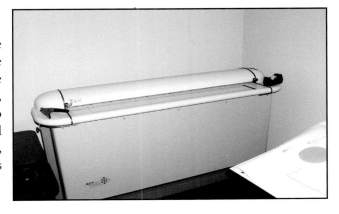

Let's take a look at how we can use technology to actually make our job as fire protection professionals easier and more efficient. Efficiency is important. By now you no doubt will have learned that fire departments will continue to face having to do more with less. One way to compensate for that is to work smarter and more efficiently. That you will also have to work harder is a given because there is a good chance that you will face less than adequate staffing in the field of fire prevention. The work force of the 21st century is more accustomed to electronic technology and grasps its use more easily than some of today's fire prevention veterans.

An important function of both managing and working in fire prevention is record and/or data management. The nature of the work in fire prevention bureaus is conducive to creating tons of paper records (**Figure 14.1**). Essentially, fire prevention bureaus and their staffs are data collectors and managers. How we use that data will determine the effectiveness or ineffectiveness of our fire

Figure 14.1 The scanning of documents, blueprints, and other paper items can be invaluable in the storage and retrieval of data. Pictured are (**a**) a large blueprint scanner and (**b**) a large plotter, used for reproducing blueprints and other large documents.

> How we use the data we collect will determine the effectiveness of our fire prevention efforts.

prevention efforts. Think about what goes on during typical fire prevention activities conducted by fire departments. Fire inspections are one of the first things that come to mind. What happens during a fire inspection? The inspector conducts an inspection and generates inspection data. The inspection data may consist of a number of items such as the following:

- Business name
- Business license
- Occupant contact
- Emergency contact
- Fire alarm system information
- Fire pump
- Key box
- Building square footage
- Hazardous material information
- Violations noted
- Address
- Plan review comments
- Acceptance test data
- Utility shutoff information

Fire prevention bureaus also are involved sometimes in developing the preincident plans that incident commanders use at emergency incidents. Even if the task of gathering the preincident data is performed outside of the fire prevention bureau, the data collected are very similar if not the same. Data typically collected as part of the preincident plan include:

- Occupant contact information
- Address
- Building construction details
- Building dimensions
- Hydrant location
- Available water supply
- Hazardous materials
- Fixed fire suppression (i.e., sprinklers)
- Key box information
- Fire lanes
- Fire department access
- Utility shutoff

For discussion purposes, we will consider a fire department in the process of conducting a hazard risk assessment similar to the one we examined in Chapter 6. Some of the information gathered in this process would include the following:

- Occupancy classification
- Building construction details
- Building dimensions
- Number of building stories
- Occupant load
- Available water supply
- Hydrant location
- Fixed fire suppression (i.e., sprinklers)

Now compare the data collected in each of these tasks. **Table 14.1** clearly illustrates a redundancy. This redundancy will not just be for these three tasks. Consider other tasks, such as construction document reviews and fire investigations, and all will repeat some of the same information. How we as fire professionals collect and use that data is critical to our effectiveness. For example it is not very effective to collect the same data in different visits to the same occupancy if it all could be collected in one visit (assuming, of course, that the data are not constantly changing so fast that they require very frequent updates).

Table 14.1 Data collected during fire prevention activities			
Data Collected	**Activity**		
	Inspection	**Preplanning**	**Risk Survey**
Address	X	X	X
Business name	X	X	X
Business license	X		
Emergency contact	X	X	
Occupant contact information	X	X	
Building construction details	X	X	X
Building square footage	X	X	X
Building dimensions		X	X
Number of building stories		X	X
Occupancy classification	X	X	X
Building dimensions		X	X
Hydrant location		X	X
Available water supply		X	X
Hazardous materials (chemical inventory)	X	X	X
Fixed fire surpression (i.e. sprinklers)	X	X	X
Fire pump	X	X	
Fire alarm system information	X	X	
Knox box information	X	X	
Fire lanes		X	
Fire department access		X	

For instance, an engine company conducts a preincident plan of a senior-citizen housing complex. The data collected are very similar to those we listed above for preincident planning. Later that same month the fire prevention bureau inspector comes to the same location and conducts a fire inspection, again collecting data, this time the data listed above for fire inspections. Finally, an engine company visits the same location later in the year to conduct a risk assessment. The data for the occupancy noted above may not pertain only to fire prevention activities. Some could be used as dispatch information for emergency response. Coordinating all data collection activities and sharing access to that data would benefit the customer and the fire department.

Coordinating all data collection activities and sharing access to that data benefits the customer as well as the fire department.

Fire departments are now placing computers in their apparatus (**Figure 14.2**). These computers are used by the incident commanders and company officers, both while en route to and at the emergency scene. The amount of

Figure 14.2 Many fire department company officers have become reliant on their vehicle laptops to communicate information.

information that can be provided to the responding units is limited only by the department's ability to define and collect it. The responding units can be provided with specific directions of how to get to the scene as well as a map. The communications system also can provide plan review data if it has been collected and managed properly in the beginning.

Computer technology is having equally far-reaching effects on fire prevention technology. Many departments are utilizing some means of computerization in their fire prevention efforts (**Figure 14.3**). This can range from simple word processing to using handheld computers and geographical information systems (GIS). It is one thing to collect and maintain data, but it is another thing to manage that data. Of course, we can put all the data in the world into our super fire prevention database, but what will we use it for? What do we actually need to collect? Are these data already available somewhere else in another format? It is also important to remember the adage, "Garbage in, garbage out." Do not collect superfluous or incorrect data, as they will only be as useful as they are relevant and accurate.

Look again at Table 14.1. If all of these program managers kept separate databases they would be performing redundant tasks. Do not limit to the fire department your questions about who is collecting what data. For example, some of the information you need might have been collected or be maintained by another municipal department in the community. Maybe the department responsible for water billing or business licenses is also collecting and

Figure 14.3 Computers play a vital role in almost all we do, but do not forget to be human and deal with customers appropriately.

maintaining this data. What about the building department? Are they keeping the same construction project information as the fire prevention bureau? Throughout this text we have emphasized the needs to build coalitions and to have the assistance of others. Creating coalitions to collect and manage data should be no different than for fire and life safety education programs.

Most fire departments do not have a full-time person assigned to information technology (IT) or management information systems (MIS). But this is not to say that no one in the department is performing those tasks. In many fire departments, the time has not come where they can contract or be able to hire full-time people assigned this duty. Granted, some departments may not warrant a full-time position because of their size and scope of responsibility. However, this is a critical function that can enhance the fire department's operation. Or if not managed correctly, it can hinder the department's operation. So, should all fire departments begin to eliminate one line firefighter or officer and hire a full-time IT or MIS person? It may be needed, but eliminating shift personnel is hard to justify when they are so difficult to get in the first place.

The best situation is to have a person who is trained in fire department operations and also has a formal education or at least a strong background in MIS. Any MIS person hired to fill the spot will need some time to become familiar with fire department operations. It may even be feasible to use another municipal department's MIS person if the size of your departments does not justify a full-time position. This is another instance where coalitions can pay off.

The "typical" data fields that we have discussed are only a small sample of the data that can be collected. The data noted do not include the details of the deficiencies recorded during the inspection or the results of fire investigations. These are actually the type of data that are most useful in tailoring the fire prevention program to the community.

The development of handheld or tablet computers and the use of personal digital assistants (PDAs) has provided another means for fire prevention bureau personnel to collect data. Fire departments typically collect data on paper forms. The data are then stored in one fashion or another. They may be stored in their original paper format or entered into a computer and stored electronically. The electronic data may or may not be systematically placed in a database format for retrieval and statistical analysis. Fire departments are finding that the sooner they can format the electronic data for retrieval, the more accurate and useful they are. Since computer technology has improved our means to retrieve data quickly, we need to ensure we can enter them at a comparable pace. Nothing is more frustrating than collecting data by computer only to find out that your data entry is a year behind.

One method to keep your data current is to enter them directly during the inspection, emergency incident, or survey. To do this, some fire departments have started utilizing PDAs and tablet computers (**Figure 14.4, on next page**). Data entered in these devices can be transferred electronically from the device to the location where the database is stored via either a computer or a

> Creating coalitions to collect and manage data should be no different than for any other area of fire prevention.

Figure 14.4 Fire inspectors now use tablet computers when performing their inspection tasks. *Photo courtesy of the Mount Prospect Fire Department*

dedicated network or even through radio-data links. An effective method to collect and transfer data is to develop an electronic inspection and gathering program using the latest technology available. One way to do this is to utilize a handheld computing device that stores the information when it is gathered until it can be electronically transferred to the permanent database. The data would be entered once into the handheld device during the fire inspection, preplan inspection, or risk survey. They then could be downloaded at the office or fire station and made available to all personnel in a matter of hours instead of weeks or months. Emergency response personnel could use the information from this almost instant data base during an emergency incident in nearly real-time.

Another possible fire-prevention use for computer technology is cataloging and tracking plan submittals through the use of bar codes. A number of commercially available software products can enhance the fire department's ability to use the data after they have been collected. The key is to ensure the right data are being collected for the intended outcome. For example, if you are collecting data pertaining to the color of exit signs, it is important that this information will be used at some time. Never collect useless data. All it does is take up room, and then like your junk drawer, the database will need to be cleaned.

What data should be collected? That will depend on the fire prevention efforts determined in the strategic planning process (see Chapter 4). The data should help to evaluate the effectiveness of your fire prevention efforts or identify new areas that need attention.

Collect those data that will help to evaluate the effectiveness of your fire prevention efforts or identify new areas that need attention.

Global Information Systems

Global information systems (GIS) are the way of the future. These systems are an extremely powerful and unique way to share information with not only fire department staff but also the public we serve and the policy makers who provide the resources to accomplish our mission. The kinds and levels of analysis available now to researchers, policy advisors, and decision makers were only dreamed of as recently as a decade ago. With every passing day, more and more information and potential uses come to light.

Global information systems work by taking base data of given parameters and laying those data over other layers of data. An example would be gathering information on fire hydrant locations, which are specifically catalogued by geo-based coordinates. They are placed into a map format that is called a layer. A second layer of data can be created—a satellite photo of the community, for instance—that reveals the exact footprint of each structure and all the streets within the study area. By combining these two layers, basically laying one over the other, the footprint of the structures along the streets with specific hydrant locations can be placed on a map.

The base data come from any number of sources, such as private contractors, survey companies, public and private utilities, government agencies, and the military. These data can be in the form of infrared, topographical, photographic, or other images. Tabular data are easily placed into map layers that are graphical images. For example census data can be layered over postal zip code tracts to provide an accurate picture of demographic information for use in public information programs. Similarly, fire incident data can be transferred to fire demand zone (FDZ) layers.

The fullest potential for this type of information has yet to be seen. When the tragic events of 9-11 unfolded, GIS information was used to show accurately where buildings and open spaces used to be versus where they were after the disaster. The information was shared with all of the emergency response teams, and the photos could even be seen over the Internet. This provided invaluable information for search and recovery operations. Another example is the use of satellite imagery during the severe wildfire season of 2002. Infrared satellite images of fires such as the Hayman fire in Colorado and the Rodeo-Chediski fire in Arizona provided real-time pictures of where the flame fronts were advancing, yielding accurate understanding of time relationships to trigger points that had been established for initiating community evacuation orders.

The fullest potential for the use of GIS information has yet to be seen.

Are We There Yet . . . Is Technological Advancement Over?

Technology will continue to advance. The progressive fire protection professional should be aware of those advances and constantly explore how to incorporate them into his or her work. Technology should be used whenever possible if it enhances your job performance or improves the way you do business (**Figure 14.5, on next page**).

Figure 14.5 Roadway signs are now providing lots of information not only about road closures but also about fire danger ratings, evacuation orders, and the like.

Most choose to ride out the waves of new technologies until the "bugs" are worked out and the price of the product falls within their budget. For example, when digital cameras were first introduced, they were very costly and difficult to use because most computers had difficulty supporting them. The legal system was unsure that they could be used in a court of law due to the possibility of photo enhancement or recreation that could nullify an image's validity. Now the price of digital cameras has dropped, the quality has improved, and most all computers can support them. The courts have even ruled that they can be used for photographing evidence.

The use of digital photos for fire inspections and fire service training is becoming very common. These digitized images are useful not only for in-house applications but also for board of appeals hearings, city council meetings, and other venues. More fire prevention bureaus are using digital cameras to document fire safety deficiencies or existing conditions during inspections. For example, restaurants often modify their cooking appliance arrangement to accommodate their changing menus. These modifications can alter the effectiveness of the automatic extinguishing system. Taking a digital picture of the approved cooking equipment allows the fire inspector to compare what he or she sees in the restaurant a year later to the digital photo. The digital photo can be loaded on the handheld computer along with other photos of the occupancy. Not only will the first responders have a map of where they are going on their vehicle laptops; they may even have a photo of the building.

For the fire protection profession to advance, we must be willing to accept new technology and the changes associated with it. We do not want to be left on the corner as an opportunity to improve the way we prevent and mitigate fires passes us by.

For the fire protection profession to advance, we must be willing to accept new technology and the changes associated with it.

Summary

Technology continues to play an important role in fire prevention. The use of personal computers for data collection and fire prevention bureau management is just one of the many technological advancements that have assisted fire departments. The computer has allowed further advancements such as global information systems (GIS). This permits fire departments to access information that may range from the street location of the incident to the nearest hydrant. Other important information such as topographical details can be essential during a wildland fire. Other advancements such as personal digital assistants, tablet computers, digital cameras, and in-vehicle laptops have enabled the fire departments to improve efficiency and reduce costs. This is critical to justify purchase of such equipment. Technology will continue to advance, and fire departments must constantly monitor the environment for opportunities to use the latest technology to handle hostile fires through suppression and prevention.

Chapter 14 Review Questions

14.1 Why is the use of technology important in the field of fire prevention? _____

_____

14.2 What technological advances in the past 5 years have impacted the fire department's ability to prevent fires? Why?_____

_____

_____

_____

_____

_____

_____

_____

_____

_____

_____

14.3 How would you present a request to purchase an item such as a digital camera for use in the fire prevention bureau?_____

_____

_____

_____

_____

_____

14.4 How can global information systems benefit a fire department? _____

_____

_____

_____

14.5 Give examples of where the technology available today needs to advance to a higher level to improve the way fire departments prevent fires. _____

_____

_____

_____

_____

14.6 To keep up with the advances of technology, should fire departments purchase the latest products as soon as they become available? Why or why not? _____

_____

_____

_____

_____

14.7 What do the following acronyms abbreviate: GIS, IT, MIS, and PDA?

_____

_____

_____

_____

14.8 What are some of the benefits of using digital cameras on routine inspections? _____

_____

_____

14.9 Do courts allow digital images to be used as legal evidence?_____

_____

_____

14.10 Discuss other ways that technology could be used in the field of fire prevention. _____

_____

_____

_____

_____

_____

Fire Prevention Applications
Chapter Review Exercise Answers

Chapter Review Exercise Answers

Chapter 2

2.1   An understanding of the relevance of historical fire events lays the groundwork for how we got where we are today in the field of fire prevention. Fire prevention professionals will at times be asked to explain why we need to do something or what is the purpose or intent of the code requirement. If fire professionals understand what led to the development of fundamental code requirements, then they will be capable of explaining the purpose of or reasoning for code requirements. Fire protection professionals can also use historical events to gain insight into what contributed to a fire loss and apply those lessons in preventing similar losses.

2.2   A tragic event creates media attention. The public tends to show an interest in preventing the event from occurring again. Many times the codes are changed as a result of tragic fires.

2.3   In 1189 the first lord mayor of London mandated that houses be built of stone. Some buildings were required to have party walls with rings for hooks.

In 1608, a fire in Jamestown, Virginia, led to requirements for thatch roofs and wood chimneys.

2.4   The Iroquois Theater fire provided a number of lessons:

Stages need to be protected by automatic sprinklers. At the time of the fire, the building had none.

Draperies, such as the stage curtain, need to be fire resistive.

Permitted occupant load limits must be obeyed.

Employees need to be trained in evacuation procedures.

2.5   One of the most significant findings was that a building's means of egress must include a sufficient number of stairs in fire resistant shafts with rated fire doors at each opening.

2.6   At the National Fire Protection Association's annual meeting in May 1911, R. H. Newborn presented a paper on exit drills and educating factory workers. A year later Newborn's paper became the NFPA's first safety-to-life publication under the title "Exit Drills in Factories, Schools, Department Stores, and Theaters."

2.7   The lessons learned from the Our Lady of Angels incident included:

Automatic sprinklers with water flow alarms would have reduced or eliminated the loss of life at this incident.

The open stairways created vertical passageways for the smoke to travel. Like the other fires, this event again demonstrated the need for enclosed stairs.

The dangers of transoms over doors and combustible finishes were also identified.

2.8   The building had undergone many additions and had no automatic sprinklers. The interior finishes along the walls and ceiling in many areas of the building were combustible. The facility's occupant load was exceeded. Exits were obstructed or locked. Some exits were not clearly identified.

2.9   Both fires occurred in an industrial occupancy that resulted in large life loss. The Triangle Shirtwaist fire was the basis for the establishment of what later became the Life Safety Code. The food processing fire occurred 80 years later at a time when the Life Safety Code was already established and when technology was on the rise. In both fires, contributing factors to the loss of life included the lack of automatic sprinklers and blocked or obstructed exits.

2.10   The conferences are a virtual "Who's Who in the American Fire Service" with the purpose to discuss issues of emerging interest and importance as well as to reevaluate our current roles and responsibilities as a fire service.

2.11   The six basic issues identified in the 1996 Wingspread Conference are:

Customer Care. The emergency services have an opportunity to increase their value at little cost by preparing the community to deal with natural disasters, fires, medical emergencies, and other incidents. These programs are not directly connected with emergency response or operations but in fact are more in line with prevention and mitigation functions, such as public information and education.

Managed Care. Escalating health care costs and insurance costs are driving more people than ever before to use 911 as their source of medical care. This discussion spawned ideas to radically change the delivery of emergency medical services. Again, this attempt at managed care is an opportunity for fire prevention bureaus or divisions to explore their potential in public education, wellness awareness education and information, and making the right decision.

Competition and Marketing. Wingspread's intent was to recognize that if the fire service is to survive, it must market its services and demonstrate their value.

Service Delivery. This topic speaks to deployment, response times, and service level objectives of the overall system.

Wellness. This issue addresses the need for fire service employees to make sure they are physically fit, mentally prepared, and emotionally healthy. In order to provide proper support and service, we must be at our best.

Political Realities. This topic stresses the overall importance of good labor/management and customer relations to maximize our overall impact on our communities.

2.12 Rankings will vary based upon the importance identified. The ranking choice should be substantiated based on the individual community's fire problem or fire service issues.

Leadership. This discussion expressed a critical need for leadership development to move the fire service into the future, particularly with our dynamic environments and evolving political and fiscal challenges.

Prevention and Public Education. This discussion again emphasized the need to expand this resource.

Training and Education. This topic addresses managers' increasing their professional and leadership roles in order to remain credible to policy makers, administration, staff, and the public.

Fire and Life Safety Systems. This issue concerns the need for adopting and supporting more codes and standards that mandate these protective systems' use.

Strategic Partnerships. Participants explored the need for the fire service to reach out and enlist the support of other individuals and groups in accomplishing the overall mission of fire protection and emergency service response.

Data. Measurable data are crucial to understanding where we have been and where we are going.

Environmental Issues. These issues concern the need for the fire service to comply with local and federal laws both in mitigating incidents and in providing for the safety and welfare of our employees and partners.

2.13 *America Burning* is a document that explains America's overall fire problem going into the 1970s and the issues that needed to be addressed.

2.14   The nation needs to place more emphasis on fire prevention.

The fire services need better training and education.

Americans must be educated about fire safety.

In both design and materials, the environment in which Americans live and work presents unnecessary hazards.

The fire protection features of buildings need to be improved.

Important areas of research are being neglected.

2.15   The standard test was developed using wood and other combustibles. It is used to compare how things burn and often is applied today as a benchmark to draw a comparison of a product used in construction.

2.16   There needs to be more research on providing cost effective fire protection features for residential occupancies such as the single-family home. This is just one of the many areas that need to be addressed to reduce fire deaths.

2.17   The National Fire Protection Association. This organization promulgates codes and standards.

2.18   Underwriters Laboratories and Southwest Research Institute

2.19   The functions may vary from state to state but typically include: code enforcement, fire and arson investigation, construction document review, inspections, fire data collection, fire legislation development, fire and life safety education, fire service training, and licensing.

2.20   The United States Fire Administration (USFA) administers the federal data and analysis program and serves as the primary agency to coordinate arson control programs at the state and federal levels. This agency also administers a program concerned with firefighter health and safety.

2.21   The tragic fires identified in this text all resulted in multiple loss of life. The facilities had some form of exit deficiency such as blocked or obstructed exits. The facilities lacked the installation of automatic sprinklers throughout. Installing automatic sprinklers and providing adequate exits could have altered the outcomes. An aggressive fire safety education program combined with the installation of the built-in fire protection features is also an important component of altering the outcome of the tragic fires studied in this text.

Chapter 3

3.1   Buildings or structures collapsing. Buildings constructed poorly. Pressure from the insurance industry.

3.2   A body of law systematically arranged to define requirements pertaining to the safety of the general public from fire and other calamities. The purpose of codes is to establish *minimum* requirements for life safety.

3.3 ISO provides an analysis of the community's fire protection system.

3.4 The best rating is one.

3.5 Ten percent.

3.6 Standards dictate how something is to be done.

3.7 Codes typically are thought of as written documents that answer the questions who, what, when, and where concerning various requirements and their enforcement. A code will tell when something is required. A standard will tell you how to do it. The building code requires a sprinkler system and the standard, NFPA 13 *Standard for the Installation of Automatic Sprinklers* indicates how the sprinkler system is to be installed.

3.8 Appendices in model codes or individual standards contain a great deal of information ranging from background material, history, simplified tables, or interpretations to good fire protection practices. They are not enforceable unless specifically adopted.

3.9 Those that govern the construction and occupancy of a building when it is being planned

Those that govern the construction and occupancy of a building when it is being constructed

Those that regulate activities conducted within a building once it has been constructed

3.10 The building code specifies how to construct a building to prevent the spread of fire by construction features or hazard arrangement.

3.11 The four model codes were the *National Fire Codes*, the *BOCA National Fire Prevention Code*, the *Uniform Fire Code*, and the *Standard Fire Prevention Code*.

3.12 The reasons for code consolidation include the need for consistency in all parts of the country. The codes that have evolved from consolidation include the *International Building Code* and the *National Fire Protection Association Building Code*.

3.13 These codes differ from the prescriptive model codes in that they have no standards for reference but utilize an engineering approach to determine protective measures.

3.14 Performance based codes are used in large, irregularly shaped facilities with complex industrial processes that may not be addressed in the prescriptive codes.

3.15 The performance-based codes provide flexibility for the building designer.

3.16 The performance-based design is based upon the conditions of the building at the time of construction as well as the anticipated use of the facility. Once the building is constructed and occupied, the building may undergo changes that impact the performance-based design. The fire official is continually responsible for the building and must monitor changes that impact the performance-based design.

3.17 Technical committees or groups formulate drafts of new codes as requested. A standards council or other similar group generally issues the approval for certain codes or standards to be drafted and or revised if it is not already on a set printing schedule. Technical committees also may hear numerous appeals throughout a given code cycle. Once the assigned committee or group makes drafts or revisions, the drafts are put out for public comment. The technical committee receives the comments and then makes changes. In some cases, staff makes these changes rather than a technical committee. The revised proposal is then republished for public comment. Often, hearings are held to discuss the proposals and potentially to receive comments from the floor. In other instances, residents submit comments again and the technical committee makes one last revision. The code is then ratified, accepted, and printed.

3.18 Code renewal cycles repeat approximately every four years. The renewal process offers an opportunity for code committee members as well as the general public to submit requests for changes.

3.19 The federal government's facilities are exempt from compliance with local ordinances. However the municipality may request compliance in order for the facility to get water or emergency service protection from the municipality.

3.20 The level of authority is actually situational. There are cases where the local authority does not have jurisdiction and the state does. The level of authority will also vary from state to state. In some states, the community can adopt codes and ordinances stricter than the state codes. The most stringent codes would then apply.

3.21 The appeals process must be spelled out in a form of ordinance or part of the adopted model codes. The process begins with a written appeal of a fire official's code interpretation. For example, the adopted appeals procedure may require the appeal to be made to an appointed board of professionals or to an individual such as the city manager.

3.22 The level of authority will be determined by the structure of the two entities. For example there are municipalities where the fire department is responsible for the building requirements and vice versa. If, for example, the fire marshal manages the fire prevention bureau and the building department, then he or she will have more authority. The authors of the text believe that the building department and the fire department should have equal authority and strive to work together to address all areas of life safety.

3.23   Codes cannot be written and approved at the same pace that technology may advance. While the codes are in the revision cycle, technology is already creating new products or commodities that may not be in the codes.

3.24   The authority having jurisdiction.

Chapter 4

4.1   Empathy for clients

Try to be more of a customer advocate. Understand that your organization likely knows far more about fire code issues than customers do. Be their resident consultant regarding your policies, procedures, and laws.

Remember that every time you open your mouth or put pen to paper while doing code enforcement work, you are likely costing somebody a lot of money.

Be mindful of community economic conditions and try to be flexible. Meet the intent of the code, not necessarily the rigid prescriptions listed in the document. Your job is to help business, commerce, and quality of life in your community, not stifle it.

4.2   3–5 percent

4.3   Change is inevitable and economics is a large driver. The fire service will likely be pricing itself out of a job if it does not begin to consider better and more efficient ways of providing a necessary service for a lower cost. While we are not a business, we should try to be more businesslike.

4.4   Privatization

Enterprise

Cost recovery/fee based

Revenue offset

4.5   To expedite and better control their interests. The less regulation on their industry, the better their performance in their world.

The result, whether good or bad depends solely on the local community and what they desire and get for their money.

It can free up general fund monies to sustain other fire department operational needs or help improve other city financial concerns.

It prevents governmental agencies from squandering fire prevention operational funds.

It typically is cheaper to operate and run than traditional Civil Service employee options.

It enhances consistency in operation and congruency in code enforcement due to reduced employee turnover.

4.6 Which method is best depends solely upon local conditions, organizational culture, community demands and policy decisions. The key is to have flexibility, technical knowledge, economies of scale, and economically sound business practices.

4.7 Familiarity with operational procedures

Organizational promotional opportunities

Experience with organizational culture and policies

Familiarity and respect among sworn ranks.

4.8 High costs

Frequent turnover

Limited experience

Limited flexibility with talent

4.9 Low cost

Consistency

Good training investment (they stay after you pay)

Tenure

4.10 Requires careful search and preemployment screening for qualified candidates

Potentially limited knowledge of local policies and procedures

Organizational respect issues

4.11 Upward organizational mobility

Consistency

Educational opportunities

4.12 Our external environment (business, community and governmental) changes constantly.

Fire and injury problems change.

Employee personality types change (X Gen vs. XY Gen types).

4.13 *Any three of the following:*

Help people get rid of the old stuff before moving to the new.

Provide answers to questions while change is taking place.

Involve people in the process.

Don't just talk the talk, but walk the walk.

Communicate, communicate, communicate.

4.14. Who are we?

What basic social or political needs do we exist to meet?

What do we do to recognize, anticipate, and respond to problems?

How do we respond to our stakeholders?

What are our philosophy, values, and culture?

What makes us distinctive or unique?

4.15 Answer will be based on local issues.

4.16 Much of what a fire prevention division does impacts not only community injury but response times, organizational costs, resource planning, and overall community risk management.

4.17 *Any five of the following:*

Proactive education programs at nursing homes

Low-hazard inspections reduced from annually to every five years

Fewer vehicles responding to selected types of incidents

Public education programs for EMS

Smoke detector blitzes in key areas like housing projects

Aggressive inspection programs

Public education and awareness programs

Ambulance service providers taking nonemergency medical calls

4.18 *Any four of the following:*

Defines the purpose and objective for specific hazards based on organizational mission and values

Creates an environment where your entire department has ownership

Creates synergy by pushing everyone to be his or her best all at the same time

Communicates goals and strategies to your clients and the policy makers

Helps make sure you are using your department's resources to their fullest

Provides a benchmark or baseline from which to measure progress

4.19 Yes. Dead-end jobs are not always attractive. Promotional opportunities and enrichment should be attempted and provided whenever possible. This not only satisfies the employee but helps the organization hold onto valuable resources.

4.20 Whether change is good or bad depends on the circumstances. One certainty is that change is difficult to manage. Change is always going to occur. People are uncomfortable with change. So the manager must remember various rules and strategies to assist everyone in the process.

Chapter 5

5.1 The different methods of staffing the fire prevention bureau include sworn personnel, civilian personnel, or a combination of both, as well as either full-time or part-time employees.

5.2 The differences between using sworn and civilian personnel will vary from department to department and from person to person. Generally speaking, however, sworn personnel can offer an understanding of firefighters' needs as they relate to built-in protection systems and fire department access. They have an extensive knowledge on how things burn in a fire. They can use these skills to mitigate and prevent fires. Civilian personnel may offer some technical training such as fire protection engineering that most sworn personnel do not have. Some civilian personnel can be hired at a lower cost than a sworn firefighter.

5.3 Outsourcing is sending work outside the organization for completion.

5.4 Outsourcing can reduce workloads and use specifically trained or educated individuals to perform certain tasks (for example, outsourcing construction document reviews to a fire protection engineering firm).

5.5 Education, engineering, and enforcement. Education takes place mainly in fire and life safety education presentations. Engineering aspects are found mainly in the construction document review. Enforcement includes ensuring compliance with codes.

5.6 The position is typically an assistant chief or battalion chief who reports to the chief.

5.7 Prevention or suppression

5.8 Organizational structure

Staffing options (i.e. civilian vs. sworn)

Number of employees

Level of service to provide

Budget

5.9 Span of control is the number of people a person can directly supervise effectively.

5.10 Construction documents related to zoning

Building construction (architectural)

Roadways (civil)

Fire suppression and fire detection

5.11 Historically, fire prevention bureaus were staffed with individuals who did not fit the mold of a firefighter. Fire prevention bureaus have been known to be the depository for the sick, lame, or lazy. This has led to staffing of fire prevention bureaus with the less desirable employees.

5.12   Performance designs allow the builder to select construction methods and materials as long as they can be shown to meet the performance criteria through an engineering analysis.

5.13   Forcing firefighters to work in fire prevention bureaus may cause turnover if they are reluctant to perform fire prevention tasks. The firefighter may have entered the fire service with suppression tasks in mind. The civilian employee may become frustrated with the pay structure and lack of promotional opportunities.

5.14   Options include using a third party for construction document review and inspections.

5.15   Those departments that choose to contract out will lose some degree of ownership as they will not have direct control over all the aspects they otherwise could. In many cases, there will be a lack of quality control regarding a true vested interest in the overall fire department's mission. More importantly suppression personnel within the fire department are among the customers supported. It is imperative that all fire prevention bureau personnel have the interests of fire suppression personnel in mind when they are performing their fire prevention duties.

5.16   The engineering section is responsible for construction document review and inspection of fixed systems. The fire and life safety education section is responsible for conducting fire and life safety education presentations. The inspection sections conduct routine fire inspections. The investigation section is responsible for investigating the cause and origin of fires. The public information section serves as a primary media contact at emergency incidents in the capacity of public information officer.

5.17   NFPA 1031 is *Professional Qualifications for Fire Inspector and Plan Examiner.*

5.18   Types of inspections can include business licenses, complaints, and inspections of existing occupancies.

5.19   Preincident planning is the process of identifying specific occupancies, buildings, or locations likely to require special treatment or operations should an emergency occur.

5.20   NFPA 1033 is *Professional Qualifications for Fire Investigator.*

5.21   Policies and guidelines for conducting fire investigations

Fire origin and cause determination

Data collection methods

Relationships with various legal authorities within the jurisdiction

5.22 These sectors support the fire victims and many times the businesses that have been adversely impacted by the emergency incident.

5.23 The prevention and mitigation of wildland fires

5.24 The fire prevention bureaus need to ensure the staff is adequately trained and has a grasp on current technology and the ever-changing codes. The ability of fire prevention staff members to perform their job relies heavily on continuous education.

Chapter 6

6.1 Risk is the chance of injury, damage or loss.

6.2 Identify your strengths and weaknesses

Identify and classify risks as typical or higher in severity

Communicate with your public

Provide strategic planning

Identify targets for mitigation and prevention efforts

6.3 Credible and accurate data for strategic planning

Communicate better with your public and elected officials

Identifying the right targets

6.4 The answer will depend upon local area and culture.

6.5 Mitigation is simply the modification of an unwanted outcome to a level that is sustainable, survivable, or nearly nonexistent due to active protection measures.

6.6 Mitigation changes the outcome or severity of an event, where prevention actually stops the event from ever occurring.

6.7 A typical risk could be a simple single-family residence classification that your department routinely handles time and time again. No special effort, equipment, or training is required to deal with the event. Another typical risk could be a small office building.

6.8 A measure of the severity and probability of an unwanted event

6.9 The actual value of the risk. This is basically the public's opinion of the risk.

6.10 So that policy makers, citizens, and elected officials will be better able to communicate priorities for dealing with the right issues and in the best time frame

6.11 The act of engaging the public with factual information concerning issues that are important to them and learning from them "what they want and can't live without"

Chapter 7

7.1. The five-step planning process consists of the following steps that can be used for a variety of fire and life safety education programs:

Step 1: Identification of major fire problems. Identification is typically accomplished by conducting a community analysis that will determine the major fire hazards, the high-risk locations, the high-risk times, the high-risk victims, and the high-risk behaviors.

Step 2: Selection of objectives for education program. Selection assists in determining the targeted audiences and begins the process of finding sources for developing the community partnerships essential to a successful fire and life safety education program.

Step 3: Design of the program plan. Design determines what to say in the fire and life safety education program based on the intended message and the available resources.

Step 4: Implementation of the program plan. This step consists of delivering effective programs to their target audiences.

Step 5: Evaluation of the program's impact. The evaluation tools allow the fire and life safety educator to show that his or her efforts are reaching the target audience and that the target audience grasps what was presented.

7.2 The goal is to focus on human behavior modification to reduce deaths and losses from the effects of fire.

7.3 Fire and life safety education is a proven method to motivate the public to act in a fire-safe manner. It is also an opportunity to teach people what to do.

7.4 Fire departments have expanded their role in educating the public to act safely in a number of areas. The inclusion of additional prevention topics led to the term fire and life safety education.

7.5 Fire departments have expanded their emergency response from just putting out fires to other services that include emergency medical services, swift water rescue, ice rescue, hazardous materials, and other specialty teams. Because of the increased services, fire departments were witnessing citizens being injured from a variety of activities. Fire departments then began to incorporate prevention topics for these activities.

7.6 Topics may include: water safety, bike safety, seatbelts, car seats, ice safety, babysitter training

7.7

Relating Evaluations To Specific Prevention Themes	
Prevention Theme	**Examples Of Measures To Use**
Use of smoke detectors	# households with detectors # reported fires (early detection leads to occupant extinguishment and fewer reports) # fire deaths
Getting out quickly from residential fires	# injuries while attempting fire control in residential fires # fire deaths # severe injuries
Need to clean chimneys	# chimney fires
Careless smoking	# fires or deaths involving careless smoking
Safe storage of flammable liquids at home	# nonarson fires where flammable liquid was material first ignited
Children playing with lighters or matches	# residential fires where heat of ignition was a match (or lighter) and ignition factor was "children playing" # children injured in above type of fire

Source: *Proving Public Fire Education Works.*

7.8 The effectiveness of a fire safety education program should be measured by its impact on the "bottom line." In this case, the bottom line would be the reduction or elimination of the community's fire incident, injury, and death rates.

7.9 The following can be obtained from the United States Fire Administration (www.usfa.fema.gov). Funding for grants, juvenile fire setter intervention handouts, after-the-fire brochures, reports on residential sprinklers, America Burning Revisited, and Beyond Solutions 2000 publications.

The following are available from the National Fire Protection Association at www.nfpa.org. Fire statistics in the United States, firefighter deaths, fire reports for specific occupancies, Fire Prevention Week information, fire and life safety education articles.

The Consumer Product Safety Commission offers information on product recalls that may have contributed to fires.

7.10 Programs can include a fire engine ride to school for children who successfully accomplish an academic goal determined by the school principal (i.e., reading a set number of books), having the fire chief read a fire safety related book out loud to the children, sponsoring a fire safety education poster contest, producing a fire safety education calendar, having a save-our-senior day with fire prevention topics for the seniors, and inviting a senior housing complex to the fire station for a cookout and conducting a presentation.

7.11 Sign boards or message boards can be used for a variety of ages. Web pages with interactive fire and life safety messages are good for children. Stickers and coloring books are effective for preschool age children. Newsprint is a medium for adults and seniors.

7.12 A firefighter speaking to the group works well with seniors; puppets or clowns work well with younger children. Children in kindergarten through grade 5 learn well with videos, TV, and compact discs.

7.13 Answer will depend on local circumstances.

7.14 The report indicated that fire prevention could not be effective without public education.

7.15 The report should address the recommendations that focus on targeting the high-risk groups by improving fire safety in the areas of egress, early alarm notification, and fire sprinkler protection. It also should explain in detail how each of the areas of improvement will impact fire safety for the targeted groups.

7.16 Answer will depend on local circumstances.

7.17 The paragraph should address the appropriate method of presentation for the audience and why it is important to know the audience. The presentation to the younger audience may include the use of puppets while the older audience may be better served by a presentation by a firefighter.

7.18 Topics can range from planning a home fire escape plan to the need to install residential sprinklers.

7.19 The media can be used to present a fire and life safety education message with each fire that occurs. The media can be used to portray the fire department in a positive manner. The effective use of the media is an essential component of a fire and life safety education program.

Chapter 8

8.1 NFPA 1035, *Professional Qualifications for Public and Life Safety Educator*

8.2 To communicate with the public those things that will maintain the department's image, to inform the public of emergencies, to communicate events, to keep audiences motivated in fire and life safety behaviors

8.3 Community Relations

Media Relations

Writing

Public Speaking

Audio/Visual Presentation

Fire Department operations and functions

8.4 Who works, invests, and maintains a high profile within the community

Awareness of organizational relationships and partnerships within the community

Community views regarding emergency preparedness and their political opinions and volunteer involvement

Cultural and religious values and beliefs

8.5   Answer will depend on local circumstances.

8.6   Answer will depend on local circumstances.

8.7   Answer will depend on local circumstances.

8.8   Important things are not important unless they are different.

Emotional messages are better than factual messages.

Keep information in small bites.

Create shelved "canned" messages for immediate release.

Keep information easy to get and easy to give.

Treat the media with respect by answering their questions directly.

Repeat messages just as in teaching.

Never make stuff up.

Never speak for another agency or official.

Don't give personal opinions.

Assume you are always on camera or tape.

If you don't want something on the national news, don't say it.

8.9   Worksheet should include at least the following:

Cause of event

Place for eyewitness accounts

How many and what type of resources responded to the incident

Statistics (money, loss, deaths, injuries, etc.)

Past history of similar events

8.10   Answer will depend on local circumstances.

8.11   *Any four of the following:*

Looking sloppy

Holding onto a podium when speaking

Pacing from side to side

Reading to any audience

Using hypnotic filters

8.12   Answer will depend on local circumstances.

Chapter 9

9.1   Fires are investigated to determine how they started and/or why they behaved as they did. The data are then collected for future use.

9.2 Fire prevention bureau personnel can use the fire investigation information to try to prevent similar events. One excellent method of using this information is through fire and life safety education. The information gained from a fire investigation can and should be used to educate and inform the public of potential fire causes.

9.3 An investigation to determine where (origin) and how (cause) fires started by analyzing the area of origin, the heat of ignition, the combustible or flammable materials involved, and the actions of the occupants at the time of the fire

9.4 *Some of the most significant mistakes investigators make on fire scenes include:*

Failing to take enough photographs

Not digging and scraping to the bottom of the fire scene

Not digging and scraping with care

Not documenting where the evidence samples were taken

Failing to get and document accurate statements from witnesses

Assuming something happened without making certain

Failing to write a comprehensive report

Failing to seek the assistance of outside agencies

Failing to seek the assistance of experts

9.5 Arson, in the laws of the United States, is the act of willfully and maliciously setting fire to a house, building, or other property.

9.6 Arson can be costly to the taxpayers for the investigation as well as result in the loss of tax revenue if a business is destroyed. Arson can be deadly and take innocent lives.

9.7 NFPA 921, *Standard for Fire and Explosion Investigations*

NFPA 1033, *Professional Qualifications for Fire Investigator*

9.8 Just as conducting a fire inspection, determining the origin of a fire requires a systematic approach.

9.9 The data collected by the cause of fires can be used to develop a code that would prevent the incident for occurring again. For example if the use of charcoal grills on wooden balconies in large combustible apartment complexes causes a number of fires, the code could prohibit charcoal grills on wooden balconies in multi-family residences.

9.10 The list should include at least the following: address, deaths, cause of fire, material ignited, time of fire, names of witnesses, names of suppression crews, time and day of fire, injuries, insurance company, dollar loss, occupancy classification.

9.11 *The list should include at least the following:*

Personal protective equipment

- Helmet
- Coat
- Gloves (heavy and light)
- Boots
- Respirator or self-contained breathing apparatus (SCBA)
- Coveralls

Flashlight

Cell phone or portable radio

Pump can (for hotspot touchups and cleaning the floor after debris removal for better examination)

Portable electrical lights

Hydrocarbon sampling device

"Get after it and dig for it" equipment

- Trowel
- Scraper
- Shovel
- Small saw
- Chisel/hammer
- Wire cutters
- Multipurpose scissors
- Needle-nose pliers
- Vise grips
- Goose-neck pliers
- Pry bar
- Garden tools
- Battery powered reciprocating saw

Measuring tape

Ruler

Camera and film (digital work well)

Barrier tape

Paper

Pen or pencil (pencils always work in a variety of climates!)

9.12   *The answer should include at least the following:*

Day of the week fires most often occur

Time of day fires most often occur

Most common type of fires

Most common ignition sources causing fires

Most common locations where fire occurs

Trend identification is also important for justifying requests for more resources.

9.13   Extreme climate conditions, the potential for falling objects, the instability of the structure, and poor air quality

9.14   *Answer should include at least the following:*

Develop good policies and procedures for everyone to follow.

Integrate fire investigation functions into the mission of the fire department.

Train everyone on the job about what it means to do good fire investigation.

Get management's commitment to this process.

Provide proper training and equipment.

Develop arson task forces where appropriate.

Gather and track good data.

Develop an arson early warning system.

Develop a progressive public education program citing all aspects of fire.

Partner with community organizations.

Develop relationships with law enforcement agencies and prosecutors.

Support advances in fire investigation technology.

Chapter 10

10.1   The construction document review is an opportunity for the fire department to begin building a fire prevention coalition with the owners of the building and is an opportunity to identify potential hazards and risks that will impact the safety of the occupants and the firefighters who may be called there in the middle of the night to mitigate an emergency incident.

10.2   Building officials have a responsibility to enforce the building code that contains elements that protect firefighters.

Insurance companies want to ensure their level of risk is minimized through adequate construction methods.

State fire marshals have jurisdiction to enforce state codes in some construction document reviews.

10.3　Firefighter safety

　　　Occupant safety

　　　Enforcement of codes

　　　Preincident planning

　　　Property conservation

10.4　*The construction document review package will include:*

　　　Architectural drawings: the fire department will be concerned with egress and passive fire protection features.

　　　Structural drawings: the fire department will be concerned with how the building is put together and how it may fail during a fire.

　　　Mechanical drawings: fire department concerns include how the mechanical systems will effect firefighter operations.

　　　Electrical drawings: the fire department concerns pertain to the emergency lighting, generators, fire pump wiring, egress lighting, and location of transformer vaults.

　　　Site, landscaping, civil, utility drawings: the fire department will focus on access, hydrants, and vegetation management.

　　　Plats: the fire department will review elements that may impact fire protection access.

　　　Fire protection drawings:

- Sprinklers
- Standpipes
- Fire detection and alarm

　　　The fire department's concern is compliance with the applicable standard as well as the impact the systems will have on fire department operations.

10.6　Preconstruction meetings provide the architect, other design professionals, and owner the opportunity to ask the construction document review team specific questions regarding the project.

10.7　The preconstruction meeting is an excellent opportunity for everyone involved in the project to meet all of the individuals from the design team and construction document review team. The architects and designers benefit from such a meeting because they will reduce or eliminate design mistakes, and the construction document review team benefits because ensuring their concerns are addressed in the initial design will most likely shorten the review time.

10.8　Conceptual designs are preliminary documents and are not intended to be used for construction or permit approval. Conceptual drawings typically serve as a means to facilitate a meeting of the construction document review team with the owners and their design professional.

10.9   A certificate of occupancy is issued to the occupant when the building has been determined to be safe to occupy and has been inspected to meet the code requirements.

10.10   1. The deficiency. What is the problem with the document under review?

         2. The code and code section of the deficiency. Where can the design professional go to find more information?

         3. What is needed to correct the deficiency? What must the design professional do?

10.11   Fire protection drawings include a variety of different systems and elements pertaining to the building's fire protection systems.

10.12   1. The need is determined.

         2. A design professional is contacted.

         3. Conceptual designs are prepared.

         4. Construction documents are prepared.

         5. Construction documents are reviewed.

         6. Construction document review comments are completed.

         7. Construction document revisions are submitted.

         8. Construction document revisions are approved or denied.

         9. Permit is applied for and issued.

         10. Construction begins.

         11. Construction is inspected.

         12. Construction is completed.

         13. Certificate of occupancy is issued.

         14. Occupant moves in.

         15. Business license is approved.

         16. Periodic fire inspections continue.

Chapter 11

11.1   Research

        Interior inspection

        Exterior inspection

        Documentation

        Explanation to owner(s)

11.2 Yes. A fire inspector must be credible for fire prevention and code issues to be accepted and trusted by an owner or occupant.

11.3 To provide a reasonable degree of safety to the occupants of commercial and public buildings. Americans typically rely on safe buildings just as they rely on fire engines or ambulances to be available in an emergency.

11.4 Research the occupancy and any past history.

Contact the owner/manager to schedule an appointment.

Be punctual.

Be prepared with all your necessary equipment.

Examine the exterior for various requirements such as access, fire hydrants, etc.

Begin the interior inspection in a top-down or bottom-up procedure (just be consistent).

Document the inspection findings, both positive and negative.

Close the inspection with a verbal summary of the findings.

11.5 Ensuring that a building or process is safer than when an inspector entered it

11.6 Occupants conduct their own inspections and provide a copy of the inspection report to the fire department.

11.7 *Advantages:*

More people involved in the inspection and accountable for their own safety

Inexpensive

Can touch more businesses annually

Disadvantages:

No guarantee the inspection will be done

No professional guidance

No quality control

Potential that occupant may lie

11.8 Because the history of the findings and the end results are important not only for future reference but possible legal defense in civil or criminal litigation. Documentation is critical to any fire prevention work.

11.9 Communication

Research capabilities

Code knowledge

Fire department knowledge

Familiarity with hazards and processes

Interpersonal skills

Conflict resolution skills

Salesmanship

11.10 Conduct research

Be familiar with the occupancy and processes

Gather tools and equipment

11.11 Digital organizer

Laptop or tablet computer

Clipboard

Pen

Paper

Rulers or tape measure

Flashlight

Cell phone

Radio

Forms

Camera

11.12 Answer will depend on local circumstances.

11.13 A reasonable time frame as established by the inspector and the business owner. However, the inspector has the final say based on the severity of the violation and hazard.

11.14 To provide guidance to the inspection staff and provide and promote continued focus on mission and purpose

11.15 To provide a safe environment for the public

11.16 Let the occupant know how and why a violation is a problem and why it must be fixed. Provide good information as to the risk and the exposure and how that relates to the occupant's business operations and to firefighters as well.

11.17 Identify your fire problem. Those with the most significant potential losses (life and then property) are your targets. Place them in descending order and you will have a prioritized list. However, do not forget about large significant risks that may not have suffered a loss yet. That future single event may cause more damage than all the others combined.

11.18 *Any ten of the following:*

Fires

Fire alarms

Request for service

Outstanding fire code violations

Construction permits/alterations

Occupancy changes

Process uses

Written correspondence

Permit activity

Fire alarm test results

Suppression system inspection /test results

11.19 They are equally important as one must have the technical knowledge to understand and communicate the violations and then be skilled enough to communicate the needs and problems so as not to offend the owner/occupant.

11.20 Domination

Compromise

Integration

11.21 No method is necessarily better as long as the inspector is consistent.

Chapter 12

12.1 A condition or element that provides a source of ignition for a hostile fire or that contributes to the spread and severity of a hostile fire

12.2 Heating and cooking. While some years the statistics may vary, these two generally lead the list. Smoking used to be very prevalent, but over the years this cause has begun to decline.

12.3 A hazard that is common among occupancies or locations.

12.4 A hazard that is isolated to specific operations or locations like concentrated hydrogen peroxide storage—not a common sight in most homes.

12.5 Selecting those occupancies where your most commonly occurring fire incidents take place or where extreme life risk exists.

12.6 Create a team   Implement the plan
Create a mission statement   Evaluate
Establish strategic goals
Establish strategies to achieve the goals
Sign a contract document affirming the goals and strategies

12.7 Suppression systems: extinguish the fire in its smallest incipient phase

Smoke control systems: evacuate smoke and/or pressurize certain compartments to keep smoke out

Detection and alarm systems: detect fire in an early phase to alert occupants or the fire department

12.8 Active fire protection systems do something to suppress, warn, or control fire when it occurs. Passive fire protection involves design features that do not actively attack a fire but by their mere existence prevent fires or prevent them from getting worse or spreading.

12.9 Life safety

Property protection

12.10 Yes, very! This is the last and least effective fire protection and suppression measure because of time delays, reliance on human beings, and dependence on various factors.

12.11 Typically, flame retardant properties can be incorporated in the manufacture of various materials making them inherently flame resistant. If something will not burn, it does not have to be protected.

12.12 Compartmentation is the physical separation of one area from another, which keeps fire or toxic gases from moving between the areas.

12.13 Defending in place involves protecting people or processes without evacuation or significant relocation.

12.14 Notification

Safe and unobstructed paths of egress or methods of escape

12.15 This curve represents a standard test fire but does not adequately or accurately reflect the type of fire that commonly occurs nowadays.

12.16 An area or series of areas separated by sufficient fire resistive construction that occupants can move through it or into it for safety

12.17 A process of risk and hazard assessment that identifies consequences and decisions that dictate the design of a building or process.

Chapter 13

13.1 Any hostile fire in the outdoors that is not prescribed or purposefully managed

13.2 While it will help prevent disasters from occurring to some extent, it also prohibits nature from "taking care of business" by cleaning the forest of noxious weeds, insects, and overgrowth. This just increases the severity of the problem so that when an event does occur, it likely will be well beyond anyone's capability to stop or defend.

13.3   Interface mix: structures scattered throughout a rural area surrounded by undeveloped land

Occluded interface: isolated area of forested land surrounded by homes or structures

Classic interface: homes or structures pressed directly against the forest or wildlands

13.4   Water

Wildlife

Air

Plants

Timber

Soil

13.5   *Answer will depend on local circumstances. Agencies may include:*

USDA

USFS

State forest service

Local fire department

Neighborhood associations

County

Land trust owners

City and county parks

13.6   Operating plans are typically mutual aid or operational plans established by various cooperating agencies that respond to fire emergencies in the wildland-urban interface. They establish the ground rules for response, mitigation, and prevention and are renewed on an annual basis.

13.7   Vegetation management

Control burns

13.8   Fire has always been a major method of reclamation and restoration for old, dead, and dying forests. It has been the mechanism for rejuvenating new growth and clearing out overgrowth. It has been around as long as forests and, in fact, probably did the best job of managing forests until we intervened.

13.9   It called for all fires to be extinguished by 10:00 A.M. the day after their discovery. This caused an environmental imbalance by allowing vegetation to become too dense and overgrown, which weakened some species allowing additional insect infestation to also impact various forested areas.

13.10 Fire and life safety education

Prevention and mitigation

Suppression

13.11 Water

Air

Wildlife

Timber

Soil

13.12 Fuel

Weather

Topography

13.13 What are the loss impacts to the community

What is the community's assessment of which losses are and are not acceptable?

What is our ability to mitigate hazards that have been identified?

13.14 Because wildfires cross many boundaries and no one department has the resources to deal with a situation once it occurs.

13.15 Fuel

13.16 Ground fuels

Surface fuels

Crown fuels

13.17 A large wildfire that moves into the crown of large vegetation. This event creates enormous amounts of heat release, generally burning so hot that it sterilizes the soil underneath. Obviously, no vegetation can survive these extreme temperatures.

13.18 Assume adults living in large homes in forested areas are educated, understanding, and responsible.

Assume that these same adults do not know much about the natural fire environment or their actual risk.

Assume that they want to do the right thing if they are informed, if they have the capability, and if they can measure their progress.

Be factual, be truthful, and make clear all expectations about survivability and fire suppression capabilities.

Chapter 14

14.1   Technology can allow you to work smarter and accomplish more with less. Technology can also improve efficiency.

14.2   The advancement of the personal computer has enabled fire prevention bureaus to work more efficiently.

        The global information system permits fire departments to share information in layers. An example would be fire hydrant location with a second layer of streets or topographical information.

        Digital cameras can provide a cost effective means to document conditions that need to be corrected.

        Tablet computers can be used by fire prevention bureau inspectors to conduct inspections and reduce paper work.

        Data base software is an affordable means to track fire loss data and determine the areas on which to focus fire prevention efforts.

14.3   *Answers will vary. In any case, the item needs to show a benefit either of reducing cost or improving efficiency. For example, the digital camera can reduce photo-processing costs and eliminate the time it takes inspectors to take film to a lab for processing.*

14.4   Global information systems can determine hydrant locations, locate streets for emergency response, and identify topographical information that may benefit the wildland mitigation and prevention efforts.

14.5   *Answers will vary. One possible answer is given below:*

        The fire deaths in the United States continue to be the highest in our homes. It is important that technology advance to reduce residential fire deaths. Progress has been made toward the installation of residential sprinklers. Residential fire safety improvements are just one area to be addressed by technological advancements.

14.6   It is not always wise to purchase products as soon as they become available because of the cost associated with the first generation of the product. Typically the second generation of the product corrects any product deficiencies and further improves upon the product's first generation.

14.7   GIS: global information systems

        IT: information technology

        MIS: management information systems

        PDA: personal digital assistant

14.8   Digital cameras are a cost-effective means to document the conditions at the time of the inspection. This documentation can be archived for future reference. Since the photo is digital, it can be saved electronically without taking file storage space.

14.9   Yes

14.10 Technology can be used to identify a community's fire problem by tracking the frequency and causes of fires through a computerized database. The information of the property where an inspection is being conducted can be sent to the fire inspector's laptop in his or her vehicle. Technology can provide the inspectors with real-time data while they conduct their inspection.

Fire Prevention Applications
Bibliography

Bibliography

Amdahl, G. (2001). Disaster Response: GIS for Public Safety. ESRI Press, Redlands, CA.

Arno, S. F. and Steven Allison-Bunnell (2002). Flames in Our Forest: Disaster or Renewal? Island Press, Washington, DC.

Babcock, Chester, and Rexford Wilson, "The Chicago School Fire," NFPA Quarterly (January 1959).

Beakley, George C., and Herbert W. Leach, Careers in Engineering and Technology, 2nd ed. New York: Macmillan, 1979, p. 3.

Best, Richard L., "Tragedy in Kentucky," Fire Journal (January 1978).

Best, Richard L., Investigation Report on the MGM Grand Hotel Fire National Fire Protection Association, Quincy, Mass., 1982.

Bryson, J. M. (1995). Strategic Planning for Public and Nonprofit Organizations. Jossey-Bass, New York.

Cohen, Jack D., "Wildland-Urban Fire: A Different Approach," Missoula Fire Sciences Laboratory, Rocky Mountain Research Station, Forest Service, U.S. Department of Agriculture, 2002.

Coleman, R. J. (1997). "It's the Fire Service, Not the Fire Business." Fire Chief, (April)

Colorado Springs (Colorado) Fire Department Wildfire Mitigation Plan, 2001.

Cote, A. (1991). Fire Protection Handbook, 17th ed. National Fire Protection Association, Quincy, MA.

Cote, R., ed. (2000). Life Safety Code Handbook, 8th ed. National Fire Protection Association, Quincy, MA.

Covey, Stephen R., Principle Centered Leadership (Summit Books, 1991), pg. 173.

Custer, R. L., and B.J. Meacham, (1997). Introduction to Performance-Based Fire Safety. National Fire Protection Association, Quincy, MA.

Dungan, K.W. (2001). "Risk-Based Methodologies." Fire Protection Engineering (Spring 2001), Society of Fire Protection Engineers, Bethesda, MD.

Employment Policy Foundation (2000). The American Workplace, 1998. Retrieved February 21, 2000, from the World Wide Web: http://www.opf.org/labor98/98intro1.htm.

Favreau Donald F., Fire Service Management (New York: Donnelley, 1969).

Federal Emergency Management Agency (2001). Public Fire Education Planning: A Five-Step Process (brochure). Federal Emergency Management Agency, Emmittsburg, MD.

Federal Emergency Management Agency, United States Fire Administration (1998). Strategies for Marketing Your Fire Department Today and Beyond (brochure). Federal Emergency Management Agency, Emmittsburg, MD.

Illinois State Fire Marshal (2000). Media and Budgeting Resource Guide for the Fire Service (brochure). Illinois State Fire Marshal, Springfield, IL.

International Association of Fire Chiefs, et al., The Fire and Emergency Services in the United States, Wingspread IV, October 23–25, 1996.

International Fire Service Training Association (1998). Fire Inspection and Code Enforcement, 6th ed. Fire Protection Publications, Stillwater, OK.

International Fire Service Training Association (2000). Fire Investigator, 1st ed. Fire Protection Publications, Stillwater, OK.

International Fire Service Training Association (1997). Fire and Life Safety Educator, 2nd ed. Fire Protection Publications, Stillwater, OK.

International Fire Service Training Association (1993). Fire Service Orientation and Terminology, 3rd ed. Fire Protection Publications, Stillwater, OK.

International Fire Service Training Association (2000). Public Information Officer, 1st ed. Fire Protection Publications, Stillwater, OK.

Kiurski, T. (1999). Creating a Fire Safe Community: A Guide for Fire Safety Educators. Fire Engineering, Saddle Brook, NJ.

Machlis, G. E. and Artley, D., eds. (2002). Burning Questions: A Social Science Research Plan for Federal Wildland Fire Management. National Wildfire Coordinating Group, Washington, DC.

Mathis, Mark, Feeding the Media Beast (West Lafayette, Indiana: Purdue University Press, 2002).

McEwen, Tom, Fire Data Analysis Handbook. Washington, D.C.: U.S. Fire Administration

National Fire Protection Association (1994). NFPA Inspection Manual, 7th ed. National Fire Protection Association, Quincy, MA.

National Fire Protection Association (1998). Professional Qualifications for Fire Inspector and Plan Examiner (NFPA 1031). National Fire Protection Association, Quincy, MA.

National Fire Protection Association (1998), NFPA 1033, Professional Qualification for Fire Investigator National Fire Protection Association, Quincy, Mass.

NCFPC, America Burning: Report of the U.S. National Commission on Fire Prevention and Control (Washington, D.C.: U.S. Government Printing Office, 1973).

North American Coalition for Fire and Life Safety Education (January 2002). Beyond Solutions 2000. Retrieved February 1, 2003, from the World Wide Web http://www.usfa.fema.gove.

Osborne, D., and T. Gaebler, (1992). "Anticipatory Government." In Reinventing Government (pp. 223–226). Addision-Wesley Publishing Company, Reading, MA.

Pages from the Past, "Flammable Decorations, Lack of Exits Create Tragedy at Coconut Grove," Fire Engineering (August 1977).

Pages from the Past, "Theater Was 'Fireproof' Like a Stove but 602 Persons Lost Their Lives," Fire Engineering (August 1977).

Powell, P., and M. Appy, (1997). "Fire and Life Safety Education: The State of the Art." In Ron Cote, ed. Fire Protection Handbook, 17th ed., pp. 2–55. National Fire Protection Association, Quincy, MA.

Pyne, S. J. (1997). "World Fire: The Culture of Fire on Earth." University of Washington Press, Seattle.

Robertson, J. C. (1979). Introduction to Fire Prevention, 2nd ed. Glencoe Publishing Co., Inc., Encino, CA.

Teague, Paul E., "Case Histories: Fires Influencing the Life Safety Code," in Ron Cote, Life Safety Code Handbook (Quincy, Mass.: National Fire Protection Association, 2000), pp. 931–933.

TriData Corporation (1987). Overcoming Barriers to Public Fire Education in the United States. TriData, Arlington, VA.

TriData Corporation (1990). Proving Public Fire Education Works. TriData, Arlington, VA.

Wallace, William H., Community Risk Issue: Structure Fires, Colorado Springs, Colorado: Colorado Springs Fire Department, 1997.

Wallace, William H., Colorado Springs Fire Department, Summary of Survey Responses, page 25, January 3, 2003.

Wolski, A. (2001) "Risk Perceptions in Building and Fire Safety Codes." Fire Protection Engineering (Spring 2001), Society of Fire Protection Engineers, Bethesda, MD.

Fire Prevention Applications
Glossary

Glossary

A

adoption by reference a local jurisdiction's formal decision to follow state laws exactly as drawn

arson the act of willfully and maliciously setting fire to a house, building, or other property

assembly a particular construction method that details specific types of materials, their specific manufacture or installation, and components

C

classic interface area with homes and other structures, especially in small dense neighborhoods, pressed directly against the forest or wildlands

code a body of law systematically arranged to define requirements pertaining to the safety of the general public from fire and other calamities

common hazard hazard that is found among many occupancies or locations

community injury any significant loss of property or monetary value, as well as physical injury or death

compartmentation the use of passive (and in some cases active) protection features to prevent fire spread

compressed workweek scheduling system that permits full-time employees to perform the equivalent of a week's work in fewer than five days

compromise method of resolving conflicts in which each side gives up something in order to reach an agreement

conceptual design preliminary document that is not intended to be used for construction or permit approval

D

defending in place protecting people or processes without significant relocation or evacuation

domination method of resolving conflicts in which one side is the victor and one side is the loser

E

electrical drawing drawing that reflects the details of the building's electrical system

enabling act method of adopting state regulations that allows the local jurisdiction to amend them based on local needs or preferences

enterprising running a service organization or a division of the organization so that it operates fully on a cost-recovery basis

F

fire protection drawing drawing that indicates the systems and elements pertaining to a building's fire protection systems

G

grading (fire suppression rating schedule) method of evaluating fire suppression capabilities and crediting them to individual property fire insurance rates

H

hazard a condition or element that provides a source of ignition for a hostile fire or that contributes to the spread and severity of a hostile fire

hostile fire any unwanted or destructive fire

I

incendiary fire any fire that is set intentionally

injury personal injury, monetary impact, job loss, or aesthetic impact

integration method of resolving conflicts in which a mutual solution is found and both sides achieve their goal to some degree with neither being wrong or bad

interface mix rural area with structures scattered sparsely throughout

L

ladder fuels fuels that are configured so that a ground fire can become a surface fire and a surface fire can become a crown fire

M

maintenance code code that details how to properly safeguard the activities or operations in a building

mechanical drawing drawing that indicates the elements of the building's mechanical systems, such as plumbing, heating, air conditioning, etc.

mission statement a description of the purpose of the organization

mitigate to make less harsh or hostile or to make less serious or painful

mitigation the prevention or reduction of severity of an undesired event

O

occluded interface isolated area of forested land or wildlands surrounded by homes or other structures

P

paradigm shift a change from old ways of thinking that opens the door for new insight, new methods, and different views

performance-based code code that allows designers to determine how best to meet an individual building's unique fire protection needs

plat legal document illustrating the legal description of a property as well as any legally binding easements

preconstruction meeting meeting during which the people involved in a building project review the conceptual designs

preincident planning the process of identifying specific occupancies, buildings, or locations that will likely require special treatment or operations during an emergency

prescriptive code code that lists specific design requirements, such as number of exits, fire separation, construction type, and fire suppression systems

privatization the transfer of functions or duties previously performed by a government entity to a private organization

public information information provided to the general public so they remain informed about events, become better educated and/or prepared for various situations, and remain motivated in fire- and injury-prevention behaviors

public process the act of engaging the public with factual information concerning issues that are important to them and learning from them "what they want and can't live without"

R

risk the exposure to possible loss or injury

risk assessment process of analyzing the risk impact and the risk perception and then combining the results

risk impact a measure of the probability that something will occur and the severity of its results

risk perception the actual "value" of a risk

S

service delivery deployment, response times, and service level objectives of the overall fire service system

site drawing drawing that indicates a variety of details concerning topography, landscaping, and civil engineering details

specific hazard hazard that is isolated to particular operations or locations

standard document that details how something is to be done in order to comply with the applicable codes

Standard Fire Test published results of research that determined time/temperature measurements of a typical large fire in the early twentieth century

structural drawing drawing that provides details on how a building is put together

T

target hazard location or building that is different than those that are "typical" throughout a jurisdiction

10:00 A.M. policy policy mandating that any fire be controlled by 10:00 A.M. the day it is reported or, failing that, by 10:00 A.M. the day following, ad infinitum

V

value statement a summary of the ethical priorities for everyone's behavior when working on the mission

vision statement a brief description of how the fire department, or more specifically the fire prevention bureau, will operate

W

wellness being physically fit, mentally prepared, and emotionally healthy

wildfire any hostile fire in the outdoors that is not prescribed or purposefully managed

Fire Prevention Applications
Index

Index

A

Accelerants, 211. See also Arson
Acceptable risk, 124–125
Active fire protection, 225, 238, 277
Adjustments to the organization, 71–73
Administration
    civilian personnel, 90–92
    generally, 81
    organizational framework, 85–86
    outsourcing, 92–95
    scope, 81–83
    staffing levels, 83–85
    staffing options, 87–90
    sworn personnel, 90, 91
    volunteer departments, 95
Adoption by reference, 41, 373
"After the Fire" packets from FEMA, 108
AHJ (authority having jurisdiction), 81, 283. See also Fire marshal
AIA (American Insurance Association), 35
Alarm panels, 87, 88
Alarm systems. See also Sprinklers
    automatic, 278, 279–281
    fire prevention bureau challenges, 87–88
    in fire protection drawings, 233
    human, 279
Alternate means and methods, 289, 290
America at Risk, 139
America Burning
    fire and life safety education, 139
    fire prevention emphasis, 82
    identification of fire problems, 20
    importance of education, 156
    insufficient research, 47
    overview, 19
America Burning Recommissioned, 139
American Insurance Association (AIA), 35
Apartments. See Multi-family dwellings
Apathy of fire problem, 20, 21, 126
Apollo space program fire investigation, 192
Appeals of code requirements, 42–44
Appendices, 38
Architects and construction document review, 219
Architectural drawings, 225–226
Arson
    accelerants, 208
    benefits of fire investigation, 190, 191
    defined, 199, 203, 373
    Happy Land Social Club fire, 16
    investigations, 201–211

    completing the report, 209
    criminal penalty, 201–202
    exterior examination, 204
    interior examination, 204–208
    origin and cause, 200–201
    procedures, 200–208
    prosecutions, 208–209
    solutions, 209–210
    training and equipment, 197–200
Assembly, 284, 373
Assessment, quantitative, 48
ATF (Bureau of Alcohol, Tobacco, and Firearms), 26, 65
Audio presentations, 180
Augustus, Caesar, 10
Authority having jurisdiction (AHJ), 81, 283. See also Fire marshal
Automatic fire detection
    home fire protection, 4
    sprinklers. See Sprinklers
    suppression and control systems, 277–278

B

Bar codes, 228
Bark beetle, 304
Basic Code, 46
BATF (Bureau of Alcohol, Tobacco, and Firearms), 26, 65
Beverly Hills Supper Club fire, 14–15
Beyond Solutions 2000, 142
Big brother/big sister mentoring program, 70
Big Red Truck (BRT), 20, 100
Biological weapons, 63
BLM (Bureau of Land Management), 301
BOCA. See Building Officials and Codes Administrators International
BOCA National Building Code, 46
BOCA National Fire Prevention Code, 45, 46
Brannigan, Francis L., 284
Bread-and-butter operations, 105
Building codes
    construction document review, 218
    purpose, 44
Building Construction, 284
Building Construction for the Fire Service, 284
Building departments, 21, 44–45
Building design
    construction document review, 218
    construction materials, 23
    cost of prescriptive code requirements, 89
    fire protection engineers, 96
    improvements, 22–23
    performance-based, 289–290, 291

preparation, 224
Building Exits, 45
Building Exits Code, 12
Building officials, 219–220
Building Officials and Codes Administrators International (BOCA)
    BOCA National Building Code, 46
    National Fire Prevention Code, 45, 46
Building permit process
    application and issuance (step 9), 234–26, 237
    beginning construction (step 10), 236
    business license approval (step 15), 239
    certificate of occupancy (step 13), 238
    communication of comments (step 6), 234–235
    conceptual design preparation (step 3), 224
    construction completion (step 12), 238
    construction document review (step 5), 248
    construction document revision submittal (step 7), 235
    construction document submittal (step 4), 224–234
        architectural drawings, 225–226
        electrical drawings, 229–230
        fire protection drawings, 233–234
        plats, 232–234
        site, landscaping, civil, and utility drawings, 230–232
        structural drawings, 226–228
    construction inspection (step 11), 238
    contacting design professional (step 2), 222, 224
    fire inspections (step 16), 239
    flowchart, 222
    need determination (step 1), 222
    occupant moves in (step 14), 238–239
    revision approval or denial (step 8), 235
Built-in fire protection systems. See Automatic fire detection
Bureau of Alcohol, Tobacco, and Firearms (ATF), 26, 65
Bureau of Indian Affairs, 301
Bureau of Land Management (BLM), 301
Bureau of National Affairs, 68
Business decisions, risk perception, 122–123
Business license approval, 239
Businesses
    hazard identification, 273
    office fire investigations, 106
    office hazard risk, 120–121
    target protection plan, 274–275

C

California, bankrupt cities and counties, 59
Cause determination. See Origin and cause determination
Certificate of occupancy, 238
Changes to the organization, 71–73
Chemical compounds, 23, 286
Chicago fire, 35
Chicago nightclub inadequate exits, 141
Chief, Fire, 126
Children's flame retardant sleep wear, 283

CIGNA
    design deficiency study, 99
    importance of inspections, 102
City manager's office, construction document review, 222
City of Make-Believe, 39–40
Civil engineering drawings, 230
Civilian Conservation Corps, 301
Civilian personnel, 90–92
Class 1 through 10 grading schedule, 37
Class A building codes, 36
Classic interface, 302, 373
Clean agent suppression systems, 278
Clown and puppet troupe for fire and life safety education, 154
Coconut Grove fire, 13, 191
Code
    after Triangle Shirtwaist fire, 11, 12
    appeals, 42–44
    appendices, 38
    building, 44, 218
    Building Exits Code, 12
    building official review, 219–220
    current problems, 47
    defined, 35, 373
    development, 46
    enforcement, 101–103
    enforcement and fire prevention, 281
    fire department enforcement, 220–222
    fire inspections and, 247
    fire protection systems, 234
    history, 9, 19
    judgment of available methods, 286
    Life Safety Code. See Life Safety Code
    model, 46–47
    model organizations, 45–46
    National Electrical Code, 230
    overview, 50
    prescriptive, 88–89
    principles, 41–42
    product manufacture and performance, 283
    purpose, 35
    results, 42
    review. See Construction document review
    stairwell safety, 15
    standard vs., 37–38, 50
Code of Hammurabi, 35
Cohen, Jack D., 311
Coleman, Ronny J., 57
Collapse and compartmentation, 284
Colorado
    building departments, 59
    Taxpayers Bill of Rights, 59
Colorado Springs
    business education, 99–100
    community risk analysis, 250
    fire and life safety education, 154, 307
    fire resistant building elements, 311

FireWise trailer, 306
minimum job requirements, 92
mission statement, 62
organizational chart, 85
preincident planning, 106
public education of risk, 128–129
safety messages to media, 104
wildfire prevention, 311–312
wildland risk management, 109
workload survey, 63–64
Columbus Method, 123
Combustibles
factor in American tragic fires, 12, 13
inspections, 102
Common hazard, 271, 373
Communication
construction document review, 234–235
education, 22, 284
fire prevention, 311–313
fire prevention bureau and law enforcement agency, 107
media. See Media
organizational changes, 72
performance-based codes, 48
progressive prevention programs, 82–83
public speaking by public information officer, 179–180
wildfire prevention, 304
written, by public information officer, 177–178
Community
coalitions for education, 142–143
fire prevention level, 4
growth and regional departments, 59
injury, 35, 373
preparation for emergencies, 17
relations of public information officer, 168
Community injury, 35, 373
Community risk analysis, 250
Companion documents, 44–45
Compartmentation
defined, 283, 373
Navy warships, 288
objective, 284
Competition, privatization of services, 93
Competition of service, 17
Compliance, voluntary, 254–255, 258
Compressed workweek
defined, 68, 373
disadvantages, 69
scheduling alternative, 68–69
Compromise, 255, 373
Computers
for data collection, 324–326
design modeling, 48, 89
digital photos, 328
engineer documentation, 98
holes for cables reducing fire barrier, 284
risk assessment tool, 130

used for research, 23
worthless data, 146
Conceptual design
defined, 224, 373
preparation, 224
Conferences, impact on service, 17–18
Construction document review
architects, 219
building officials, 219–220
construction start, 236
documentation, 239
enforcing codes and standards, 218–219
fire department, 220–222
insurance rating bureau, 220
overview, 217–219, 240
permit coordination process, 222–239
beginning construction (step 10), 236
business license approval (step 15), 239
certificate of occupancy (step 13), 238
communication of comments (step 6), 234–235
conceptual design preparation (step 3), 224
construction completion (step 12), 238
construction document revision submittal (step 7), 235
construction document submittal (step 4), 224–234
construction inspection (step 11), 238
contacting design professional (step 2), 222, 224
fire department review (step 5), 234
fire inspections (step 16), 239
flowchart, 223
need determination (step 1), 222
occupant moves in (step 14), 238–239
permit application and issuance (step 9), 235–236, 237
revision approval or denial (step 8), 235
purpose, 217–219, 239
state fire marshals, 220
Consumer Product Safety Commission (CPSC), 26, 39, 283
Corps of Vigils, 10
Costs
building design and review, 218
fire and life safety education, 143
reductions, 58
risk assessment consideration, 130
staff, 58–59, 73
unfunded mandates, 39
wildfire management, 305
Covey, Stephen R,, 126
CPSC (Consumer Produce Safety Commission), 26, 39, 283
Cray Supercomputer, 23
Crown fuels, 310
Cultural impact of fire problem, 100
Customer care, 17
Cyclical fire inspections, 251

D

Data
collection forms, 98
computer storage, 324–326
Conference report, 18
coordination of collection, 323
efficiency of technology, 321–322
fire and life safety education, 155
fire investigation, 192, 195
information checklist, 323
mobile terminals, 106
national fire databases, 146
nationwide information, 24
risk assessment, 123–124
risk impact, 121–122
use in target identification, 273
Deaths by fire, 3
Deckert, Dr., 301
Defending in place, 286–288, 373
Deficiencies found during fire inspections, 248
Demographic impact of fire problem, 100
Department of Health and Human Services (HHS), 39
Detail view, construction drawing, 227
Detection and alarm systems. See Alarm systems
Detection devices in fire protection drawings, 234
Development review group, 97–98
Digital photos, 328
Documentation
construction document review, 239
digital photos, 328
fire inspection record keeping, 260–261, 262–263
fire investigations, 203
fire protection engineers, 98
performance-based building design, 290
Documents, companion, 44–45
Dogs used for accelerant detection, 208
Domination, 255, 373
Draperies, fire resistive, 11
Dry chemical extinguishing systems, 278
Drywall flame retardant properties, 284
Dupont Plaza Hotel fire, 192

E

Earthquake, San Francisco, 35–36
Ecological impact of wildland fires, 302–303
Ecosystem, 302–303. See also Wildlands
Education, 21. See also Three Es
Conference report, 18
fire and life safety. See Fire and life safety education
fire inspection deficiencies, 248–249
fire investigators, 198–199
fire prevention, 5, 81, 276
fire safety, 21–23
life safety educator, 86
public, 18

Egress. See Exits
Einstein, Albert, 73, 110
Electrical drawing, 229–230, 373
Elements needed for fires, 137
Elevation view, construction drawing, 226
Elevator evacuation, 286
Elk Grove Rural Fire Protection District, Illinois, 94
e-mail communication, 22
Emergency response, 280–282
Employment Policy Foundation, 68
Enabling act, 41, 373
Enforcement of fire prevention, 5, 81, 276. See also Three Es
Engineering. See also Three Es
civil engineering drawings, 231
construction document review, 221
emergency response, 280–281
fire prevention, 5, 81
fire prevention bureaus, 95–99
hazard control, 276
performance-based concept, 48
ranked priority, 280
Engineers, fire protection, 86, 110
Enterprising, 94, 373
Environment and wildfires, 299
Environmental issues, 18
Equipment
arson investigations, 204–205
fire inspection, 257
fire investigation, 201–202
risk assessment and, 119–121
Escape plans, 137. See also Evacuation
Evacuation
drills, 12
employee training, 11, 13
high-rise buildings, 137
occupant safety, 285–286
school example, 287
Evaluation of fire and life safety education program, 148, 149
Examples
bark beetle, 304
Beverly Hills Supper Club fire, 14–15
Chicago fire, 35
City of Make-Believe, 39–40
Coconut Grove fire, 13, 193
Colorado Springs. See Colorado Springs
defending in place, 287–288
Dupont Plaza Hotel fire, 194
federal laws and properties, 39–40
fire inspection and code enforcement, 101
food processing plant, 16
Happy Land Social Club fire, 15–16
Hayman fire, Colorado, 328
holiday lights testing, 282
Iroquois Theater fire, 11
Los Alamos, New Mexico, fire, 110, 302
media portrayal of messages, 166–167

mentoring program, 70
Mesa Verde National Park, Colorado, 302
MGM Grand Hotel fire, 15
mission statement, 62
organizational chart, 85
Our Lady of Angels School fire, 13–14
outsourcing, 93–94
paradigm shifts, 126
performance-based design, 289
preventable injuries, 141
public acceptable risk, 124
risk assessment, 120
risk perception, 122
Rodeo-Chediski fire, Arizona, 328
San Francisco earthquake, 35–36
sprinklers, 88
Triangle Shirtwaist fire, 11–12
truth hurts, 127
wildland risk management, 110
window in office door not rated, 282–283
worthless data, 146
Exits
    Chicago nightclub inadequate exits, 141
    Coconut Grove fire, 13
    Life Safety Code requirements, 248
    marking clearly, 15
    minimum construction, 286
    Triangle Shirtwaist fire, 12
Exterior fire inspections, 206–207, 263

F

Factory Mutual Global Loss Prevention Data Books, 24
Factory Mutual Research Corporation, 25, 282
Factory Mutual System, 24
FDZ (fire demand zone), 328
Federal Emergency Management Agency (FEMA)
    "After the Fire" packets, 108
    America Burning Recommissioned, 139
    Fire and Data Analysis Handbook, 146
    National Fire Incident Reporting System (NFIRS) database, 146
    Public Fire Education Planning: A Five-Step Process, 147
Federal fire protection organizations, 25–26
Federal laws and properties, 39–40
Feeding the Media Beast, 104, 167, 169–170
FEMA. See Federal Emergency Management Agency
Feshe course objectives
    codes and standards, 34
    construction document review, 216
    fire and life safety education, 136
    fire inspection procedures, 244
    fire investigation, 188
    fire prevention bureaus, 56
    fire prevention technology, 320
    hazards, 270
    history and development of fire prevention, 8

organizational structure and function, 80
public information officer, 164
risk assessment, 118
wildland fires, 298
Finishes, combustible, 14, 15
Fire, 19
Fire and Data Analysis Handbook, 146
Fire and life safety education
    activities, 152–153
    benefits of fire investigation, 190
    effectiveness, 144
    evaluation, 144–145
    by fire prevention bureau, 65
    history, 139–144
    importance of, 138–139
    objective, 137, 145, 156
    overview, 99–100, 155–156
    presentations, 154–155
    program planning, 147–148
    public information, 155
    public information officer roles, 165
    purpose, 138–139
    systems, 18
    target audience, 147, 148, 149–151, 152–153
    topics, 152
    wildfire management, 306–307
Fire and Life Safety Educator, 145, 150–151
Fire chief, 126
Fire Data Analysis Handbook, 192
Fire demand zone (FDZ), 328
Fire department construction document review
    architectural drawings, 226
    during construction, 236
    construction inspection, 238
    design approval, 235
    electrical drawings, 230
    fire protection drawings, 233–234
    mechanical drawings, 229
    plats, 233
    purpose, 220–221
    site, landscaping, civil, and utility drawings, 231–232
    structural drawings, 228
Fire department emergency response, 280–282
Fire Detection and Suppression Systems Manual, 278, 280
Fire Incident Data Organization, 146
Fire Inspection and Code Enforcement, 247, 272, 284
Fire inspection procedures
    analysis of needs, 246–247
    arrival at inspection site, 257–258
    compromise, 262
    coordination with other community agencies, 256
    data collection, 322
    documentation, 260–261, 262–263
    enforceable regulations, 247
    equipment, 257
    evaluation, 259

exterior inspections, 259
goals, 249
identification of problem, 250
inspector's level of training, 247–249
interior inspections, 258–259
overview, 262–263
periodic, 239
policies and procedures, 249
preparation, 251–253
priorities, 250–251, 262
professionalism, 260
professionalism of inspectors, 246
public relations, 254–255
purpose, 245
reasons for, 245
scheduling, 256–257, 260
self-inspection program, 255
steps, 259–261
unannounced visits, 257
Fire inspectors
appeals of codes, 43
fire and life safety education, 144
indifference of public, 20
procedures. See Fire inspection procedures
professionalism, 246, 254–255
small department, 21
Fire investigations
arson investigations, 201–211
completing the report, 209
criminal penalty, 201–202
exterior examination, 204
interior examination, 204–208
origin and cause, 200–201
procedures, 200–208
solutions, 209–210
training and equipment, 197–200
benefits, 190–192
determining origin and cause, 200–201
equipment, 199–200
fire department responsibility, 196
fire prevention bureau, 106–108
fire prevention information, 189–190
goals, 210
indentifying trends, 192–196
overview, 210
significance of data, 189
training, 198–199
Fire marshal
administrative functions, 81
functions, 26, 220
Fire Marshals Association of North America (FMNA), 25
Fire prevention bureau
data collection, 322
digital photos for documentation, 328
mission statement, 60–62
organization. See Organizational structure

overview, 73–74
roles, 58, 61
staffing, 84, 87–88
strategic plan, 63–66
tasks
engineering, 95–99, 111
fire inspection and code enforcement, 101–103, 111
fire investigations, 106–108
occupant service section, 108–109
preincident planning, 104–106
public information, 103–104
safety education, 99–100, 111
wildland risk management, 109–110
training, 110–111
Fire prevention resulting from fire investigations, 189–190
Fire prevention technology
advancements, 327–328
computers, 324–326
data collection, 322–326
efficiency, 321
global information systems, 327
overview, 329
redundancy of tasks, 323, 324–325
tools, 321
Fire protection drawing, 233–234, 373
Fire protection engineers, 86
Fire Protection Handbook, 24, 272
Fire Protection Publications, Fire Inspection and Code Enforcement, 247
Fire Safety Consultants, Inc., 93
Fire suppression rating schedule, 36–37, 373
Firesafety Educator's Handbook, 100
Flextime, 68
Floor plans, 225–226
FMNA (Fire Marshals Association of North America), 25
Foam suppression system, 278
Follett, Mary Parker, 255
Follow-through of target protection plan, 276
Food processing plant fire, 16
Forest Service. See United States Forest Service (USFS)
Fuel for wildfires, 309–311, 312
Funding. See Costs

G

General Services Administration (GSA), 40
Geographical information system (GIS), 106, 324
"Gigantica", 154
GIS (geographical information system), 106, 324
GIS (global information systems), 327
GIS mapping, 251, 308, 310
Global information systems (GIS), 327
Government
compliance mandates, 255
judgment of issues, 167

Grading
    defined, 36, 373
    schedule, 36–37
Grass-roots level of fire service, 5
Ground fires, 300
Ground fuels, 310
GSA (General Services Administration), 40

H

Happy Land Social Club fire, 15–16
Hayman fire, Colorado, 327
Hazard
    common, 271, 373
    compartmentation, 283–284
    control as fire protection, 276–277
    defined, 271, 374
    detection and alarm fire protection, 279–280
    fire department operations, 280–282
    occupancy, 252–253
    occupant safety, 284–288
    overview, 290–292
    performance-based design, 289–290
    product manufacture, 282–283
    resources to assist with protection plan, 275
    specific, 271, 375
    suppression and control fire protection, 274–276
    target protection plan, 274–276
    targeting, 272–274
Hazardous materials incident worksheet, 173–174
Health and Human Services (HHS), 39
Health department, construction document review, 222
HHS (Department of Health and Human Services), 39
High-rise buildings, 137
Historical building risk assessment, 130
History
    American tragedies, 10–16
        Beverly Hills Supper Club, 14–15
        Chicago fire, 35
        Coconut Grove, 13
        Coconut Grove fire, 191
        Dupont Plaza Hotel fire, 192
        food processing plant, 16
        Happy Land Social Club, 15–16
        Iroquois Theater, 11
        Jamestown fire, 19
        MGM Grand Hotel, 15
        Our Lady of Angels School, 13–14
        Triangle Shirtwaist, 11–12
    early laws, 10
    fire and life safety education, 139–144
    fire prevention, 9–17
    Forest Service, 301–302
    occupancy, for fire inspection, 252–253
    overview, 27
    reason for study, 9–10

Holiday light testing, 279
Holistic fire protection approach, 5
Homeland defense and collaboration of departments, 190
Homeland Security, 3
Homes. See Single-family dwellings
Hospital, defending in place, 288
Hostile fire
    causes, 277
    dealing with, 111
    defined, 271, 374
    human identification, 279
Hotel and Motel Fire Safety Act of 1990, 192
Human factor
    behavior modification, 137
    detection of fires, 279
    in fires, 276–277
    impact of sleeping on awareness, 279
    wildfires, 299–300
Human resource management trends, 68

I

IAAI (International Association of Arson Investigators), 25
IABPFF (International Association of Black Professional Fire Fighters), 25
IAFC (International Association of Fire Chiefs), 25
IAFF (International Association of Fire Fighters), 25
ICBO (International Conference of Building Officials), Uniform Fire Code, 45
Identification of problems for education, 147, 148
IFSTA. See International Fire Service Training Association
IGA (intergovernmental agreement), 66
Ignition source determination, 210
Ignition zone, 311
Implementation of fire and life safety education program, 148, 149
Incendiary fire
    defined, 197, 374
    determination of cause, 210
Incident cheat sheet, 105
Indifference to fire problem, 20, 21, 126
Information technology (IT), 326
Injury, defined, 19, 119, 374
Inspections and code enforcement, 101–103
Inspectors. See Fire inspectors
Insurance
    arson investigations, 204
    Chicago high risk fire area, 35
    fire investigations, 196
    payment for wildfires, 304
    rating bureau, 220
    San Francisco earthquake area, 35–36
    unprotected home coverage, 110
    wildfires, 110
Insurance research organizations, 24–25
Insurance Service Organization (ISO) water supply evaluations, 231
Insurance Services Office, Inc. (ISO), 24–25, 36–37

Integration, 255, 374
Intel Corporation fire and life safety CDs, 154
Interagency cooperation for wildfire management, 305–306
Interface mix, 302, 374
Intergovernmental agreement (IGA), 66
Interior fire inspections, 204–208, 258–259
International Association of Arson Investigators (IAAI), 25
International Association of Black Professional Fire Fighters (IABPFF), 25
International Association of Fire Chiefs (IAFC), 25
International Association of Fire Fighters (IAFF), 25
International Conference of Building Officials (ICBO), Uniform Fire Code, 37–38, 45
International Fire Code, 38, 45
International Fire Service Training Association (IFSTA)
    Building Construction, 284
    Fire Detection and Suppression Systems Manual, 278, 280
    Fire Inspection and Code Enforcement, 272, 284
    Public Fire Educator, 100
    resources, 25
International Personnel Management Association, human resource management trends, 68
Internet used for research, 23
Investigations. See Fire investigations
Iroquois Theater fire, 11
ISO (Insurance Service Organization) water supply evaluations, 231
ISO (Insurance Services Office, Inc.), 24–25, 36–37
Isolation. See Compartmentation
IT (information technology), 327

J

Jamestown fire, 19
Jensen, Gary, 94
Junior Fire Marshal Program, 139
Jurisdiction
    adoption of standards, 38
    authority having jurisdiction (AHJ), 81, 283. See also Fire marshal
    fire investigations, 190
    functions, 40

K

KISS acronym, 128
Kubler-Ross, Elisabeth, 71

L

Laboratories, research, 25
Ladder fuels, 310, 374
Landscaping drawings, 230–232
Laws
    federal, 39–40
    fire prevention, 10
    knowledge by public information officer, 181
    local, 41
    ramifications of improper procedures, 259–260
    state, 40–41

Leadership Conference report, 18
Learn Not to Burn program, 100
Lessons learned
    Beverly Hills Supper Club fire, 15
    Coconut Grove fire, 13, 193
    fire investigation, 191–192
    Happy Land Social Club fire, 16
    Iroquois Theater fire, 11
    MGM Grand Hotel fire, 15
    Our Lady of Angels School fire, 14
    Triangle Shirtwaist fire, 12
Level of services
    determination, 66–67
    fire inspections, 246
Liability and fire investigation, 191
Life Safety Code
    exit requirements, 45, 248
    history, 12, 13
Life safety education. See Fire and life safety education
Life safety educator, 86
Life safety group, 97
Linden, Russ, 71–72
Lloyd's of London, 35
Local laws and ordinances, 41
Local research organizations, 26–27
Los Alamos, New Mexico, fire, 110, 302

M

Maintenance code, 41, 374
Managed care, 17
Management information systems (MIS), 327
Manufacturing plant risk assessment, 130
Marketing of service, 17
Mathis, Mark, 104, 167, 169–170
McEwen, Tom, 192
McHenry Township Fire Protection District, 70
Mechanical drawing, 228–229, 374
Media
    advisories, 178
    age of information, 103–104
    audio/visual presentations, 180
    benefits of fire investigation, 190
    education, 22
    fire and life safety education, 155
    instant news releases, 166
    journalism school, 169
    news conferences, 179–180
    news releases by public information officer, 177–178
    portrayal of messages, 166–167
    public information officer relationship, 168–170, 177, 181–182
    spin on messages, 167
    target protection plan publicity, 275
Memorandum of understanding (MOU), 66
Mentoring programs, 69–70

Mesa Verde National Park, Colorado, 302
MGM Grand Hotel fire, 15
Mills, Bill, 307
MIS (management information systems), 324
Mission statement
    defined, 60, 374
    examples, 62
    fire prevention bureau role, 61
    guidelines, 61–62
    prevention and emergency response, 60–61
Mitigate
    defined, 277, 374
    hostile fires, 277
Mitigation
    benefits of fire investigation, 193
    defined, 119, 374
    hostile fire, 276
    wildfire, 310–313
Model code organizations, 45–46
Model codes, 46–47
Modification of fire codes, 42–44
Montreal Protocol on Substances that Deplete the
    Ozone Layer, 278
MOU (memorandum of understanding), 66
Mount Prospect, Illinois
    fire and life safety education, 153, 154, 155
    mission statement, 62
    preincident planning, 106
Multi-family dwellings
    fire inspections, 250
    hazard identification, 273
    target protection plan, 274–275
Murphy's Law, 288

N

NASA (National Aeronautic and Space Administration), 47, 127
National Aeronautic and Space Administration (NASA), 47, 127
National Board of Fire Underwriters (NBFU), 35–36
National Building Code (NBC), 35–36, 46
National Electrical Code, 230
National Fire Academy, 20, 26
National Fire Codes, 45
National Fire Incident Report, 192–195
National Fire Incident Reporting System (NFIRS) database, 146
National Fire Prevention and Control Administration education
    model, 147
National Fire Protection Association (NFPA)
    Building Exits Code, 12
    code development, 46
    Committee on Safety to Life, 12
    fire department call statistics, 99
    Fire Incident Data Organization, 146
    fire prevention bulletins, 139
    Fire Protection Handbook, 24, 272
    fire protection system codes, 234

Firesafety Educator's Handbook, 100
    inspector training courses, 247
    Learn Not to Burn program, 100
    model codes, 46–47
    National Electrical Code, 230
    National Fire Codes, 45
    national fire database, 146
    protection system installation standards, 280
    research, 24
    Risk Watch program, 100
    Sparky the Fire Dog, 138, 139
    Standard 34, Standard for Dipping and Coating Processes
        Using Flammable and Combustible Liquids, 252
    Standard 921, Standard for Fire and Explosion Investigations,
        197
    Standard 1031, Professional Qualifications for Fire Inspector
        and Plan Examiner, 96, 101
    Standard 1033, Professional Qualifications for Fire
        Investigators, 107, 197
    Standard 1035, Professional Qualifications for Public Fire and
        Life Safety Educator, 99, 165
    Standard 1500, Occupational Safety and Health for the Fire
        Service, 63
    Standard 1710, Standard for the Organization and Deployment
        of Fire Suppression Operations, Emergency Medical
        Operations and Special Operations to the Public by Career
        Fire Departments, 63, 74
    standards for professionals, 139
    statistics, 3
National Park Service (NPS), 301
Nature's fire cycle, 303–305
Navy warship compartmentation, 288
NBC (National Building Code), 35–36, 46
NBFU (National Board of Fire Underwriters), 35–36
New Deal, 301
New Jersey nightclub fire, 141
Newborn, R. H., 12
News. See Media
Newsletters, 180
NFIRS (National Fire Incident Reporting System) database, 146
NFPA. See National Fire Protection Association
North American Coalition for Fire and Life Safety Education, 142
Not-for-profit organizations, 501c(3), 143
Notification of occupants, 285–286
NPS (National Park Service), 301

O

Occluded interface, 302, 374
Occupancy
    hazards, 252–253, 276
    history, 252–253
Occupant
    area of refuge, 288
    defend in place, 286–288
    evacuation, 285–286

load limits, 11, 13
   safety, 284–288, 291
   service section, 108–109
Occupational Safety and Health Administration (OSHA), 16, 39–40
Occupational Safety and Health for the First Service (Standard 1500), 63
Offices
   fire investigations, 106
   hazard risk, 120–121
   window in office door not rated, 282–283
Oklahoma City news conferences, 179
On the job training (OJT), 90
Ongoing Issues of National Importance, 18
Organizational framework, 85–86
Organizational meetings to focus on mission, 62
Organizational structure
   administration, 81–95
      generally, 81
      organizational framework, 85–86
      outsourcing, 92–95
      scope, 81–83
      staffing levels, 83–86
      staffing options, 87–90
   civilian personnel, 90–92
   sworn personnel, 90, 91
   volunteer, 95
Organizations, research, 24–27
Origin and cause determination
   arson fires, 199–200
   fire investigations, 196–197, 204–208
   hazard identification, 273
OSHA (Occupational Safety and Health Administration), 16, 39–40
Our Lady of Angels School fire, 13–14
Outsourcing services, 58, 92–95
Ozone phase out, 278

P
Paradigm shift
   defined, 126, 374
   service delivery, 126–127
   wildfire management, 313
Party wall, 10
Passive fire protection
   compartmentation, 283
   designs, 277
   new construction, 225, 238
PDAs (personal digital assistants), 326–327
People. See Human factor
Performance-based code
   building design, 289–290, 291
   calculations, 48
   defending in place, 288
   defined, 47, 374

future, 49
   prescriptive code, 47–48, 88–89, 374
   purpose, 47
   worldwide use of, 89
Personal digital assistants (PDAs), 326–327
PIO. See Public information officer
Pipe schedule method, 88
Plans examination section, 95–99
Plat, 232–233, 374
Political realities, 18, 83
Powell, Colin, 87
Preconstruction meeting, 224, 374
Preincident planning, 104–106, 374
Prescriptive code, 47–48, 88–89, 374
Preventable injuries, 141
Primitive Pete, 276
Priority rank, 131, 280
Privatization
   defined, 93, 375
   examples, 93–94
   fire prevention bureaus, 59–60
   purpose, 93
Products
   liability and fire investigations, 196
   manufacture and performance control, 282–283
   safety recalls, 192
Professional Fallen Firefighters Memorial, 3
Professional Qualifications for Fire Inspector and Plan Examiner (NFPA Standard 1031), 96, 101
Professional Qualifications for Fire Investigators (NFPA Standard 1033), 107, 197
Professional Qualifications for Public Fire and Life Safety Educator (NFPA Standard 1035), 99, 165
Professional research organizations, 25
Promotional opportunities, 92
Proving Public Fire Education Works, 145
Public business of fire prevention bureau, 57–60
Public Fire Education Planning: A Five-Step Process, 147
Public Fire Educator, 100
Public information
   defined, 165, 375
   fire and life safety education, 155
   importance of, 165–167
   media, 103–104
   worksheet, 171–172
Public information officer (PIO)
   audio/visual presentations, 180
   community relations, 168
   familiarity with department operations, 181
   hazardous materials incident worksheet, 173–174
   importance of public information, 165–167
   legal issues and responsibilities, 181
   media relations, 168–170, 177, 181–182
   occupant service section, 108
   overview, 182–183

public speaking, 179–180
responsibilities, 165
strategy, 181–182
worksheet, 171–172, 175–176
written communication, 177–178
Public opinion, 122. See also Risk perception
Public process
  defined, 125, 375
  issues of concern, 125
Public relations
  education and, 155
  fire inspections and, 254–255
Publicworks, construction document review, 221
Puppets for fire and life safety education, 154

Q
Quantitative assessment, 48

R
Radio-data link, 326
Recommended Building Code, 35–36
Reconstruction of fire scene, 201
Red card training, 306
Redundancy of tasks, 323, 324–325
Refuge area, 288
Regional departments, 59
Reports of fire investigations, 201, 209
Research
  delays of code advancement, 47
  federal fire protection organizations, 25–26
  improvements, 23–24
  private organizations, 24–25
  state and local organizations, 26–27
Restaurant photos for fire inspections, 330
Risk
  acceptable, 124–125
  analysis, 120, 129–131
  assessment. See Risk assessment
  defined, 119, 375
  equipment or methods and, 119–121
  impact. See Risk impact
  management, 131
  preception. See Risk perception
  wildfire, 305–306
Risk assessment
  benefits, 123
  community-based decision process, 126
  defined, 121, 375
  information gathering, 123–124
  overview, 132
  paradigm shifts, 126–127
  procedure, 129–131
  public acceptable risk, 124–125
  public education of risk, 128–129
  purpose, 123

risk impact, 121–122
risk perception, 122–123
truth hurts, 127
Risk impact
  defined, 121, 375
  information gathering, 121–122
  measurement, 122, 130–131
  priority ranking, 131, 280
Risk perception
  defined, 122, 375
  evaluation, 122, 131
  hazard, 272
Risk Watch program, 100
Roadway sign information, 328
Rodeo-Chediski fire, Arizona, 327
Roles
  fire prevention, 83–95
  fire prevention bureau, 58, 61
  fire safety education, 138–139
  impact of terrorism, 3
  scope, 81–83
Rome fires, 10
Roosevelt, Franklin D., 301
Rural Metro Fire Department, Arizona, 93

S
"Safe Trek", 154
"The Safety Hop", 154
Safety issues
  firefighter, 281
  occupant, 284–288, 291
Salary as motivation, 67
San Francisco earthquake, 35–36
Satellite imagery, 328
SBCCI (Southern Building Code Congress International), Standard Fire Prevention Code, 45
Scheduling, 68–69
School
  defending in place example, 287, 288
  risk assessment, 130
Section view, construction drawing, 227
Selection of audience for education, 147, 148, 149–151, 152–153
Self-inspection program, 255
September 11 events
  apathy prior to September 11, 126
  fire service response, 20
  global information system use, 327
  increased communication among agencies, 108
  World Trade Center, 182, 189
Service delivery
  agreements, 66–67
  benefits, 17
  competition, 73
  defined, 17, 375
SFPE (Society of Fire Protection Engineers), 25

Signboard communication, 22

Silcox, Ferdinand, 301

Simpson, O. J., 21, 209

Single-family dwellings

    building in wildlands, 300

    fire inspections, 250

    materials as wildfire fuel, 305–307

    sprinklers, 4

    target identification, 273

    target protection plan, 274–275

Site drawing, 230–232, 375

Sleep wear, flame retardant, 283

Sleeping and fire awareness, 279

Smoke from wildfires, 303

Smokey Bear, 307

Society of Fire Protection Engineers (SFPE), 25

SOGS (standard operating guidelines), 249

Solutions 2000, 142

Southern Building Code Congress International (SBCCI),
    Standard Fire Prevention Code, 45

Southwest Research Institute (SwRI), 25

Sparky the Fire Dog, 138, 139

Sparky the puppet, 154, 307

Specific hazard, 271, 375

Sprakey Mutant Ninja Turtle, 307

Sprinklers

    amended requirements, 88

    automatic suppression system, 278

    fire and life safety education, 144

    fire protection drawings, 233

    industrial buildings with combustibles, 12

    installation, 38

    media portrayal of messages, 166, 167

    pipe schedule method, 88

    residence, 4

    Uniform Fire Code, 37–38

    use in performance-based building design, 289–290

Staffing issues

    civilian personnel, 67, 90–92

    costs, 58–59, 73

    determining staffing levels, 83–86

    motivation, 67–70

    options, 60, 87–90

    overview, 74

    promotions, 92

    retention, 67–70

    sworn personnel, 90, 91

    turnover, 92

    volunteer departments, 95

Stairways

    enclosed, 14

    passageways for smoke, 14

    reentry requirements, 15

Stand replacement fires, 300, 310

Standard

    code vs., 37–38, 50

    defined, 37, 375

    principles, 41–42

    purpose, 37

    review. See Construction document review

Standard 34, Standard for Dipping and Coating Processes
    Using Flammable and Combustible Liquids, 252

Standard 921, Standard for Fire and Explosion Investigations,
    197

Standard 1031, Professional Qualifications for Fire Inspector
    and Plan Examiner, 96, 101

Standard 1033, Professional Qualifications for Fire
    Investigators, 107, 197

Standard 1035, Professional Qualifications for Public Fire and
    Life Safety Educator, 99, 165

Standard 1500, Occupational Safety and Health for the Fire
    Service, 63

Standard 1710, Standard for the Organization and
    Deployment of Fire Suppression Operations, Emergency
    Medical Operations and Special Operations to the Public by
    Career Fire Departments, 63, 74

Standard Fire Prevention Code, 45

Standard Fire Test, 23, 375

Standard for Dipping and Coating Processes Using Flammable
    and Combustible Liquids (NFPA Standard 34), 252

Standard for Fire and Explosion Investigations (NFPA
    Standard 921), 197

Standard for the Organization and Deployment of Fire
    Suppression Operations, Emergency Medical Operations
    and Special Operations to the Public by Career Fire
    Departments (NFPA Standard 1710), 63, 74

Standard operating guidelines (SOGs), 249

Standpipes in fire protection drawings, 233

State fire marshals, 220

State laws and statutues, 40–41

State research organizations, 26–27

Statistics

    fire department calls, 99

    fire occurrences, 3

    forest protection, 301

    local vs. national norms, 146

    wildfire, 299–300

Stop, Drop, and Roll, 124, 137, 138

Storage inspections, 102

Strategic partnerships, 18

Strategic planning process

    benefits, 64

    documentation, 66

    future results, 64–65

    level of services, 67

    models, 65–66

    target identification, 273–274

Structural drawing, 226, 375

Structure guys and gals group, 306

Subrogation claims, 198

Suppression

    automatic protection systems, 4, 278, 279

education on use of, 281–282
rating schedule, 373
sprinklers, 282. See also Sprinklers
wildfire, 312
Surface fuels, 310
Sworn personnel, 90, 91
SwRI (Southwest Research Institute), 25
Systems group, 98

T

TABOR (Taxpayers Bill of Rights), 59
Target audience for fire and life safety education, 149–151
Target hazard
defined, 105, 375
identification of, 273
Target identification, 123
Target protection plan, 274–276, 291
Taxpayers Bill of Rights (TABOR), 59
Technology. See Fire prevention technology
10:00 A.M. policy, 301–302, 375
Terrorism, 3. See also September 11 events
apathy prior to September 11, 126
defending in place, 287
emergency preparedness plans, 141
fire investigations, 191
GIS used September 11 events, 327
impact on fire department budgets, 58
public information officer responsibilities, 182
September 11 events and increased communication
among agencies, 108
training, 63
World Trade Center, 182, 189, 285
Three Es
evacuation education, 285
fire protection systems, 291
identification of hazards, 276
motto, 280
planning and implementation, 81
principles of fire prevention, 5
Time line of events affecting public fire and life safety
education, 140
Topography, impact on wildfires, 307–309
Toxic gases from wildfires, 303
Training
arson investigations, 202–203
cross-training groups, 98
fire inspectors, 247–249
fire investigators, 197–199
fire prevention bureau, 110–111
improvement, 20
technical, 21
Wingspread Conference report, 18
Trends learned from fire investigations, 192–196
Triangle Shirtwaist fire, 11–12
TriData Corporation's Proving Public Fire Education

Works, 145
Trust accounts for fire and life safety education, 143
Truth hurts, 127
Turnover staffing rates, 92
Twain, Mark, 71

U

UL (Underwriters Laboratories, Inc.), 25, 282, 283
Underwriters Laboratories, Inc. (UL), 25, 282, 283
Undetermined cause of fire, 209
Unfunded Mandates, 39
Uniform Building Code, 45
Uniform Fire Code, 37–38, 45, 190
United States Department of Labor, OSHA. See
Occupational Health and Safety Administration
United States Fire Administration (USFA)
Fire and Data Analysis Handbook, 146
fire education programs, 100
National Fire Incident Reporting System (NFIRS)
database, 146
Public Fire Education Planning: A Five-Step Process, 147
purpose, 25
United States Fish and Wildlife Service, 301
United States Forest Service (USFS)
forest protection statistics, 301
history, 305–306
purpose, 26
Urban search and rescue (USAR), 20, 21
USAR (urban search and rescue), 20, 21
USFA. See United States Fire Administration
USFS. See United States Forest Service
Utility drawings, 230, 231

V

V pattern fires, 206, 208
Value statement, 60, 375
Van Dyke, Dick, 138
Vegetation in wildlands
crown fuel, 310
ground fuel, 310
impact of stress, 304
modification for fire prevention, 309
overgrowth, 299, 302, 305
surface fuel, 310
Vision statement, 60, 375
Visual presentations, 180
Voluntary compliance, 254–255, 258
Volunteer departments, 95, 246

W

Wallace, William H., 250
Watchdog group, Consumer Product Safety Commission,
26, 39, 283
Water pollution by wildfires, 303

Water shortage
    performance-based building design, 289–290
    threat of fire and, 110
Water suppression systems, 282. See also Sprinklers
Watershed pollution, 302, 314
Weather, impact on wildfires, 307, 309
Wellness
    benefits, 17
    defined, 18, 375
Wentworth, Franklin, 139
WFS (Women in the Fire Service), 25
Wildfire
    causes, 303–304
    defending in place example, 287, 288
    defined, 299, 375
    elements of behavior and movement, 307–309
    environment and, 299
    management, 305–313, 314–315
        fire and life safety education, 306–307
        interagency cooperation, 305–306
        paradigm shift, 314
        prevention and mitigation, 311–313
        prevention tools, 307–311, 314–315
        suppression, 313
    Nature's fire cycle, 303–304
    risk assessment, 130
    risk factors, 304–305
    statistics, 299–300
Wildlands
    ecological impact of fires, 302–303
    Forest Service, 301–302
    impact of fires, 302–303
    risk management, 109–110, 231–232
    urban interface, 302
    vegetation overgrowth, 299, 302
    wildfires, 299–301
Wingspread Conference, 17–19
Women in the Fire Service (WFS), 25
Work life issues, 68, 69
Workforce, traditional, 68
Workload survey, 63–64
Worksheets
    hazardous materials, 173–174
    public information, 171–172
World Trade Center, 182, 189, 285

Y

Yellow shirt group, 306

Z

Zoning, construction document review, 222